The Emperor Panda

by Alison Reynolds
illustrated by Ki-Hun Yu

a Capstone company — publishers for children

Engage Literacy is published in the UK by Raintree.
Raintree is an imprint of Capstone Global Library Limited, a company incorporated in England and Wales having its registered office at
264 Banbury Road, Oxford, OX2 7DY – Registered company number: 6695582

www.raintree.co.uk

10 9 8 7 6 5 4 3 2

Printed and bound in India

The Emperor's Panda

ISBN: 978 1 4747 1822 6

Contents

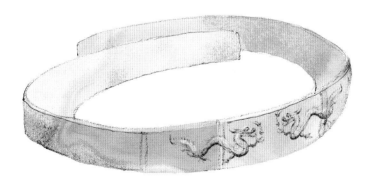

Chapter 1

Hung and Líng Líng

Hung chewed the end of his calligraphy brush. No matter how much he tried, his Chinese characters always looked like dark, inky spots.

"Ah, Hung," said his teacher, who taught all male children of noble, or high-class, families living in the Emperor's palace. "You must practise. Our Emperor still practises every day. To be thought of as a person worthy of the kingdom, your writing must be perfect."

His teacher smiled. "I know you will show us that you are a very important member of our Court, as was your father."

Hung nodded slowly. He wanted to prove to his teacher that he belonged in the kingdom, but he had some doubts. He had trouble keeping up with the other boys because of his leg, which was not like the legs of other boys.

Hung's father was the Emperor's cousin and a very noble man. Both he and Hung's mother died three years ago. The Emperor wanted Hung and his sister Mai to be raised with the other children in the royal palace.

Hung's teacher turned to face the other boys in the classroom. "School is over for today. Enjoy the sunshine."

"One day, I will earn the right to wear my father's golden buckle. This will show that I'm a good and worthy man," whispered Hung to himself.

He followed the other boys into the palace courtyard. "Let's fly kites," Hung suggested.

Cheung Yeow licked his finger and held it in the air. "There is no wind for kites, but it is a great day to ride horses. Would you like to come with us?" asked Cheung Yeow as he pointed to the blue sky above the palace roof.

Hung sighed and said, "No, that's okay. Have a good ride."

Hung watched his friends ride off, and he limped to the stables where the Emperor kept his pets. The lion roared from its bamboo cage, but Hung did not pay attention to it. An elephant lifted its trunk and trumpeted a hello. Hung gave the elephant a quick scratch under its huge ear. Then he walked past a cage of black bears to the last cage. A small black and white panda sat there.

"Hello, Ling Ling," said Hung, and he lifted up the door. The panda's round, white face with its black patches around the eyes looked up. Hung hugged him.

"Are you supposed to be doing that?" demanded a voice.

9

Chapter 2

The Emperor's plan for Ling Ling

Hung looked over the soft black fur of Ling Ling's shoulder and saw Mai, his younger sister.

"Aren't you supposed to be writing calligraphy and learning poetry?" Mai sounded angry.

"My teacher let us go a little early. The other boys are riding horses, but I can't ride because of my leg."

"I'm sorry," said Mai. "How is Ling Ling doing today?"

She reached forward to pet the panda. A long jade flute, or xiao, fell from the sleeve of her pink silk robe.

"Mai," gasped Hung. "How did you get our mother's flute? The Emperor's wife is caring for it."

"I saw it lying out, so I took it. Sometimes I take it to remind me of her, and one day I shall play as well as she did."

Hung nodded and said, "One day you will. But you're only nine years old. You must be older before you're allowed to study the flute. Until then, the flute is very dear and must be well cared for."

Mai buried her head in Ling Ling's soft neck. "All right."

Mai said, "I'm happy here, Hung. I enjoy learning to dance and sing, but one day ..."

"You will play our mother's long jade flute and be famous throughout China," said Hung, patting her arm.

Mai's brown eyes glanced at Hung. "Do you think I will?"

"Of course," said Hung as he raised his arm. "Now, watch what Ling Ling can do."

He drew a circle in the air, and Ling Ling did a perfect flip.

"Wow," said Mai. "You taught him that?"

The children heard soft footsteps. Ching, the pet keeper, walked towards them. "Excellent, Hung. The Emperor will be delighted, especially as Ling Ling is going to leave us."

"What?" gasped Hung.

14

"The Emperor is giving Ling Ling to the country of Japan as a sign of friendship," said Ching. "He will be well cared for."

"Can I go with him to Japan?"

Ching shook his head slowly and said, "I'm sorry, but you can't. Your place is here with the Emperor and the other noble children."

"But he's my friend. He can't go away."

Ching shrugged and said, "I know this is hard for you, but it must happen. The Japanese visitors are already here."

Hung and Mai watched Ching pick up a wooden bucket and walk quickly to the well.

The panda's dark eyes gazed at Hung.

"Ling Ling cannot leave me," said Hung.

"But what can you do?"

Hung bit his lower lip and said, "We can run away together. All three of us."

Chapter 3

Hung the protector

Mai crossed her arms and said, "No."

"What do you mean?" asked Hung.

"I'm not going with you, and you can't leave me. I'm the only family you have, Hung," said Mai.

"But I can't let Ling Ling go to Japan. Ling Ling is my best friend." Hung squeezed Mai's hand and said, "You must come."

Ling Ling crawled up to Mai, and she stroked the panda's soft head. "You could talk to the Emperor. He is a wise and fair man. Look at how he has cared for us."

"He won't understand because he has to act according to tradition," said Hung as tears filled his eyes. "I love Ling Ling, and now he's going away."

"But I can't leave here." Mai waved at the high walls of the palace. "We live well here, and outside we would be poor. We would have to work on farms. We'd also live in one-room huts with many other people."

"I don't care what happens to me without Ling Ling," said Hung as he gripped Ling Ling's paw. "We can't be separated."

"Talk to the Emperor," she said as she grabbed Hung's free hand. "You can't leave me."

Hung gazed down at Ling Ling's furry paw and Mai's soft hand with its long fingers. Their mother always said Mai had the hands of a musician. If they left the palace, Mai would never be able to play the flute.

"If you won't come, Mai, I'll just have to make sure that Ling Ling doesn't leave us."

Mai asked, "How? We must follow the orders of the Emperor. It is the law."

Hung smiled and said, "But what if nobody can find Ling Ling? You can't send away a panda that's disappeared."

Chapter 4

Painting Ling Ling

Hung crept through the halls of the palace. He walked softly on the red, blue and yellow tiles. Then he climbed the stairs to the schoolroom.

He slipped through the door. The large jar of ink stood on the windowsill. Hopefully there would be enough ink to cover Ling Ling's white fur.

"Hung," said his teacher as he stood in the doorway. "I'm surprised to see you here."

"I came for extra practice," said Hung as he picked up a calligraphy brush. "I want to be as good at writing as the Emperor."

His teacher asked, "Really?"

Hung unrolled a sheet of paper as he replied, "Yes."

"I will leave you to it then. I must visit the Emperor to help him. We need to make our friends from Japan feel welcome."

"When do the visitors leave?" Hung asked. He used a ladle to pour ink from the jar into a small inkwell that the boys used.

"They leave late tonight. The Emperor will be pleased to hear that you are taking your studies so seriously," said his teacher.

Hung started to paint the Chinese character for panda.

"Please leave everything just as you found it," said Hung's teacher.

Hung nodded, and his teacher left the room. Hung waited until the room was totally silent, and then he picked up the heavy jar of black ink. Ling Ling was about to change into a black bear.

"Couldn't you have gotten bigger brushes?" asked Mai. "This is taking forever."

"Calligraphy brushes need to be small, so you can paint all the parts of characters," said Hung. "We've finished. Now get up, Ling Ling."

Ling Ling jumped up.

Mai pointed to Ling Ling and said, "We forgot to paint where Ling Ling was sitting."

"Whoops," laughed Hung.

Mai quickly inked in the final white patch.

It was amazing. The black ink was perfect. Ling Ling looked like a black bear.

"Hung," shouted Ching from the courtyard gate. "I've been searching for you. I thought you would like to say goodbye to Ling Ling."

Ching looked around and asked, "Where is Ling Ling?"

Hung scratched his head. "I don't know. Mai and I have been playing with this black bear."

Mai pointed to Ling Ling's empty cage and said, "No pandas here."

Ching frowned and said, "Ling Ling was here earlier. I need to find the panda, or I'll be in trouble. Help me find Ling Ling."

Ching wandered through the courtyard towards a pond. He shouted, "Ling Ling, where are you?"

Hung, Mai and the black bear followed.

Ching said, "I don't remember that bear."

"He's new," said Hung. "One of the nobles brought him in just before."

"He found the bear in the forest," added Mai.

"Oh," said Ching as he patted the black bear's head. "You'll be safe here."

Hung pointed across the pond and said, "Isn't that Ling Ling over there?"

Ching looked at the pond and asked, "Where?"

"Behind those trees," said Hung. "I'm positive I saw a panda."

"Thanks, I'll find him," Ching said.

Ching, Hung, Mai and the black bear stared into the cool pond. Then, suddenly, there was a *splash*. The black bear plunged into the water, and the black ink began to wash away.

Ching moved closer to the pond and asked, "Is that Ling Ling?"

The panda raised his head, and Hung and Mai pulled him out of the water.

Ching looked from Hung to Mai and said, "I won't tell the Emperor about this. Say farewell to Ling Ling. I'll return soon to take him to the Japanese visitors. Tonight they leave with Ling Ling." He marched away.

"This was meant to be a good plan," said Mai.

"I forgot that pandas can swim," said Hung. "I'll think of something else."

Chapter 5

Hiding Ling Ling

Hung looked around. He and Mai just needed to hide Ling Ling until the Japanese visitors left.

Alongside one of the palace walls was a patch of bamboo. The leaves were so dense that nothing could be seen behind them.

"Let's hide Ling Ling there," said Hung.

"Sorry, Ling Ling," said Hung. He then tied the panda's leg to a thick stalk of bamboo with his sash. "We're not taking any chances."

There was noise at the courtyard gate. Ching and four guards marched up to Hung and Mai.

"It's time," said Ching.

"We're here for Ling Ling," announced the tallest guard.

Mai looked around and said, "Ling Ling is around here somewhere."

Crunch, crunch.

"What's that noise?" asked Ching.

"Me," said Hung. "I like to chew on bamboo leaves."

He grabbed a handful and chomped on them loudly.

"We need the panda," said Ching.

"I can't see Ling Ling anywhere," said Hung. "Can you Mai?"

She shook her head and said, "No."

Then Ling Ling poked his head through a hole he'd made by eating bamboo.

"I should have remembered that pandas eat a lot of bamboo," said Hung, sadly to himself.

Ching untied Ling Ling and handed the sash back to Hung. Ching said angrily, "I suppose you didn't know where he was, Hung?"

Ling Ling reached his paw towards Hung, who took it. Ching turned his back on Hung to talk to the guards.

Hung said, "Come on, Ling Ling. They can't take you away."

They charged through the courtyard to the palace. Hung's heart pounded as they ran down hallway after hallway to his room.

Hung looked out of the window onto the courtyard. There was a figure dressed in yellow surrounded by people. It was the Emperor.

"You'll have to stay here until the visitors return to Japan," said Hung. Then he shut the door behind him and raced towards the crowd in the courtyard below.

Hung looked for Ching. "Ling Ling ran away. I'm sorry."

The crowd started to laugh. Hung turned around to see where they were looking. Ling Ling was balanced on the tiled roof below Hung's bedroom. The panda searched the crowd. He saw Hung and leapt down. Seconds later, the panda stood beside Hung.

Hung dropped his head. He should have remembered that pandas were excellent climbers. Taking Ling Ling's paw, he walked to where the Emperor, his wife and the visitors sat.

Chapter 6

Ling Ling's fate

"Emperor. Here is the panda," said Hung. Hung tried not to cry, but tears kept falling.

"Wait, please take this instead of the panda," cried Mai as tears ran down her cheeks. She offered the visitors her jade flute.

"Stop," said the Emperor. "My kingdom is not to be filled with the tears of children."

Hung's teacher stepped forward and said, "Hung loves Ling Ling. Ling Ling is Hung's friend. And Mai is trying to help."

The Emperor said softly, "Hung, you should have told me."

Hung's cheeks burned red as he said, "You are a busy man."

The Emperor then softly said, "You must tell me, so I can help. Our friends, will you understand if we do not give you the panda?"

One of the visitors nodded and said, "Of course. The panda must stay with the boy who loves him."

The Emperor's wife whispered into the Emperor's ear.

He smiled and said, "My wife suggests that Mai play her special jade flute for our guests. Will you play for us, Mai?"

Mai's fingers shook as she brought the jade flute to her lips. Mai's music was like a beautiful bird song.

Everyone clapped, and Mai smiled widely.

"You will receive all the teaching we have, Mai. You have the gift of music and must play your flute every week for my people and me," said the Emperor. "Do you agree?"

Mai's eyes shone. She was too happy to speak, but she nodded.

"And you, Hung. Would you like to be in charge of Ling Ling?" asked the Emperor.

"Yes!" shouted Hung.

"You and Ling Ling will never be parted. And you will wear your father's golden buckle to show that you are noble."

Hung, Mai and Ling Ling hugged each other.

"Thank you," said Hung. "You've made me the happiest boy in China."

And from that day forward, he was.

TUSCANY

www.marco-polo.com

Sighseeing Highlights

The list of sights in Tuscany is long. Be it cultural attraction, pastoral landscapes or pretty seaside resorts – we've put together what you should definitely not miss.

❶ ✶✶ Alpi Apuane
There's no end to the variety: marble, mountains, hiking, cave explorations, seaside.
page 152

❷ ✶✶ Lucca
The formerly wealthy silk trade city is a pearl among all of the beautiful Tuscan towns.
page 297

❸ ✶✶ Florence
The absolute tourist highlight of Tuscany – here the history of the Renaissance and Humanism comes alive.
page 231

❹ ✶✶ Medici Villas
The wealthy family's magnificent residences around Florence
page 281

❺ ✶✶ La Verna
St Francis is supposed to have received the Stigmata here.
page 170

❻ ✶✶ Pisa
Everyone thinks of the Leaning tower first – but Pisa has so much more to offer than the Field of Miracles.
page 357

❼ ✶✶ Chianti
Wine region and cultural landscape
page 195

❽ ✶✶ Arezzo
The cycle of frescos by Piero della Francesca is fascinating.
page 156

❾ ✶✶ San Gimignano
The Manhattan of Tuscany
page 400

©BAEDEKER

Do You Feel Like...

... Tuscan super-towers, unusual museums, good organic products like wines or olive oil, modern art between the many Renaissance highlights, sweet delicacies or health spas, in short: your very personal Tuscany experience? Maybe these ideas will help.

BACKGROUND

PRICE CATEGORIES
Restaurants (main dish without a drink)
€€€€ = over €25
€€€ = €18–€25
€€ = €12–€18
€ = up to €12
Hotels (double room)
€€€€ = over €150
€€€ = €100–€150
€€ = €70–€100
€ = up to €70

Note
Billable service telephone numbers are marked with an asterisk: *0180…

ENJOY TUSCANY

TOURS

Always well-visited: Piazza dei Miracoli in Pisa

SIGHTS FROM A TO Z

PRACTICAL INFORMATION

The cathedral of Siena with its famous mosaic floor

BACKGROUND

What to know about this travel destination in the heart of Italy, about the land and its people, politics and the economyand about everyday life in one of Europe's most beautiful and popular holiday regions.

Facts

Natural Environment

Tuscany is an old cultural landscape; its typical cypress-lined roads, olive groves and fields of poppies have for the most part replaced the original local plants. The popular Italian travel destination was originally covered with dense virgin forests.

LANDSCAPES

Tuscany is a landscape in the middle of Italy and one of 20 national regions (Regione Toscana). In the west it extends to the Mediterranean Sea, in the north and east it borders on Liguria, Emilia-Romagna and the Marche, in the south on Umbria and Latium. The seven islands of the Tuscan archipelago (Arcipelago Toscano), of which Elba, Giglio and Capraia are the biggest, also belong to the region's territory.

Regione Toscana

At the mention of Tuscany olive groves, vineyards and cypress avenues winding along gently rolling hillsides come to mind. But the scenery is more varied than this – and by no means always as charming as the picture postcards suggest. Most of the region is hilly, and the north-west is actually mountainous, but in the south-west, in the Maremma and on the coast, the landscape is flat: this area was once marshy and is now partly a nature reserve. The densely populated belt between Pisa and Florence in the north contrasts with the less densely populated areas of fields, forests and isolated farms that mainly lie in the south.

Landscape

The Apennines, a mountain range which runs through all of Italy, form the mountainous backbone of Tuscany, and are here called the Tuscan or Etruscan Apennines. Northern Tuscany is characterized by the so-called Northern Apennines, which are formed of grey sandstone and have their highest peak, Monte Cimone (in Emilia-Romagna, 2,165m/7,103ft), just north of Tuscany.
The Apuan Alps lie to the south-west of the Apennines. Their rocky formations reach almost 2,000m/6,600ft and are reminiscent of high mountain ranges. They rise steeply from a coast famous for its marble, which is quarried near Carrara and Massa among other places.

Apennines and Apuan Alps

The basins that formed between the Apennines and the coast in northern and central Tuscany are **valleys** today: the Lunigiana, for

Valleys in the north, hills in the south

Take a break in restful Tuscan nature

example, Garfagnana, Mugello, Casentino and Valdarno as well as Val di Chiana. South of the Arno the Tuscan landscape is completely different. Although the elevations in the Colline Metallifere are in part quite high, the area is characterized not by connected mountains but by gently rolling hills from which individual mountains rise. Erosion has made some of the slopes very steep, forming deep gorges and erosion channels, as can be seen near Volterra or the so-called Crete of Siena. The ground is very fertile and is intensively used for agriculture. The **highest peak** in Tuscany is the 1,738m/5,735ft-high Monte Amiata, an extinct volcano in the extreme south-east.

Coastal plains

Tuscany has a coastline of about 300km/190mi. In the north the coastal plain is a narrow strip before the Apuan Alps, with long, **sandy beaches** and a well-developed infrastructure for tourism. From the mouth of the little Cecina River southwards to Civitavecchia in Latium the coastal plain is known as the Maremma. This straight sandy coast was feared for centuries because its swamps were infested with malaria. The Maremma was cultivated and densely populated during the Etruscan period, and then again from the 19th century.

Tuscan islands

The **Tuscan archipelago** consists of seven main islands and several small ones, which lie off the Tuscan coast in the part of the Tyrrhenian Sea that is bordered by the Italian mainland in the east and the French island of Corsica in the west. Social and economic life in the archipelago is limited for the most part to four islands: Elba, Giglio, Giannutri and Capraia. Gorgona, the site of an Italian prison, may only be visited with special permission. In 1990 parts of the Tuscan archipelago were made into a national park to protect the flora and fauna. In 1998 the entire islands of Montecristo (▶Elba), Gorgona (Livorno), Pianosa and Giannutri, 85% of Capraia, 55% of Elba and 50% of Giglio were placed under protection.

Rivers

Several rivers flow through Tuscany, all of them from the **Apennines** or the hills to the **Mediterranean**. The Arno, Tuscany's longest river, rises north of Arezzo at Monte Falterona and flows through Florence and Pisa almost 250km/155mi to the sea. The other major rivers are the Magra, Serchio, Cecina, Ombrone and Fiora. Extreme differences in water level during the course of the year are typical of all these rivers for climatic reasons.

PLANTS

Man-made landscape

Tuscany is an area of ancient settlement, and the plants and animals originally native to this area have accordingly been pushed into the margins. Outside the cities and tourist areas most of the land is used

Typically Tuscan: country roads lined by cypress trees

for agriculture; olive groves, vineyards and wheat fields predominate. The three characteristic trees of the region are the **olive tree** with its green-silver shiny leaves, the slender, dark-green **cypress** and the **stone pine** with its umbrella-like crown.

Tuscany was originally covered with dense forests – oak, beech or fir trees depending on the elevation. However, for the most part these forests were already cleared during ancient times. The erosion that followed washed away the earth and in many parts of the mountains left bare rock without any plant cover. On the hills and in the valleys between the foothills the ground that was not used for agriculture was soon covered by macchia : evergreen, low shrubs with small, often leathery leaves which protect the ground from evaporation and form an impenetrable and thorny thicket. Just like the Mediterranean heath which can often be found at higher altitudes, macchia is characteristic of the Tuscan landscape. In the spring it is transformed into a colourful sea of flowers. Many plants contain **aromatic resins and**

Macchia

essential oils that produce an intense perfume. The main plants of the macchia are varieties of heather, broom, laurel, sage, arbutus, juniper, cistus, myrtle, mastic, pistachio and bramble.

Forests Tuscany has been **reforested** since the early 20th century, especially since the end of the Second World War. Today 37% of the region is forest, making it now one of the Italian regions with the most tree cover. These efforts have been concentrated in the Apennines and other mountainous regions, where today beech, oak, ash, fir, spruce and larch are growing again. Chestnuts, too, can often be found up to elevations of about 900m/2,950ft. In the Tuscan coastal areas pine, cedar, black and white poplar as well as local eucalyptus trees have also been planted. In the southern coastal and hilly regions cork oaks can occasionally be found.

ANIMALS

The natural fauna has been pushed back even more than the plant world in Tuscany. Thus of the once rich stocks of game – deer, wild boar, rabbits – the only significant remaining populations live in less accessible mountainous regions. Not only dense human habitation, intensive use of land and disappearance of the original forests have drastically reduced the original fauna; air and water pollution and the popularity of shooting, which claims the lives of many birds every year, have also played a part. About 30,000 **white long-horn cattle** live in herds in the Maremma, where they are herded by cattle drovers (butteri). The **Maremma horses** of the butteri have adapted completely to the climate of the Maremma.

Population · Economy · Politics

Regione Toscana is Italy's fifth-largest region and has had partial autonomy since 1970. It has been sub-divided into ten provinces since 1992.

Population With a population density of 162 residents per sq km (419 per sq mi) Tuscany lies considerably below the Italian national average of 199 residents per sq km (515 per sq mi). But there are great variations within the region. About 70% of the inhabitants live in the **densely populated urban areas** of the Versilia and northern Tuscany, which together account for about 20% of the land area. The hills of southern Tuscany, above all the provinces of Siena and Grosseto, as well as the

Apennines, are **sparsely populated**. Here above all – as in Tuscany as a whole – the population has declined in the past decades. Migrants from other parts of Italy and other European countries compensate this somewhat.

Today there is still a distinct division into traditional urban and rural areas. On the one hand the historic cities like Florence, Pisa and Lucca have an urban culture and lifestyle that have developed over centuries, while on the other hand there is a typical rural settlement pattern in the valleys and remote hilly regions, with villages and many individual farms that lie in the middle of their fields. The villas of landowners from the cities, which were mostly only occupied during the summer and the hunting season, connected the urban and rural lifestyles. They were part of the »**fattoria**«, the estate, while as part of the »**mezzadria** « (»half-lease«) system the land was placed in the hands of farmers whose farmhouses (casa coloniche) were in the middle of their fields. Even though the mezzadria system has now been abolished and the rural population has been reduced drastically by the exodus to the towns, this settlement pattern is still characteristic of southern Tuscany in particular. Today many fattorie are used as holiday apartments or second homes.

Cities, villages and fattorie

Anarchy and Communism have a long tradition in Carrara: two members of one of the numerous Brigate Garibaldi

Welcome to Everyday Life!

Experiencing Tuscany away from the tourist crowds for once, meeting »normal« people or actual residents -- here are some tips.

LANGUAGE COURSES WITH AN ADDED EXTRA ...

The culture centre C.C.I.C. »Piero della Francesca« in the old city of Poppi ideally combines language and culture acquisition. It offers overnight stays in hotels and Agriturismo venues as well as rooms with Italian families; in addition it offers courses on the lives of Piero della Francesca, Dante Alighieri, cooking and gourmet courses, courses on Italian opera and even on stonemasonry including excursions into the Casentino region.

Via Cesare Battisti 5, Poppi, Tel. 05 75 52 97 74, http://www. parlital.it/Italian-Language-School. html

TRADING FLATS – B & B IN PRIVATE HOMES

Staying in private homes gives you a chance to experience everyday life. B & B Italia has a large selection to choose from – a great variety of criteria are also taken into consideration: age, family or single etc. Trading flats or taking in guests from Tuscany is another way to experience Tuscany. This makes it possible to stay with a family in Tuscany, but not always at no cost.

B&B Italia, www.bbitalia.it
Trading flats, www.airbnb.com

EXPERIENCE NATURE TOGETHER

Enthusiastic locals guide tours into the National Park of the Tuscan Archipelago (►Elba) or in Parco Naturale della Maremma, for example Paolo Fanciulli (»Il pescatore«) in Talamone or Naturalmente Toscana in Alberese.

www.paoloilpescatore.it
www.naturalmentetoscana.it

ARCHAEOLOGICAL DIGS

People interested in archaeology – not just students – can take part in excavations including interesting excursions and lectures. Participation is organized by the University of Florence in cooperation with CAMNES (Center for Mediterranean and Near Eastern Studies) and the Lorenzo de' Medici Institute, among other places. Additional information can be found at the following websites.

CAMNES, Via del Giglio 15, Florence, Tel. 05 52 39 92 57, www.camnes.org
www.archeotoscana.beniculturali.it
www.amitie.it/voch/minetti_ppt.pdf
www.archeoempoli.it/scavi.htm

WORKING WORLD IN INDUSTRY AND ORGANIC BUSINESSES

Many manufacturing sites are also attractive for sightseeing. These include the pasta factory Martelli in Lari near Pisa, which offers tours. Many olive planters and winegrowers offer tours, the latter usually including winetasting – however this is not always cheap. Some businesses, like the organic farm La Selva, or Wwoofer offer jobs to interns who can work in the fields and help with the harvest from May to October in return for free room and board without sacrificing holiday fun at the seaside only 3km/2mi away. WWOOF Italy has information on other ways of getting to know organic projects and farming in Tuscany.

Martelli Pasta facatory: www.martelli. info, La Selva: www.laselva-bio.eu , WWOOF Italy: www.wwoof.it/en

PISA AS YOU LIKE IT

Explicitly individual, highly qualified guided tours in Italian, German or English are offered by the cooperative Pisatour; this is a way to get to know Pisa in interesting personal encounters beyond the art-historical details.
www.pisatour.it

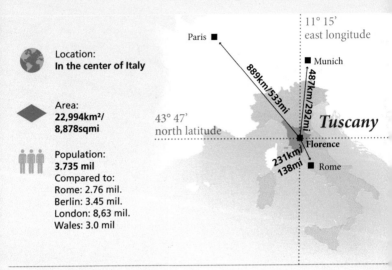

Location:
In the center of Italy

Area:
**22,994km²/
8,878sqmi**

Population:
3.735 mil
Compared to:
Rome: 2.76 mil.
Berlin: 3.45 mil.
London: 8,63 mil.
Wales: 3.0 mil

▶ **Regione Toscana**

Tuscany is one of the 20 regions of Italy. The present ten provinces
are supposed to be reduced to seven to eight provinces.

Capital:
Florence (Firenze)

A: Arezzo
B: Firenze
C: Grosseto
D: Livorno
E: Lucca
F: Massa-Carrara
G: Pisa
H: Pistoia
I: Prato
K: Siena

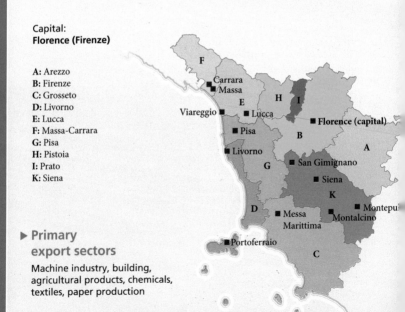

▶ **Primary
export sectors**

Machine industry, building,
agricultural products, chemicals,
textiles, paper production

▶ Economy

per capita income:
about 27,500 Euro
Maximum: Prov. Florence
33,750 Euro
Minimum: Prov. Massa-Carrara
22,750 Euro

Employment structure:

Services

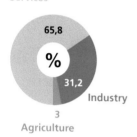

65,8

%

31,2

Industry

3
Agriculture

Unemployment rate: **8.7 %**
Youth unemployment
(15-24 yrs.): 33.4%

▶ Climate

Average temperatures

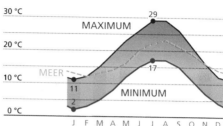

| 30 °C | | | | | | | | 29 | | | | |
| MAXIMUM |
| 20 °C |
| MEER | | | | | | | | 17 |
| 10 °C |
| 11 | MINIMUM |
| 2 |
| 0 °C |
| J F M A M J J A S O N D |

Precipitation

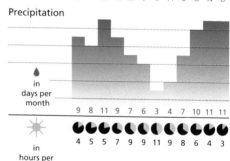

in
days per
month

| 9 | 8 | 11 | 9 | 7 | 6 | 3 | 4 | 7 | 10 | 11 | 11 |

| 4 | 5 | 5 | 7 | 9 | 9 | 11 | 9 | 8 | 6 | 4 | 3 |

in
hours per
day

J F M A M J J A S O N D

▶ Palio di Siena – the world's toughest horse race

The world's toughest horse race is held twice a year on the Piazza del
Campo. The 17 contrade represent the city districts of Siena and compete
against each other. The graphic shows the contrade winners
from 1900 to 2015.

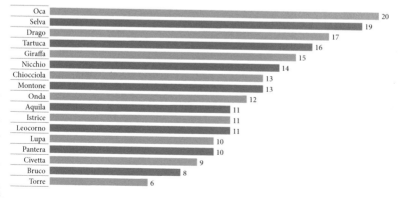

Contrada	Wins
Oca	20
Selva	19
Drago	17
Tartuca	16
Giraffa	15
Nicchio	14
Chiocciola	13
Montone	13
Onda	12
Aquila	11
Istrice	11
Leocorno	11
Lupa	10
Pantera	10
Civetta	9
Bruco	8
Torre	6

ECONOMY

Economic structure

Tuscany, like the neighbouring Umbria, lies on the border between the wealthy industrialized north of Italy and the poorer south, the mezzogiorno. Within Tuscany, too, there is an **economic divide** between the north with its large cities and the sparsely populated south. The region has a very versatile economy. Like everywhere else, the number of people employed in agriculture is declining drastically and is presently less than 2%. About 24% work in industry or as craftsmen, more than 63% in the service sector. Florence is not only politically important as the capital of Tuscany but also economically as a centre of commerce and trade fairs, and as the home of large publishers as well as an excellent science centre.

Agriculture

Agriculture remains the economic factor that marks the face of the region. For centuries the system of mezzadria dominated agriculture. The landowners lived in the cities and turned over the land to farmers in a system by which the owners paid half of the costs (for example for seed) in return for half of the crop and other services. Farms tended to be mixed farms, with grain, wine and olive or fruit trees. These have all but disappeared today. Old leases were dissolved and many small businesses that supplied additional income were closed. This led to the formation of modern medium-size to large businesses with high degrees of specialization. Tuscany mainly produces grain, sugar beets, olives, wine (for example in the famous Chianti region between Florence and Siena), fruit, vegetables and sunflowers. The EU-wide overproduction of wine and sugar are a problem here as elsewhere. Livestock (cattle, pigs) plays less of a role, as does fishing, which is mainly concentrated in the harbour of Livorno.

Mining

The production of metals, marble and clay has a long tradition in Tuscany. Iron, copper, lead, zinc and other ores (mercury, antimony) have been mined in the **Colline Metallifere**, on Elba and at Monte Amiata since Antiquity and the Middle Ages. Both mining and smelting have now largely stopped. Only manganese and pyrite are still mined. However, the marble quarries near Carrara and Massa in the Apuan Alps and the processing of marble continue to be important. The quarries for the world-famous white marble go back to antiquity, but today face tough foreign competition (▶MARCO POLO Insight p. 186). Lignite mining at Ombrone has all but stopped. Geothermal energy from the Colline Metallifere is increasingly being used and converted to electricity in a large power plant near Larderello.

Industry

Agriculture is the basis for multi-faceted **industrial activity**. This includes production of sugar, edible oils, leather and shoes as well as wine, and also wood-processing industries such as furniture and

Next to wine olives are the most important agricultural product

paper factories on the edge of the forested mountain ranges. The textile processing industry has a long tradition as well – Tuscany is to this day one of the centres of the Italian **textile and clothing industry**, which consists mostly of small and mid-sized businesses concentrated around Florence and especially Prato. New fabric was produced from old clothing in Prato after the Second World War, which earned it the unflattering nickname »rag city«. Meanwhile it continues to be a leading producer of high-quality fabrics that are made in artisan workshops. Both mass and craft production exist in the traditional **glass and ceramics industry** in the Elsa valley near Siena, as well as in the making of gold and silver jewellery in Arezzo. The capital goods industry, above all machine and auto manufacturing, is located mainly in the industrial belt from Pistoia to Prato and Florence, as well as along the Arno valley via Pontedera to the coast near Livorno.

Tuscany is the fourth most popular Italian holiday region, after Emilia-Romagna, Lombardy and Latium. 40 million visits are recorded annually, of which about 21 million include overnight stays. Italian (21 mil.) and foreign visitors (19 mil.) are about equal in number. Florence counts about 7.5 mil. visitors annually. 40% of the income   Tourism

produced by tourism comes from the Versilia beaches around Viareggio, followed by city and cultural tourism. Thermal spas and active tourism (cycling, hiking, golf etc.) are growing in popularity. The most significant area of growth in Italy's emergence into the 21st cent. is the culture industry with an annual national growth of 3.0% (other economy: + 0.3%). Tuscany is the leader, gaining 5.4% of the GDP in this sector in 2010. Italy-wide the number one in creative culture industry is surprisingly **Arezzo**. Clever businessmen are bringing in 8.5% of the income and have created 10% of the jobs through attractive cultural activities. **Pisa** is in fifth place Italy-wide. In the shadows of the Leaning Tower cultural activities and tourism bring in €800 mil. annually, which secure 8.8% of the jobs. **Florence** is in inth place in Italy; the culture industry brought in about 29% of its income through tourism.

The Leaning Tower of Pisa was a fun background for taking photos in the 1950s already

Roots of Urban Culture

When it is claimed that urban culture has its roots in a certain Italian region, then Tuscany is probably the region that best fits the bill. The successors to the autonomous Etruscan cities were medieval city states, whose architectural heritage shapes the appearance of the region to this day.

PREHISTORY AND EARLY HISTORY

The earliest archaeological finds date from the Stone Age. Remains of simple stone tools and bones from the Palaeolithic age were found near Arezzo and in the Apuan Alps. During the Bronze Age an autonomous culture, the so-called Belvedere-Cetona culture, developed among the **first settled Tuscans**. Near Chiusi on Monte Cetona, which gave this culture its name, the remains of a late Bronze Age village (1700 to 1000 BC) were discovered.

Between 1000 and 800 BC the transition took place to early Iron Age culture, which reached its zenith in the 8th century BC. This civilization, which spread through northern and central Italy, was named after Villanova near Bologna, the site of the main finds. The last phase of Villanova culture is also the first phase of Etruscan culture, which was later to develop into the first advanced civilization of Italy.

Villanova culture

ETRUSCANS

9th century BC	Etruscans appear on the Apennine peninsula.
6th century BC	Etruscan city states in the area of modern Tuscany and Latium
Late 5th century BC	Greeks end Etruscan naval domination.
3rd century BC	Decline of the Etruscan states

The first inhabitants of the core area of Tuscany who are known by name are the Etruscans. The Greeks, who were probably the people most closely related to the Etruscans, called them Tyrrhenoi, while their Roman neighbours called them Tusci or Etrusci. Their own name for themselves was Rasenna. Even though well over 10,000 inscriptions are known from the Etruscan period, the origins of this

Who were the Etruscans?

Once upon a time in Florence when cars were allowed on Piazza della Signorina

people remain a mystery. An inscription found on the island of Lemnos shows writing similar to Etruscan and influences from Sardinia are being examined as well. The Villanova civilization presumably mingled with the colonizers from the eastern Mediterranean region.

The Etruscans spread
Wherever the Etruscans came from, they did not conquer by force the regions they settled. It can be proved that they lived in the coastal area around the modern towns of Cerveteri and Tarquinia. From the 6th century Etruria extended north to the Po valley and soon after south to Campania.

They do not want a state ...
Most of the population were farmers, serf tenants or slaves; they were ruled by a land-owning aristocracy. The Etruscans did not want to form a state, but instead founded a loose league of cities, in which every city (and the surrounding territory) pursued its own political goals. The higher level of organization was the **twelve-city league**. Six of these main Etruscan cities lay in modern-day Tuscany: Arezzo, Chiusi, Cortona, Ruselle, Populonia and Volterra. The religious centre of the city league was the sanctuary Fanum Voltumnae (shrine of Voltumna) near Bolsena, where the delegates of the city rulers held a council once a year. Etruria was densely populated; Volterra, for example, had more than 50,000 residents.

... and they trade in the entire Mediterranean region
The Etruscans owed their power and wealth above all to their skill at working iron, copper and silver-bearing lead. Their **mining** operations for the most part concentrated on Elba, Etruscan Ilva (= iron), and the coastal region around Populonia. Etruscan metal products were greatly prized in the ancient world and extensive trade relationships existed. They penetrated northern Europe by land and shipped their precious goods throughout the Mediterranean region to Iberia, Gaul, Carthage and to the Near East. Thus there was no lack of trade-based conflicts. After victory over the Greeks around 540 BC in a sea battle near Alalia (Corsica) the Etruscans gained control of the Tyrrhenian Sea.

Rome brings the Etruscans to their knees
In the 5th century BC the Etruscans lost important sea battles against their Greek and Phoenician rivals. Their rule over the Tyrrhenian Sea was long finished when the Romans conquered the first Etruscan city, Veii, in 396 BC. The Etruscan league came more and more under the influence of the expanding Roman Empire. The lack of solidarity among Etruscan cities was advantageous for Rome. However, Etruria was allowed to remain autonomous and to continue processing metals for Rome, which used force only when opposition grew in Etruria and the league joined an anti-Roman coalition. The Samnite wars from 343 to 290 BC led to the **collapse of the Etruscan city states**. Etruria was conquered and became an unhappy ally of Rome.

ROMANS

3rd century BC	Rome expands into Etruscan territory.
From 88 BC	Roman citizenship for residents of Etruria
AD 297	Etruria and Umbria together become the fifth region of the Roman state.

In the 3rd century BC the Etruscan cities lost their autonomy to Rome. Unlike the Etruscans the Romans set about subduing all of central Italy. In order to create the necessary infrastructure for this, **military bases, bridges and roads** were first built. The Via Aurelia, which was begun in 241 BC, ran along the Tyrrhenian coast to Pisa; the Via Cassia via Bolsena, Chiusi and Arezzo to Fiesole; other military roads were added. A few cities, especially Volterra, Arezzo and Fiesole, enjoyed a renaissance. They acquired Roman **temples, theatres, thermal baths and aqueducts**. As an ally of Rome, Etruria suffered in the Roman wars against Carthage, Gaul and the kingdoms

First military bases, then temples and thermal baths

Stones with a history: the Roman road in the Etruscan city of Roselle (Rusellae)

of the Diadochi to the east. The territory made a substantial contribution to the alliance in the form of soldiers and finances. In the legendary battle against Hannibal at Lake Trasimeno (217 BC) the involuntary allies and the enemies of Rome gained new hope, for the Carthaginians inflicted a crushing defeat on Rome. Yet they did not gain the final victory.

Economic decline The 2nd century BC brought the first signs of economic decline in Etruria. The import of grain from Roman colonies led to the abandonment of agriculture and consequently to strong migration from rural areas. Mining, long the wealth of the region, stagnated. The coastal region became swampy and malaria spread. After the so-called Social Wars from 91 to 88 BC, rights of Roman citizenship were granted to Etruria, but the consequent status of political equality also meant the end of any independence.

The exodus from the land increased dramatically. Equipped with the new citizenship, thousands moved to the steadily growing city of Rome. Octavian, who took the name Augustus after 27 BC, was the first to try to halt the decline of Etruria, which threatened the cities too, by means of a land reform and administrative measures. Etruria then became the seventh region of Roman territory, together with the northern parts of Latium, but the situation improved only a little.

3rd century BC Region of Tuscia In late antiquity Emperor Diocletian redrew the boundaries of his empire. In AD 297 the old area of Etruria together with Umbria became the fifth region of the Roman Empire, named Tuscia – the term »Toscana« only appeared in the 13th century. The region was almost ruined by massive imports of grain from Egypt and Sicily. Mining and processing of ore were hardly important any longer.

Fall of the western Roman Empire With the fall of the western Roman Empire – officially in the year 476 – urban life all but extinguished in the region of Tuscia. Soon only the ruins of great temples, amphitheatres, baths and aqueducts testified to Roman rule.

MIDDLE AGES

6th century	Lombard Duchy of Tuscia
8th–9th century	The Franks conquer the Lombard kingdom and make Tuscia into a march.
12th–13th cent.	Cities prosper economically and become politically autonomous; conflicts between Guelfs and Ghibellines.
14th century	Florence becomes a financial centre.

The end of the western Roman Empire left a power vacuum that was at first filled by tribes who were looking for new areas to settle. With the Lombards, who entered northern Italy from 568 under Alboin, better times arrived. As an agrarian people they revitalized **agriculture** and took over Roman administrative structures. The capital of the Lombard Duchy of Tuscia was Lucca. The peaceful rule of the Lombards lasted about two hundred years. It brought traders, pilgrims and craftsmen into the area.

Charlemagne expanded the kingdom of the Franks towards the end of the 8th century into northern and central Italy and subjugated the Lombards. He had himself crowned as Roman emperor in 800 in Rome and became the protector of the papal state. Tuscia became a march, a border county, in order to secure the imperial boundaries. From this time Frankish counts resided in Lucca and San Miniato. From the 10th century the Holy Roman emperors tried to increase their political power in northern Italy, and made use of the bishops for imperial political purposes. Moreover the **march of Tuscia**, which belonged to the rulers of Canossa from the 11th century, became stronger. Countess Matilda of Tuscia, in particular, was adept at increasing her holdings and using them politically. She mediated during the Investiture Controversy in 1077 between Holy Roman Emperor Henry IV and Pope Gregory VII in the castle of Canossa. After Matilda died in 1115 – she had willed all her property to the pope – the conflicts between pope and emperor went on for generations. At first local nobles like the Guidi near Florence, the Gheradesca between Pisa and Volterra and the Berardenga between Siena and Arezzo profited politically.

Maritime and long-distance trade led to an increase in the political and economic importance of the cities. Textile production flourished in Arezzo, Lucca and Florence, in Siena financial institutions grew, and Pisa took on the role of a powerful naval republic with property and trading privileges in almost all major neighbouring countries on the Mediterranean. With the economic recovery the Tuscan cities also gained **political autonomy** for the first time; public assemblies were formed, consuls and podestà (city reeves) elected. Neither the emperor nor the pope could prevent the growing self-determination of the cities. The policies of both Emperor Frederick Barbarossa and Emperor Frederick II were defeated by the bitter resistance of communes, which developed into city states and were thus increasingly faced with conflicts between rival noble and patrician dynasties. Communes adopted the tactic of gaining the support of the emperor or the pope. The opposing parties in the communes during the struggle of individual families for political power were named after the battle cries **»Ghibellines«** (the imperial party) and **»Guelfs«** (the

Whose penthouse is the highest up? In the Middle Ages the nobility of San Gimignano competed to see who could build the highest tower.

papal party). There were constant rivalries between the urban centres of power. Florence, above all, was continually at odds with Siena. At the end of the 13th century Pisa's glory as a naval power had already been extinguished. Its rivalry with Genoa ended in disaster, when Pisa lost its entire fleet in the naval battle of Meloria in 1284.

Pisa loses, Florence wins

Florence profited more than Lucca and Siena from Pisa's defeat. The harbour of Pisa silted up and the centre of power in Tuscany moved inland to republican Florence. Meanwhile banking developed on the basis of trade and manufacturing, and the rich guilds of merchants and craftsmen formed an **urban oligarchy** which determined the course of politics from then onwards. In the second half of the 14th century Arezzo, Pistoia, Prato, Cortona, Volterra, San Gimignano and Colle di Val d'Elsa became economically dependent on the Guelf city of Florence, even though they were not subdued by military means. In 1406 Florence finally officially extended its control over Pisa. Only Lucca and Siena remained independent, and by the time Siena was forced to surrender its autonomous status in 1559, Florence too had ceased to be a city state.

THE RULE OF THE MEDICI

Early 15th century	Cosimo founds the Medici dynasty.
1569	Cosimo I becomes Grand Duke of Tuscany.
1737	The Medici dynasty dies out; the Grand Duchy of Tuscany passes to the Habsburgs.

At the beginning of the 15th century the noble families in Florence fought over political control of the city. At first Rinaldo degli Albizzi gained control and sent his opponent Cosimo de' Medici (1389–1464) into exile. A year later Cosimo Il Vecchio (the elder) returned amidst popular jubilation, exiled his opponents and increased his political influence by placing people loyal to him in the most important city offices. Cosimo increased the wealth of his family business, but kept the good of the city in mind and established numerous charitable foundations (►MARCO POLO Insight p. 34). — Cosimo Il Vecchio

After Piero de' Medici's short time in office Lorenzo Il Magnifico entered (1449–1492) the political stage. More than any other person of his time he embodied the manner of governing, lifestyle, world view, education and patronage of the Renaissance man. At the same time he secured for Florence the cultural and political lead in Tuscany by making use of Medici bank funds to the point of bankruptcy. Lorenzo died in 1492 at the age of 43. The **»magnificent«** was followed by the **»unlucky«: Piero**, who was driven out of the city because of his compliant attitude towards King Charles VIII of France. The Dominican monk Girolamo Savonarola seized the moment and proclaimed a theocracy, which failed in 1498 due to the resistance of the people and the papacy. Savonarola was executed and Florence again had a republican city government. — Lorenzo Il Magnifico

<table>
<tr><td>

? MARCO POLO INSIGHT *Medici Coat of Arms*

Did you know where the spheres on the Medici coat of arms come from? They represent pills as the name of the most famous Tuscan dynasty means »physicians«. The patron saints of the Medici were the two early Christian doctors Cosmas and Damian.

</td></tr>
</table>

Only in 1512 did the Medici return, with the help of foreign troops. Their political success was at first mixed until Emperor Charles V elevated the young Alessandro de' Medici to the title of Duke of Florence in 1531. The murder of Alessandro in 1537 at the hands of a relative brought Cosimo I (son of the legendary condottiere Giovanni delle Bande Nere) to power. — Alessandro

The expansionist policies of Cosimo I (1519–1574) were aimed above all at the neighbouring city of Siena, which continued to defend its — Cosimo I

Art and Commerce

The Medici – the name stands for Renaissance art and art patronage, but also for immeasurable wealth and large-scale financing. Unlike other upper-class Florentine families, they did not gain wealth and influence in the 14th century. Their rise took place later, within the century known as the quattrocento, a glorious age for Florence.

Giovanni di Bicci de Medici (d. 1429) laid the foundation for the family's wealth by giving generous loans to the popes during the schism of 1378. When Rome grew as the papal residence, the Medici were already well established as the pope's bankers, and the young Cosimo, later called the Elder, was able to continue his lucrative business deals. The Rome branch of the banking house made about 50-60% of the Medici profits at that time. The Medici managed this without much personal capital, since the high deposits made by the Curia were used to make loans

that brought in a return of up to 20%. The bank had branches in many cities: in Venice for trade with the Orient, in Bruges for trade with northern Europe, in Geneva for central Europe, in London

for the English court and the wool trade, and in Milan and Naples. The Medici also had a commercial monopoly on alum, traded in wool and silk, and sold luxury goods.

Banking Business

Their account books from 1397 to 1420 document profit increases of 5000 gold florins annually – multiply this figure by 100 for today's value in gold in euros. When **Cosimo the Elder** took over the business, profits exceeded 8000 gold florins annually until 1434, and later even increased to 13,000 gold florins annually. Cosimo was generous in making gifts but cautious in lending and kept a close eye on the creditworthiness of his clients, who were generally associated with the Curia or were members of ruling houses and could also increase the political influence of the Medici. Cosimo also hired excellent bankers for his branch offices and reinvested a large part of the profits. In contrast his grandson **Lorenzo il Magnifico** was not interested in business and loved to live beyond his means; by the time he died in 1492 the banking house was almost broke. However, the Medici position was also strengthened by international connections, and despite being exiled after 1513 they continued to rule the city with the help of the popes.

Monumental graves of the famous Medici dukes

Art Patronage

Wealthy Florentine citizens put a large amount of their wealth into charitable foundations. Thus Giovanni Tornabuoni, head of the Medici bank in Rome, had Domenico Ghirlandaio decorate the main choir chapel of **Santa Maria Novella** with wonderful frescoes »as an act of respect and love for God and to praise his house and family«. Other **motivations for patronage** can be seen in the writings of the international merchant Giovanni Rucellai (1403–81), who financed the façade of the church: »I believe that I have earned more honour by spending money than by making it.«

The dimensions of this kind of publicity can be seen in the records of Lorenzo the Magnificent, who figured from the family account books of 1434 to 1471 that his family had paid out about 664,000 gold florins to the poor, to foundations and taxes. Of these 8000 gold florins went to the decoration of the Franciscan church of Santa Croce, 40,000 gold florins to the reconstruction of the monastery of San Marco, 60,000 gold florins to the reconstruction of the parish church of San Lorenzo by Filippo Brunelleschi and 60,000 gold florins to the building of Palazzo Medici. That meant an annual expense of 18,000 gold florins, which were

Lorenzo the Magnificent. Detail of the wall painting *Procession of the Magi* by Benozzo Gozzoli

not covered by the 13,000 gold florins of profit that were made every year, but possibly through real estate.

But why these immense expenditures? On the one hand, alms were given to ease the conscience of the donor, since **loaning money** was considered to be shady business and was condemned by the church. Pious patronage allowed the church to make use of the money, and thus it indirectly condoned the business practices by accepting the donations. By choosing the buildings and the artists that they supported, the patricians showed their level of education, virtuous motives and the **cultured use of their wealth**. Their generosity also served political purposes, for the many large private contracts created jobs, were **visible proof of the economic power** of the families and brought them votes for communal offices. The conviction that not the person but the art he had made possible would outlast time and increase the family fame was also important.

Sassetti Chapel

The **Sassetti Chapel** in the church of Santa Trinita shows how subtly **piety** on the one hand and **wealth** and **political power** on the other can be demonstrated artistically. **Francesco Sassetti** had become rich as the branch head of the Medici bank in Lyon; from 1469 he was an advisor to the young Lorenzo de' Medici. In the chapel next to the choir in **Santa Trinita** he documented his **social rise** and his close **contact to the Medici family**. The confirmation of the Franciscan order by Pope Honorius III in 1223 is depicted in the political centre of contemporary Florence.

The **Sassetti and Medici families** are spectators in the foreground. Near the papal throne on the right stands the bald Francesco Sassetti with his son Federico, next to him the dark-haired Lorenzo de' Medici as well as the greying Antonio Pucci, a relative of the Sassetti and Medici supporter. On the left opposite are Sassetti's three sons Teodore I, Cosimo and Galeazzo. The children of Lorenzo the Magnificent are depicted as they climb the stairs with their tutor: little **Giuliano** first, then **Piero** and finally **Giovanni**, followed by their teacher Matteo Franco and the poet Luigi Pulci. It is interesting that the setting is not the cathedral but the political centre of Florence, a clear indication that Sassetti was more interested in a demonstration of power than in a depiction of St Francis of Assisi.

Elevation to the Nobility

The **Procession of the Magi** in the private chapel of the Medici palace makes it evident that the Medici already enjoyed the prestige of princes in the mid-15th century; it was painted by Benozzo Gozzoli in 1459–60 and depicted the family as kings. The monumental mural refers to three grand events in Florence in which the Medici played a decisive role: the council for the unification of the eastern and western Christian churches in 1439, the great festival for Pope Pius II and Duke Galeazzo Sforza in 1459, and the processions of the Brotherhood of the Magi.

Further proof of the Medici claim to kingship is the **Adoration of the Magi** (around 1475) in the Uffizi Gallery, in which Sandro Botticelli immortalized the Florentine upper class. Even though the kings – portraits of Cosimo the Elder with his sons Giovanni and Piero – are subordinated to the Holy Family, they still occupy the centre of the picture. The younger Medici, Cosimo's grandsons, stand at the side: the pensive **Lorenzo** in dark clothing and his vivacious brother **Giuliano**, who was murdered during the Pazzi conspiracy in 1478, in bright clothing. The actual theme of the picture is upstaged and serves only an excuse for ostentatious representation of the Medici and their supporters. The eldest king, who is kneeling before Mary and the Christ child, is Cosimo the Elder and his son Piero is the figure in the centre with a red cloak.

independence. But Cosimo's goal was to create a state including the whole of Tuscany. He made skilful use of the rivalry between Spain, Germany and France and arranged the conquest of Siena in 1555 by imperial troops. The ennoblement of the Medici reached its pinnacle when they were awarded the title of **Grand Duke of Tuscany** in 1569 by Pope Pius V.

The dynasty dies out

With Francesco I and Ferdinando I a weaker phase of the Medici era had already begun. They concerned themselves only with lucrative dynastic policies that would secure their power and great **splendour at court**. Cosimo II and Ferdinando II allowed their mothers and wives to take the reins of power from their hands. Cosimo III, a religious fanatic, tormented his subjects with merciless taxation policies. The dynasty died out in 1737 with the death of the last, childless Medici ruler, Gian Gastone. During the Medici era Tuscany lost its position as the centre of European textile trading, despite a renewed flowering of the arts. Trade and credit banking were affected, too. In the 16th century the urban moneyed aristocracy looked for low-risk investments and rediscovered land and large estates – the picturesque man-made landscape of Tuscany slowly began to take shape, albeit in the shadow of feudalism.

Inside the funerary chapel of the Medici grand dukes at San Lorenzo in Florence

The son and successor of Franz I was **Archduke Leopold**, who ruled from 1765 to 1790 and resolutely continued his father's policy of re-form. He dissolved the Inquisition and confiscated clerical estates in Tuscany. The abolition of torture and the death sentence (1786) was a further virtually revolutionary measure. He did not achieve the le-gal transformation of tenants into landowners, but after failed har-vests and famines great efforts were made that transformed swampy agricultural regions like the Maremma and Val di Chiana into arable land again. In 1790 the popular archduke left his residence in Flor-ence to succeed his childless brother Emperor Joseph II in Vienna. **Ferdinand III**, the son of Leopold, took over as ruler of Tuscany and proved to be much more reactionary. His policy of neutrality was in-terrupted abruptly by the French revolution and Napoleonic wars.

In 1796 Napoleon Bonaparte conquered northern Italy, and in 1799 also annexed Tuscany after Ferdinand III fled to Vienna. Napoleon turned Habsburg Tuscany into a **puppet state** called the »Kingdom of Etruria«, which was in part ruled by his sister Elisa Bonaparte Baci-occhi. After the collapse of the French empire Napoleon spent one year in exile on the island of Elba off the coast of Tuscany in 1814. The **Con-gress of Vienna** (1814–1815) re-drew the political map of Europe. Ferdinand III returned and ruled the Archduchy of Tuscany until his death (1824) with a policy of restoration. As a consequence of the Con-gress of Vienna the principality of Lucca went to the Bourbons.

Leopold II (1797–1870), son of Ferdinand III, had little opportunity for restoration policies because of the socio-political impulses of the French revolution in the early 19th century. Everywhere in Europe na-tionalist liberation movements rebelled against the old powers and dynasties, against feudal structures and princes. Leopold II also felt the wind of change known as the **Risorgimento**, the Italian movement for unity and independence. From 1830 unrest increased in all the larger cities of the region. The press supported the Risorgimento movement, and democrats demanded an assembly that would write a constitution. Archduke Leopold II was soon forced to accept the reform proposals of Florentine liberals led by Bettino Ricasoli. During the first Italian war of independence against Austria in 1848/1849, Leopold II sought the protection of the king of Naples. In Florence a republican civilian government took power. Leopold returned to Florence in 1852 with the help of Austrian troops. All progressive elements were against him. However, the Florentine-Tuscan independence movement felt unable to bring about the renewal with its own resources and thus sought the solidarity of Piedmont and its chief minister, Camillo Benso di Cavour.

TUSCANY IN UNITED ITALY

17 March 1861 Tuscany is part of the newly founded Kingdom of Italy.

L'Unità
In the decisive war of independence in 1859 Austria lost northern Italy. Leopold II abdicated on 27 April 1859. Under the ruling house of Piedmont, the only liberal constitutional state in Italy at that time, the unification of Italy was completed in 1859–1861: L'Unità. On 15 March 1860 Tuscany voted by plebiscite to join the newly planned kingdom of Italy. On 17 March 1861 it became part of the kingdom under Vittorio Emanuele II. **Florence** replaced Turin as the **capital of Italy** from 1865 to 1871 when the king entered Rome.

Industrializa-
tion
At this time the industrial age arrived in Tuscany. Heavy industry was established in Livorno, Florence, Pistoia and Piombino. Prato became a centre of the textile industry. The economic upswing also politicized of the labour force. The **Socialists** gained ground, but in the second half of the 19th century liberal democratic politicians held office in most city halls in Tuscany. Despite industrialization Tuscany remained for the most part – thanks to the agrarian policies of the Habsburgs – an agricultural region that was still farmed in the centuries-old system of tenancy.

20TH CENTURY

1921	Founding of the Communist Party of Italy in Livorno
1940	Italy enters the Second World War.
Sep 1943	Italy surrenders. Villages and cities in Tuscany are plundered and destroyed during the German withdrawal.
1966	The river Arno floods the old city of Florence.

Florence was the capital of Italy from 1865 to 1871

In 1915 Italy entered the First World War on the Allied side against the partners in the former Triple Alliance, Germany and Austria. Between 1914 and 1918 the heavy industry of Tuscany worked at full capacity.

First World War

After the end of the war Italian soldiers streamed back to their home provinces but faced immediate unemployment. Labour strikes and rural unrest in the whole region soon caused the ideological radicalization of the political parties. On 21 January 1921 the Communist Party of Italy (PCI) was founded in Livorno, Tuscany. A year and a half later the Fascist movement under **Benito Mussolini**, later known as Il Duce, prepared to take over government. After the »March on Rome« in October 1922, paramilitary organizations of the Fascists occupied all key positions in the region and the king nominated Mussolini prime minister. The antifascist resistance was stronger in

1920s and 1930s

Tuscany than in other places but Fascist forces prevailed. Mussolini's populist policies enthralled the masses, and the labour programmes of the 1930s brought about an improvement in the economy. The construction of the central line of the Italian railways (Florence–Bologna) was celebrated as a heroic feat. The **monarchy** continued to exist only on paper.

Second World War

In 1940 Italy entered the war. Tuscan cities, especially Pisa, were partially destroyed in Allied bombing raids. In 1943 the Allies landed in southern Italy. The Grand Fascist Council deposed Mussolini, who was arrested in July 1943. When Italy surrendered in September 1943, the German forces disarmed the Italian army but met with resistance from partisans in northern and central Italy. The Italian Resistenza lasted almost two years. During the German retreat the SS destroyed whole villages in the provinces of Pisa, Arezzo, Siena and Florence.

> **MARCO POLO TIP**
>
> *Tuscany during the war* **Insider Tip**
>
> The estate La Foce in Val d'Orcia is an enchanting site whose gardens attract tourists from all over the world. It is difficult to believe that war raged here. The diary of Iris Origo, the former owner of La Foce who made Tuscany her adopted home, brings these memories back to life. She tells of the hardships of the population, of their sympathy with the partisans, of the revenge of the retreating Germans and of the fearful wait for the arrival of the Allies. Iris Origo: War in Val D'Orcia: An Italian War Diary, 1943–44 (David R. Godine, 1984).

On 2 June 1946 a plebiscite proclaimed the Italian Republic with a clear majority. Vittorio Emanuele III abdicated. The Christian Democratic party (DC) won the first national elections, followed by the Socialist Party (PSI) and the Communist Party (PCI). Florence became the official capital of the Regione Toscana. The PCI won the **first regional elections** with an overwhelming majority and took the position of mayor and the top communal positions in almost all Tuscan cities and communities. The PCI remained the strongest political party in Italy until the late 1980s. In 1950 the Sila Law provided for the partial dispossession of Tuscan large landowners – the farmers finally owned their own land.

Catastrophic flood 1966

Florence suffered the worst flooding in its history on 4 November 1966. The Arno burst its banks and the water level in the old city reached six metres (20ft).

1990s

On 27 May 1993 six people were killed by a bomb in the historic quarter of Florence. The massive detonation damaged the southern and western wings of the Uffizi considerably. After years of renovation the Uffizi were restored to their former splendour by 1998.

21ST CENTURY

2011	Berlusconi resigns. Drastic austerity measures are instituted.
2012	Shipwreck of the »Costa Concordia« off the island of Giglio
2014	In February Matteo Renzi is asked to form a new government.

National elections in April brought **Silvio Berlusconi** and his party Popolo della Libertà (PdL), the successor to his Forza Italia, to power for the third time. Tuscany remained »left«, even if voting by the traditional leftist parties (reform communists, Green) is down, causing great losses.

In a nation-wide referendum in June 2011 the overwhelming majority of Italy and Tuscany voted, among other things, against a reintroduction of **atomic energy**, against the privatisation of the **water utilities** and against government attempts to introduce legislation making it possible for it to be »lawfully impeded« from possible criminal proceedings.

In August/September 2011 reduced ratings cause further problems in refinancing the high government debts. Silvio Berlusconi resigned on 12 November 2011 clearing the way for a new government under former EU commisar Mario Monti. After Mario Monti's resignation in April 2013 and that of his successor Enrico Etta in early February 2014 the social democrat Matteo Renzi is commissioned that same month with building a new government.

In January 2012 the cruise ship Costa Concordia rammed a rock just off the **island of Giglio** and began to take in water. The ship listed sideways about 65 degrees. 32 of the more than 4220 passengers and crew lost their lives. The entire surrounding coastal region, which is part of the Parco Nazionale dell' Arcipelago Toscano, was in danger of an ecological catastrophe due to the leaking fuel; it was possible to pump the fuel off the ship however. The salvaging of the cruise ship caused great problems – only in September 2013 was the wreck placed upright again and more months passed before it could be transported away. The cruise ship line, captain and other ship's personnel came under investigation since the Costa Concordia possibly deliberately sailed a course that was too close to the coastline.

After two austerity packages – one for 48 bil. euros and one for 54.2 bil. euros – as well as the adoption of an effective »debt brake« into the constitution under the Berlusconi government, the following government under Mario Monti instituted the »Decreto Salva-Italia« (Decree to save Italy) in December 2011, which included further

The cruise ship Costa Concordia rammed a rock right off the island Giglio in January 2012

drastic budget cuts of 24 bil. euros. 2012 and 2013 brought even more cuts, which affected primarily the Italian health system and the universities. All national holidays were moved to Sundays in order to create more working days. The controversial raise of the VAT from 21 to 22 % took effect in October 2013. These and other measures were meant to **reduce Italy's immense mountain of debt**, which amounted to 1,900 bil. euros or about 120 % of the GDP. The fear that the rigorous austerity measures would cause the Italian GDP to shrink made additional negotiations necessary in 2012 for a new debt payment procedure: the EU also had to start new programmes to promote the Italian economy.

The austerity measures also brought on new plans to reduce the number of Italian **provinces** as well as the ratio of **the number of politicians to the population**. These reforms have not been implemented yet due to the frequent changes of government.

Art and Culture

Art History

About 20,000 cultural monuments have been counted in Tuscany – more than in any other region in Italy. This includes graves from the Etruscan period, medieval city palaces, churches and chapels, Renaissance villas, wonderful parks and private gardens.

ETRUSCANS AND ROMANS

The first period of advanced civilization in Italy was that of the Etruscans. They settled in the area between the Arno, the Tiber, the ridge of the Apennines and the Tyrrhenian Sea from about 900 BC. Between the 8th and the 5th century BC they were organized in a federation of twelve cities: Arretium (Arezzo), Velathri (Volterra), Curtuns (Cortona), Perusia (Perugia), Clusium (Chiusi), Rusellae (Roselle), Populonia, Vatluna (Vetulonia), Volsinii (Orvieto), Vulci, Tarquinii (Tarquinia), Caere (Cerveteri) and Veii (Veio). The dividing line between Etruscan and Roman art cannot be determined in space or time.

First period of advanced civilization

There are no examples of Etruscan temples in Tuscany, but they deserve mention. Unlike Greek temples they were not placed in the surroundings like monuments, but were embedded into the landscape with sensitivity for spatial planning. Temples rested on a podium, faced a courtyard and had a deep portico. This spatial accent developed into a trademark of Roman architecture in he following centuries.

Temples

Etruscan art has been passed down above all through finds from necropolises. The end of the 8th century BC saw the emergence of the **chamber grave**,which has several rooms or even large areas for dances and games, just as an aristocratic house would have had. Only in the course of the 4th century did the chamber grave make way for the spacious, richly painted burial hall (Tomba dei Rilievi in Cerveteri). Vases filled with wine, oil or grain, gold jewellery and small art objects which were placed in the graves as funerary goods testify to the Etruscan belief in an afterlife.

Necropolises, grave finds

In Volterra and Chiusi **ash urns of alabaster and tuffstone** were produced and decorated with reliefs. Mythological themes or

Next to the Leaning Tower the Baptistry which unites Romanesque and Gothic elements is one of the main attractions of Pisa.

festivities were depicted, often framed architecturally with columns or lintels. Their expressiveness lies in the representation of the figures, which are turned and stretched, rather than in their spatial depth and detail. The Guarnacci Museum of Volterra and the Etruscan museums of Chiusi, Cortona and Florence have extensive collections of urns of the Hellenistic period (4th–1st century BC).

Sculptures Even though the Bronze Warrior in the Museo Archeologico in Florence is an example of Greek influence, Etruscan culture achieved at least partial independence in the area of sculpture too. Marked examples for the archaic character of Etruscan sculpture are the Chimera, also in Florence, as well as the Capitoline Wolf, which was created in the 5th century BC and which stands in the Palazzo dei Conservatori in Rome today. Typically for the time, the expressive strength of both figures lies in the type and not in individual characteristics. In the 2nd century BC the originality of Etruscan art was lost in the wake of Roman mixed culture. An example is the Arringatore (speaker) from the Museo Archeologico in Florence: the inscription and typical stiffness are Etruscan, but the posture and clothing are Roman.

Painting Etruscan painting has been documented since the 6th century BC and shows – in the burial cult too – **depictions from life**: hunting, fishing and banquets were part of the repertoire of the tomb paintings. An impressive example is the giant of the Tomba del Tifone in Tarquinia / Latium (late 2nd century to early 1st century BC). Without the example of Hellenistic art the great pathos of movement, the passionate facial expression, the modelling of the body and the rich colour spectrum would have been unthinkable.

Rome prevails From the 5th century BC Rome began to expand its sphere of influence and conquer the Etruscan cities, until the last one fell in 290 BC. A new **system of roads** was built, connecting Rome to the main cities of Tuscany. It corresponds essentially to the modern roads. The Romans profited from the Etruscans' technical knowledge, as in the construction of vaults or in water engineering. Cities like Volterra, Arezzo and Fiesole flourished. Temples, theatres and thermal baths were built, often using material from demolished Etruscan monuments. The strict axial outlines of Roman cities can still be seen clearly in the colony of Lucca: the two main streets, cardo and decumanus, intersect at the forum, which is Piazza San Michele today. The streets that divide the city into islands of houses (insulae) have also remained. Since the destroyed amphitheatre was used as the foundation for houses in the Middle Ages, its elliptical form is still clearly visible today.

ROMANESQUE PERIOD

Tuscan Romanesque style is also called **Proto-Renaissance** since –
unlike the Romanesque style in France, Britain and north of the Alps
– it prepared the way and was a model for the Renaissance, just as
antiquity was. Two buildings in **Florence**, both dating from around
the middle of the 11th century, mark the beginning of the Proto-
Renaissance: the baptistery of the cathedral and the church San Miniato al Monte. The baptistery, which was begun in 1059, is an eight-
sided, two-storey central-plan building with a choir chapel. It is so
close to the architectural concepts of ancient times that the Renaissance architect Filippo Brunelleschi in the early 15th century copied
the structure, assuming that it was really a building from ancient
Rome. The façade of San Miniato al Monte is thoroughly inspired by
antiquity. With its green-white marble covering and its geometric
decorations it is reminiscent of a reliquary. Architectural history was
made not only in Florence but also in Pisa, where from 1062 the larg-

Forerunner of
the
Renaissance

**The Romanesque cathedral in Pisa was the first church to be built on
a cross-shaped outline and with a transept**

Detail of a capital in the Abbazia Sant'Antimo near Montalcino

est and architecturally most important Romanesque cathedral was built. Its concept of a **church in the form of a cross with a transept** and a dome above the crossing, which goes back to Byzantine models, was new. Typical features of Pisan architecture include the blind arcades with rhombus-shaped patterns on the ground floor and the rows of pilasters with architrave on the upper floors, which refer to ancient models. The dwarf galleries of the choir are high Romanesque. Elements of the most diverse styles and cultural regions melded in the cathedral of Pisa to a new architectural language, which became the model for urban ecclesiastical buildings in the 12th and 13th centuries. This can be seen especially clearly in the church San Michele in Foro in Lucca, which not only adopts the floor plan of a columned basilica with transept, but also the system of decoration with blind arcades and marble facing around the entire building.

Rural churches From the 11th century many parish churches were built outside the villages. These simple small churches, called **pieve**, follow the basilica pattern and have one or three apses, simple square pillars, and no decoration or divisions of the walls.

Architectural sculpture plays a minor role in Italian Romanesque style, except for the capitals. Guglielmo made the figurative decorations on the upper part of the cathedral façade of Pisa, whose style – influenced by the Lombard region – shows a love of rich decorative effects and reveals influences from Byzantine, Islamic and ancient art. There were numerous commissions for sculptors for interior furnishings: baptismal fonts, pulpit and altar balustrades.

Sculpture

In the mid-13th century Nicola Pisano from southern Italy received the commission for the pulpit of the baptistery in Pisa. The artist, whose name is in the inscription around the pulpit, here laid the foundation for Italian sculpture. He departed from the traditional square pulpit form and created a free-standing hexagon, which was covered with panels of relief sculpture. From then on many pulpits in Tuscany followed this principle. The concept of reliefs that take up the entire height of the parapets was also new. The figures no longer stand out like silhouettes from the relief background; instead they overlap and give an impression of depth. The **intense study of antiquity** by the sculptor is evident not only in the direct adoption of particular figures and changed conception of relief sculpture, but also in the natural depiction of many individual figures.

Nicola (Niccolò) Pisano

Painting on panels did not have a continuous tradition. A change in the liturgy had far-reaching consequences for painting: the priest no longer celebrated mass from behind the altar, but rather in front of it. The altar could now be decorated with a painted panel, known as a retable. This resulted in a new task for painters. The oldest panels show Christ surrounded by scenes from his life; later saints were added. Guido da Siena completed a retable in 1260 on which the Virgin is surrounded by four saints. Christ on the cross was another common subject. Byzantine influence can be seen in the fact that the figure of the living Christ was replaced with the dead Christ, his body turned slightly to the left, and in the strictly hieratic composition of the figures on all of the early panels.

Painting

In the late 11th century the economic rise of the cities began. Family towers were built as the emblem of individual noble families. Their height showed the owner's importance – 15 of the original 72 towers have survived in San Gimignano. The **palazzo comunale** added another important building task in the 13th century; it was the office of the podestà and other political organs. The Palazzo Pubblico in Siena and Palazzo Vecchio in Florence impressively demonstrate the increased power of the urban population. The **Piazza Signoria in Florence** took its present form when many houses were torn down in the 14th century. A monumental axis was built between the Piazza Signoria and the cathedral and adorned with important buildings like

Palazzi and family towers

the Palazzo Vecchio, the Loggia dei Lanzi, Orsanmichele, the campanile and the cathedral. The city inhabitants took an active part in shaping their surroundings: in Florence there was a tradition from the late Middle Ages of holding a competition for the best design, which was open to everyone, when a public building or artistic decoration of a building was planned. Another Florentine characteristic was to entrust the construction, care and repair of individual buildings to various guilds. In Siena a municipal commission for the beautification of the city was founded. It was responsible for the adornment of streets and squares.

GOTHIC

Churches The beginning of the construction of the Cistercian abbey San Galgano (today in ruins), which was built from 1224 as a basilica with ribbed vaulting, a transept and a choir without an apse, is considered to be the beginning of the Gothic period in Tuscany. In this respect it followed the **model of Burgundian Cistercian churches**, while the structuring of the walls with arcades, false triforia and lancet windows showed innovation. The forms used in this church had great influence on the major building projects of the time. Above all the churches of the mendicant orders made use of this new repertoire of forms, as can be seen in San Domenico in Arezzo and elsewhere.

Siena and Florence Siena was to Gothic architecture what Florence and above all Pisa were to the Romanesque style. The Sienese first planned to give their Romanesque cathedral a new look in the early 13th century. At the east end the renovation affected the transept, the straight choir wall, the square side chapels of the choir and the massive dome over the hexagonal crossing. Vaults were added to the unusually high nave. The façade, which was renewed from 1284 by **Giovanni Pisano**, was intended to simulate a larger church through its height and rich sculptural decoration on the three doorways. About 50 years later an even more ambitious plan was made, which did not prove to be viable: the main part of the existing cathedral was to become the transept of a new, much larger nave. After part of the aisle was built, significant constructional defects were found by consultants and the enlargement was stopped. In Florence the campanile of the cathedral was the defining building project for two decades. It was begun in 1334 by Giotto, who constructed the plinth, and continued from 1337 by **Andrea Pisano**. Pisano gave the storey for the sculptural decoration a strong vertical alignment, which was continued on higher storeys. Construction was completed by Francesco Talenti who reverted to cubic storeys with an increasing number of windows with each further storey.

The sculptural decoration of the cathedral façade of Siena is among the most important figural works of the Italian Gothic period. Inspired by the sculpture of south-west France, Giovanni Pisano and his studio created a complete series of sculptures whose theme was the story of the Virgin and the coming of Christ. Unlike the French models, whose figures are part of the architecture, in Siena they stand as an independent element. The architecture became a backdrop in front of which the sculpture developed. On the pulpit of the cathedral of Siena the Pisani developed even further what had been achieved with the pulpit in Pisa cathedral: the basic form was expanded to an octagon. Scenes with many small figures predominate and seem to wind around the entire balustrade. Under the influence of French sculpture the figures are more supple with softer robes and expressive features. **Arnolfo di Cambio** and **Tino da Camaino**, who were the assistants and successors of the Pisani, allowed themselves to be influenced more by international Gothic style, so that their sculpture lost individuality and expression. The works of Jacopo della Quercia reveal a more exact imitation of nature and a close study of antiquity, combined with a high standard of Gothic stylization.

Sculpture: Giovanni Pisano

The crowds on the Siena cathedral pulpit, which Nicola Pisano carved from one block of marble

Painting:
Cimabue,
Duccio di
Buoninsegna

From the mid-13th century the two main centres of painting, which continued to be strongly influenced by Byzantine art, were Florence and Siena. Their most important representatives were Cimabue and Duccio di Buoninsegna. The style of painting of the Florentine Cimabue shows an otherworldly abstraction. He tried to capture a vision of the transcendental world on a panel. The Sienese Duccio depicts the *Virgin Mary in the Maestà*, which he created for the cathedral in Siena in 1311 (today in the Museo dell'Opera), and theMadonna Rucellai (Florence, Santa Maria Novella) in 1285 as unaffected, elegant, almost graceful. His human image is defined by classical standards, and the bodies of his figures are quite sophisticated in form. While Duccio found his models in Byzantium, his colleague Simone Martini, who together with the brothers Pietro and Ambrogio Lorenzetti created the large altar paintings for Sienese churches, took French Gothic as his inspiration.

Giotto took a step that gave a new direction to the development of painting: in his frescoes for the Peruzzi chapel and the Bardi chapel in Santa Croce (Florence), in a constant striving for harmony of proportion and balance he tried to grasp and convey a new consciousness. Realistic detail and rich colours mark the paintings of this artist, who became famous in his own lifetime, and whose influence no artist in Florence could escape.

The **painting of the large wall of the Camposanto** in Pisa was no ordinary task. Around the middle of the 14th century Francesco Traini worked on the fresco, only part of which remains today, on the subject of the joy of life and certainty of death, with depictions of the Last Judgement, paradise and hell as well as the encounter with death of knights and ladies of the court. The Great Plague of 1348 was the motivation for detailed study of this subject. Thanks to the most modern restoration techniques the rich colours of some frescos could be brought to light again.

RENAISSANCE

Beginnings of
the Renais-
sance in the
quattrocento

Florence was the centre of the early Renaissance in Italy, which developed in the first decades of the 15th century, the quattrocento. The artists were interested above all in the physical world. They tried to describe it realistically with the aid of scientific methods but at the same time to give it an ideal character. Renaissance artists took the works of ancient times for their models. A leading idea of the enthusiasm for antiquity was that the »dignity and excellence of mankind« was based on his individuality, not on divine salvation. Every person was accorded an individual sphere of knowledge and action. This had far-reaching consequences for the arts. The artist, previously no more than a simple craftsman, now saw himself as a humanist, who by the power of his »virtù«, his ability, formed individual ideas into individual works. And in truth artistic creations achieved a level of scientific, artistic, compositional and contextual intent that went far beyond the concept of craftsmanship.

Two persons had a definitive influence on Renaissance architecture: Brunelleschi and Alberti. Filippo Brunelleschi (▶Famous People), the builder of the dome of the cathedral in Florence, is considered to be the man who renewed architecture. Clear composition, geometrically proportioned forms, balanced spatial arrangement (in reference to lighting, too), the use of ancient motifs and the adoption of elements of Byzantine tradition mark his work. Leon Battista Alberti, a humanist scholar who also worked as an architect and adviser to princely courts, provided, so to speak, the theoretical superstructure with his writings on the theory of architecture.

Architecture: Brunelleschi and Alberti

The classical Renaissance façade was developed at Santa Maria Novella in Florence which, with its monumental blind arcades in the ground floor and the white-green facing, tied in to the Florentine Proto-Renaissance. Its features included large volutes, added as a connection between the nave and the lower aisles. The church Santa Maria dei Carceri in Prato, designed by Giuliano da Sangallo, was a pioneering work. Its central plan revisited the old theme of martyrs' churches.

Churches

The search for style manifested itself more strongly than ever in secular architecture. The castle-like residences of the nobility were replaced by the city palaces of princes and the leading families of the quattrocento (15th century). Palazzi were designed to look like monuments with their regular composition, clear division of storeys and a symmetrical arrangement of the façade. An important change in the floor plan was to move the stairs from the courtyard to the inside of the building. This permitted the evolution of square **arcaded courtyards**. Coats of arms and allegorical references in friezes, capitals, door and window frames glorified the owner of the building. The three-storey façade of Palazzo Rucellai in Florence (begun around 1457) adopted the order of columns of the Colosseum in Rome, with pilasters that had Doric capitals on the ground floor, Ionic capitals on the first floor and Corinthian capitals on the second floor.

Secular buildings

In Tuscany the influence of Giovanni Pisano dominated until the end of the 14th century. At the beginning of the quattrocento, however, a **fundamental change** took place. In Florence unfinished buildings required completion: the bronze doors of the baptistery, the cycle of statues on Orsanmichele, the decorations for the cathedral and the campanile – all were challenging projects for sculptors who were ex-

Sculpture

»Rebirth« of Antiquity

In the early 15th century major Italian architects began to get interested in the way antiquity used forms. They began to use Greek and Roman structures as models for their own work. Filippo Brunelleschi is considered to be the creator of Renaissance architecture. He drew up the plans for the dome of the cathedral of Florence and drew his knowledge from the study of Greco-Roman buildings. In painting the rediscovery of the central perspective was important as is made possible the portrayal of three dimensions on canvas.

ITALY

▶ **The most important people and works**

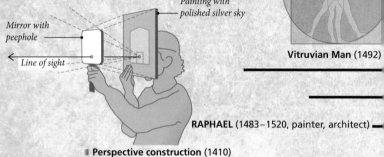

Painting with polished silver sky

Mirror with peephole

← Line of sight

Vitruvian Man (1492)

RAPHAEL (1483–1520, painter, architect)

■ **Perspective construction** (1410)

FILIPPO BRUNELLESCHI

(1377–1446, architect, sculptor)

BRAMANTE (1444–1514, master builde

David (bronze, 1430–1433?,
DONATELLO (1386–1466, sculptor)   ■ 1444–1446?)

GERMAN-SPEAKING AREA

AGRIPPA VON NETTESHEIM (1486–1535, theologian, lawyer, doctor)

ALBRECHT DÜRER (1471–1528, painter, graphic artist)

HANS HOLBEIN THE ELDER (1465–1524, painter)

SEBASTIAN BRANT (1457–1521, lawyer, poet)

1400	1450

»QUATTROCENTO«
EARLY RENAISSANCE IN ITALY

GOTHIC

MIDDLE AGES   **RENAISSANCE**

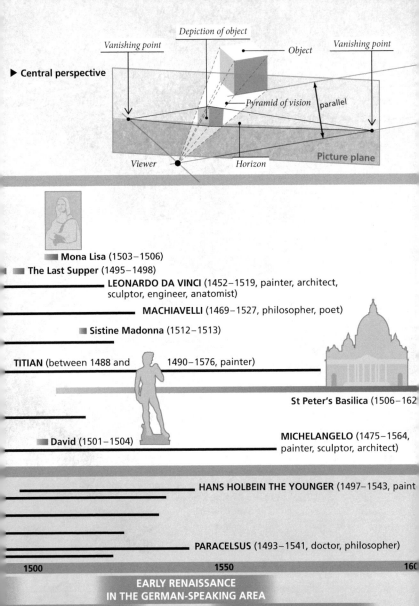

▶ Central perspective

Vanishing point

Depiction of object

Object

Vanishing point

Pyramid of vision

parallel

Viewer

Horizon

Picture plane

Mona Lisa (1503–1506)

The Last Supper (1495–1498)

LEONARDO DA VINCI (1452–1519, painter, architect, sculptor, engineer, anatomist)

MACHIAVELLI (1469–1527, philosopher, poet)

Sistine Madonna (1512–1513)

TITIAN (between 1488 and 1490–1576, painter)

St Peter's Basilica (1506–162

MICHELANGELO (1475–1564, painter, sculptor, architect)

David (1501–1504)

HANS HOLBEIN THE YOUNGER (1497–1543, paint

PARACELSUS (1493–1541, doctor, philosopher)

| 1500 | 1550 | 160 |

EARLY RENAISSANCE
IN THE GERMAN-SPEAKING AREA

»CINQUECENTO«
IGH HRENAISSANCE IN ITALY

HIGH RENAISSANCE
IN THE GERMAN-SPEAKING AREA

LATE RENAISSANCE   BAROQUE

The famous *David* by Michelangelo on the Piazza della Signoria in Florence. The original is on display in the Galleria dell'Accademia.

pected to express the new ideas about humankind in visual form. Consequently independent, free-standing sculpture was developed, a pioneering innovation that was taken up outside Italy only much later. One of the first examples of a free-standing sculpture was David by **Donatello** (▶Famous People) around 1430–1433 (Florence, Museo Nazionale del Bargello). Thorough study of a living model was the prerequisite for rendering posture and surfaces of the body on which bones, muscles and tendons appear. The sensual beauty and nudity of the figure were completely new. The sculptor learned from antiquity without copying it; he knew how to apply it in an individual manner. Donatello changed the structuring of reliefs in a fundamental way by making the background a spherical three-dimensional space. With **Lorenzo Ghiberti** this stylistic change can easily be comprehended: in the 28 reliefs on the bronze doors of the baptistery (Florence, 1403–1424) he created a work that remains strongly related to the Gothic period and takes up early Renaissance subjects only hesitantly. In contrast the Renaissance forms of the bronze statuette of St Stephen for Orsanmichele (Florence 1427–1428) are highly sophisticated: the young martyr radiates stillness and grace. **Andrea del Verrocchio's** work for Orsanmichele, including the bronze group *Christ and St Thomas*, was mostly executed on behalf of the

Medici. **Luca della Robbia** and his nephew Andrea adapted the technique of faience to large sculptures and created numerous works in majolica. At first they limited themselves to figures in white relief on blue backgrounds; later the terracottas became colourful, as in the frieze on the Ospedale del Ceppo in Pistoia.

The universal artist **Michelangelo Buonarroti** (▶Famous People) worked mainly but not only as a sculptor. Probably the most famous of his works are the much-copied marble *David* (Galleria dell' Accademia, Florence), the painting *The Holy Family* (Uffizi, Florence) and the **Medici funeral chapel** at San Lorenzo in Florence. Numerous Italian artists came to the city on the Arno to learn from Michelangelo`s example before settling down in their native regions.

When Masaccio began to decorate the Brancacci chapel in Florence in 1427, most of his colleagues still worked in the international Gothic style. His Brancacci frescoes and the painted funerary monument with the Holy Trinity in Santa Maria Novella (Florence) initiated a radical change: the **rules of perspective** were followed with scientific correctness, the figures are fixed in a space and shown in rounded detail by means of light and shade. The composition of a scene as a space in perspective was adopted by Paolo Uccello, Filippo Lippi and Andrea Castagno and developed further, while outside Florence the international Gothic style was still in use for years. From 1438 Domenico Veneziano enriched the draughtsman-like, linear orientation of Florentine painting with intense colours. In the mid-15th century painting also became more open to influences from antiquity. **Antonio del Pollaiuolo** was fascinated by complex ancient motifs of movement, which he tried to capture in his works. Space and atmosphere were intended to emphasize the expressiveness of his figures. The Carmelite monk **Fra Filippo Lippi** idealized Biblical events in his works by means of worldly beauty, as in the fresco cycle created between 1452 and 1464 in the cathedral of Prato and hisAnnunciation in San Lorenzo in Florence. The frescoes of Fra Angelico in the Florentine monastery of San Marco show astonishing **spatial depth and realism** and are marked by a deep faith. **Piero della Francesca** is considered to be the great master of perspective. His fresco cycle in the church of San Francesco in Arezzo, which was executed between 1452 and 1466, is one of the most expressive works of Renaissance painting. The Florentine **Sandro Botticelli** painted figures and forms that were full of atmosphere and represented ideal types. He placed numerous portrait figures in his paintings and emphasized linear elements of composition. His pagan mythological pictures are filled with a dreamy melancholy; they include the famous *Birth of Venus* and *Primavera*, both in the Uffizi Gallery in Florence. **Leonardo da Vinci** was a pivotal figure in the establishment of high Renaissance painting (▶Famous People). As an »uomo universale« he

Painting,
Masaccio

Detail of the famous fresco cycle that Piero della Francesca created in Arezzo

devoted himself to intense scientific and technical studies, designed architectural plans and also constructed stage machinery.

After a period of absolute artistic flowering came a century marked by plague, poverty and war. During the high Renaissance artists mastered the classical world of forms and ideas. The understanding of ancient art had reached a high standard; materials and technique were used to perfection. Florentine art began to liberate itself from the strict model of nature. The perfect balance of classical art was no longer the main goal. Artists were challenged by decay, sensuality and death, while at the same time invention, imagination and expressiveness became important concepts. New genres in painting, such as the landscape and still life, emerged. Next to the church the most important clients were the ducal house and the nobility. Theoretical interest in the history of art awakened, as the **writings of Giorgio Vasari** on the life and work of Italian artists testify. An example is Giambologna's well in the park of the Medici villa Pratolino near Florence. Its personification of a mountain range was given the form of an ancient giant whose limbs and beard melt into the rock out of which he was sculpted. The boundary between art and nature blurs as they become united as equals.

Founding of the Uffizi In Florence as early as 1582 a museum had been established in the Uffizi – which Vasari had originally designed as an administrative building – in order to house cultural treasures of the city which no longer had a liturgical function and works of the 14th to 16th centuries, as well as to present examples of Umbrian, Emilian and Venetian, Flemish and German art.

BAROQUE

Tuscany an artistic backwater The Italian centres of the Baroque were Rome, Bologna and Naples. Florence never wanted to be a Baroque city, but preferred to hold on to its Renaissance urban features. The few Baroque new or remodelled buildings there were rather sober and reserved. They lacked expansive staircases, ballrooms with ornate decorations and richly appointed door and window frames. The **late Baroque style in Florence** flourished for a short time under Archduke Cosimo III, who employed a few artists in his archducal workshops. Palazzo Pitti was one of the few buildings that was redesigned in the Baroque style; it was enlarged and newly decorated in the 17th century. The much-occupied painter and architect Pietro da Cortona, a master of illusionist ceiling painting, decorated the rooms in the piano nobile. In the second half of the 17th century Pier Francesco Silvani and Antonio Ferri gave Palazzo Corsini a monumental staircase and a richly decorated and stuccoed ballroom, which made the building closer to Roman than to Florentine Baroque. The painting of the choir of Santa Maria Maddalena dei Pazzi by Pier Francesco Silvani and Cirro Ferri is rich but comparatively crude. All in all neither Tuscan Baroque painting nor its architecture achieved the quality of Roman Baroque.

19TH AND 20TH CENTURIES

The status of Tuscany in the Baroque period as an artistic backwater did not change in the 18th and 19th centuries. The discovery of Roman antiquities and their reception by artists put Rome and archaeological excavations in southern Italy at the centre of attention. In the second half of the 19th century art schools and colonies formed in various places, as everywhere in Europe. In the late 1860s the **Macchiaioli** group of artists formed around Giovanni Fattori, who taught at the academy in Florence from 1847. They developed an independent early impressionism that was influenced by the work of Camille Corot.

19th century

Art nouveau left more traces in Tuscany than might have been expected in this region. Art nouveau buildings and interesting architectural details of this style – window frames, painted façades or shop windows – can be found today above all in **Viareggio**, where after a large fire in 1917 almost the entire seaside promenade was rebuilt in a new style, as well as in Lucca, Florence, Pistoia, Pisa and Montecatini Terme. The most famous representative of art nouveau in the region was the Florence-born **Galileo Chini** (1873–1956), who founded a ceramics factory in 1896 and soon gained international attention with his decorations. He owed many of his inspirations to a two-year stay in Bangkok, where he helped decorate the royal palace. Chini later moved his factory from Florence to Borgo San Lorenzo. The close cooperation between Chini and the architect Alfredo Belluomini brought forth the famous, oriental-style Caffè Margherita in Viareggio.

20th century, art nouveau

Painting In Italy, too, avant-garde art emerged from the cities, since artistic movements like Futurism were inextricably connected with the experience of urban life and the industrialization of society. Most young talent was drawn to the cities: Gino Severini, for example, who was born in Cortona in 1883 and with Umberto Boccioni was responsible for developing Futurism in painting. **Amadeo Modigliani** (▶Famous People), born in 1884 in Livorno, also found the inspiration for his art not in his home town but above all in Paris, which attracted artists from all over Europe in the early 20th century. One of the few internationally recognized artists to remain closely connected to his Tuscan homeland was Marino Marini (1901–1980) from Pistoia. There is now a museum of the sculptor's works in Pistoia, as in Florence too.

Architecture There are few excellent examples of urban planning and architecture of the 20th century in Tuscany, since most cities of the region have a complete historic urban fabric and thus little room for large new projects. Between 1933 and 1936 the railway station Santa Maria Novella was built in Florence. Its elements of modernist style make it one of the most important large buildings of Italian functionalism, but its marble facing is a continuation of local tradition. One of the architects responsible was Giovanni Michelucci from Pistoia, who is now honoured in his hometown (like Marini) with a permanent exhibition.

Restorations The opportunities are greater for conversions or restorations of existing buildings. A successful example is Pietro Carlo Pellegrini's conversion of the cathedral museum in Lucca, which was re-opened in 1994. He united four buildings from different eras into one complex, without blurring the architectural individuality of each one.

CONTEMPORARY ART

Special collections and exhibition venues Even though Tuscany is not a region where many modern or contemporary artists have worked, their art can nevertheless be found in a number of places. An especially prominent example is the **Giardino dei Tarocchi**, a fairytale park with fantasy sculptures near Capalbio by Niki de Saint Phalle, who died in May 2002. The sculpture park has now become a magnet for visitors to southern Tuscany. Saint Phalle's artist colleague Daniel Spoerri has followed this example and constructed an interesting sculpture garden close to Seggiano. Prato, the otherwise rather »unartistic« neighbour of Florence, has specialized in contemporary art: since 1988 the **Centro per l'Arte Contemporanea Luigi Pecci** has shown works by Richard Baquié and Willi Kopf as well as Anne and Patrick Poirier. The worthwhile private

Gori collection of the textile magnate Giuliano Gori near Montale by Pistoia can be viewed at no charge but only after a written request six weeks in advance. The unique collection currently includes 56 works from Alberto Burri through Dani Karavan, Bukichi Inoue, A. R. Penck, Richard Serra, Robert Morris, Enrico Castellani, Emilio Vedova and Pietro Coletta (Fattoria di Celle – The Gori Collection, Via Montalese 7, 51030 Santomato di Pistoia, www.goricoll.it). The exhibits in the Lu.C.C.A (Lucca Center of Contemporary Art, www.luccamuseum.com), in BLU Palazzo d' Arte e Cultura (www.palazzoblu.org) in Pisa as well as in Pisas Centro Espositivo San Michele degli Scalzi (www.comune.pisa.it/cultura/doc/CENTROSMS.htm) are all worth seeing.

The artist Mauro Staccioli, who was born in Volterra, placed some of his large sculptures noticeably around his home town between 1972 and 2009. His geometric objects are located, e.g. at the church of Kirche San Lorenzo in Mazzolla, at the driveway to the Fattoria Lischeto, at the church of Santa Lucia in Corbano or at the local road 68 (SR 68) near the town La Mestola.

Since 2011 the lawns around Pisa Airport have been decorated by new sculpture groups by the sculptor Giovanni Maria Manganelli. His project »volarearte« (»art of flying«) with the new installations *Africa, Mare aperto, Oceano* and *Psiche* is well received by arriving and departing guests.

ROBERTO BENIGNI (BORN 1952)

Some consider him to be the modern Charlie Chaplin. It is indisput-
able that Roberto Benigni,born in Misericordia near Arezzo in 1952,
is one of the greatest multi-talented individuals of the cinema today.
Thecomedian, entertainer, actor and film makerwas raised a Catholic,
but (or maybe for that reason) the Roman Catholic church has been a
favourite target for his comedy and satire since his first appearance on
stage. He began his acting career in the early 1970s in Rome with fringe
theatre and one-man shows. He made his film debut in 1977 in »Ber-
linguer ti voglio bene« by Giuseppe Bertolucci, the brother of the star
director Bernardo. Nine years later he had his international acting
breakthrough in the comedy *Down by Law* by Jim Jarmusch. His greatest success so far, *La vita è bella* (*Life is Beautiful*, 1997), in which he
played the leading role and directed, brought him the highest artistic
honours and international film prizes, including three Oscars.

Comedian, actor, filmmaker

GIOVANNI BOCCACCIO (1313 – 1375)

Boccaccio was probably born in Paris as the illegitimate son of a well-
to-do merchant from Certaldo. He grew up in Florence and first entered his father's occupation. Business took him to Naples, where he
decided to study classical languages. He remained there for many
years and became the author of works of literature in Latin and Italian. Around 1340 he was in Florence again, where he met the
humanist and scholar Petrarch and with him tried to revitalize the
Latin and Greek languages and literature. His famous cycle of novel-
las *Il Decamerone* (The Decameron), which today is considered to be
the origin of Italian prose, was written under the influence of the
Great Plague of 1348. In the 100 stories, which are told by ten people
on ten days, questions on the morals of love are discussed before the
backdrop of a catastrophe that nullifies the restrictions imposed by
the law, religion and morality. Boccaccio was an admirer of Dante,
and also wrote a *Vita di Dante* (around 1360), along with other
works, and in 1373 received the first public professorship from the
city of Florence for his interpretation of the *Divine Comedy*.

Creator of Il Decamerone

FILIPPO BRUNELLESCHI (1377 – 1446)

The Florentine architect and sculptor Brunelleschi considered to
be the true creator of Renaissance architecture. He was inspired to his

Renaissance architect

**Giacomo Puccini composed *La Bohème* and *Madame Butterfly* in his
villa on the Lago di Massaciuccoli.**

innovations by ancient monuments, which he studied in Rome together with his friend, the sculptor Donatello. He applied his new insights to the two Florentine churches San Lorenzo and Santo Spirito, among other projects. In a daring synthesis of the early Christian basilica and elements of ancient architecture (columns, pilasters, capitals, entablature) Brunelleschi created spaces with balanced proportions, bathed in light, in which the spatial whole is engaged in constant interplay with individual forms. Among Brunelleschi's great feats of engineering is moreover the massive, self-supporting, double-skin construction of the cathedral dome in Florence. But Brunelleschi also proved to be a pioneer for his painting colleagues: from Euclidian optical teachings he developed central perspective projection, i.e. the scientifically exact depiction of a three-dimensional space on a surface, which opened unforeseen possibilities for painting.

DANTE ALIGHIERI (1265 – 1321)

Author of
theDivine
Comedy

The offspring of a respected Florentine patrician family, Dante grew up in a part of the city close to the cathedral at a time when battles between the Ghibellines and Guelfs raged in the cities of northern Italy. The young nobleman studied law and then went into politics. In the year of his election to the Signoria (1300), bloody battles broke out again between the noble factions in the city, and the pope sent the French prince Charles of Valois to Florence. The Guelfs were convicted of conspiracy and their leaders were banished from the city. As their supporter Dante was sentenced to exile for life; the sentence was later changed to a death sentence. Embittered and dependent on help from others, Dante lived in northern Italy and later in Ravenna until his death in 1321.

His most important work was done during his exile years, including the *Commedia* in the Tuscan dialect, the fore-runner to the Italian national language. The word »Divina« was added later (*Divine Comedy*). The allegorical poem, which is composed of 100 songs in verse form, takes as its subject fundamental questions on theology and philosophy, church and state as well as the socio-political situation in Italy in Dante's time.

DONATELLO (AROUND 1386 – 1466)

Sculptor

Donatello (actually Donato di Niccolò di Betto Bardi) is considered to be the most important sculptor of the 15th century. In his time he was unsurpassed in expressiveness, diversity of subjects and richness of creativity. As an apprentice Donatello worked in the atelier of Ghiberti, as a master he produced statues in his home town of Florence for the cathedral as well as for the church Orsanmichele. Contact with Roman antiquity then brought him far beyond the medieval understanding of art. His *David* (1430, today in the Museo Nazionale del Bargello in Florence), was the first nude figure; his *Gattamelata* in Padua the first equestrian statue; and his *Judith Kills Holofernes* in front of the Florentine Palazzo Vecchio the first completely free-standing group sculpture. The Medici honoured the sculptor by having him interred in the crypt of Cosimo the Elder in San Lorenzo in Florence.

GALILEO GALILEI (1564 – 1642)

It took the church a long time to admit its mistake: in 1992 it lifted the ban on Galileo Galilei – exactly 360 years after it had condemned his teachings as heretical. The mathematician, physicist and philosopher received a professorship in mathematics in Pisa, the city of his fathers, when he was only 25. He is thought to have conducted ex-

»And yet it moves!« (▶MARCO POLO Insight p. 68)

periments here that led him to epoch-making discoveries: the candelabra in the cathedral induced him to experiment with the motion of a pendulum; the Leaning Tower helped him to examine free fall. He developed the laws of acceleration in Padua, where he taught from 1592. In 1609 he made a copy of the telescope which was invented in Holland a year earlier and used it to explore the heavens. Galileo's public support for the heliocentric model of the universe proposed by Copernicus brought him into conflict with the official opinion of the church, which banned his teachings in 1616. A text which Galileo composed in 1632, in which he described the earth as a ball that rotates around the sun, brought on a court trial. The sentence was pronounced on 22 June 1633: to recant his teachings and unlimited imprisonment, which he spent in Arceteri with a few interruptions. Galilei's famous statement is legendary: »And yet it (the earth) moves.«

CATHERINE OF SIENA (1347 – 1380)

One of the most honoured saints of Tuscany

Along with Francis of Assisi, Catherine of Siena is probably one of the most prominent saints in all of Italy, and certainly one of the most

And Yet It Moves!

Dass Galileo Galilei diesen Satz sagte, nachdem er offiziell der kopernikanischen
The fact that Galileo Galilei made this statement after he officially renounced
Copernicus' theory is more of a legend. But it is true that the Roman Catholic
Church only rehabilitated Galileo in 1992 – 360 years after condemning his
teachings as heretical.

▶ **Geocentric conception of
the world (schematic;
according to Ptolemy/
Aristotle)**
The geocentric conception
of the world placed Earth
and consequently also
people in the centre of the
universe. It was part of the
fundamental convictions of
the Roman Catholic Church.

SATURN ♄
JUPITER ♃
MARS ♂
☉ SUN
VENUS ♀
MERCURY ☿
☽ MOON
EARTH

ERIS PLUTO
• • - • - - Dwarf planets - - - - - -

▶ **Stations in the life of
Galileo Galilei**
Galileo was professor of
mathematics in Padua

PADUA ○

PISA FLORENCEE
○

Galileo's
birthplace
and first place
of learning ○ ROME

The family came from
Florence; after his trial Galileo
spent most of his arrest period
in Arcetri nearby

Galileo was
brought to trial
in Rome

▶ **Planets and their
respective distance
from the sun in mil. km
(schematic representation)**

NEPTUNE
4496

URANUS
2896

▲
Sector

▶ **Life, discoveries and
inventions of
Galileo Galilei**

1564 Birth of
Galileo Galilei

1592–1610
Professor of
mathematics at
the university in
Padua

1593 Galileo
invents a water
pump that is
driven by horses. In
1594 he receives a
patent for it from
the Venetian
senate.

1597 Galileo
invented the sector,
an instrument used
to calculate
proportions. Its area
of use included
surveying and
navigation.

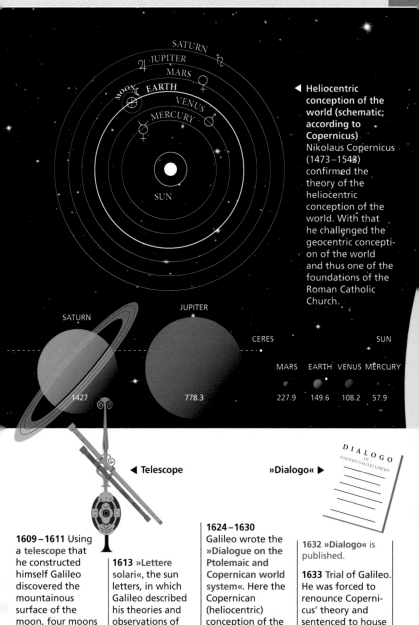

◀ Heliocentric conception of the world (schematic; according to Copernicus) Nikolaus Copernicus (1473–1543) confirmed the theory of the heliocentric conception of the world. With that he challenged the geocentric conception of the world and thus one of the foundations of the Roman Catholic Church.

SATURN 1427   JUPITER 778.3   CERES   MARS 227.9   EARTH 149.6   VENUS 108.2   MERCURY 57.9   SUN

◀ Telescope

»Dialogo« ▶

DIALOGO DI GALILEO GALILEI LINCEO

1609–1611 Using a telescope that he constructed himself Galileo discovered the mountainous surface of the moon, four moons of Jupiter and the rings of Saturn.

1613 »Lettere solari«, the sun letters, in which Galileo described his theories and observations of sunspots.

1624–1630 Galileo wrote the »Dialogue on the Ptolemaic and Copernican world system«. Here the Copernican (heliocentric) conception of the world is portrayed as the correct one.

1632 »Dialogo« is published.

1633 Trial of Galileo. He was forced to renounce Copernicus' theory and sentenced to house arrest for life.

venerated in Tuscany. The daughter of a wool dyer took a vow of chastity at the age of seven. At the age of twelve she refused to marry, but her family allowed her to enter the Dominican order only after numerous humiliations. She devoted herself to the sick and poor as a lay sister, but also to extreme acts of penance in which she experienced states of ecstasy and visions. Outside the convent walls she worked for the return of the popes to Rome from Avignon, where they had been living since 1309. On 29 April 1380, at the age of only 33, Catherine collapsed and died in Rome. She was declared a saint by Pope Pius II 81 years later. Catherine's body was buried in Rome in Santa Maria sopra Minerva; her head rests in San Domenico in Siena.

LEONARDO DA VINCI (1452 – 1519)

Engineer, artist and scientist

The Italian Renaissance produced numerous many-sided personalities, but only the genius Leonardo da Vinci united excellence as a painter, sculptor and architect with achievements as a scientist and engineer. Leonardo entered the painters' guild in Florence at the age of 20. From 1482 until 1498 he worked at the court of Duke Lodovico Sforza in Milan, then in Florence again, in Milan, in Rome until he accepted the invitation of King François I to France in 1517. Probably the most famous painting by da Vinci is the *Mona Lisa* (1503–1505) with her mysterious smile of wonderful grace. It hangs in the Louvre in Paris today, as does the *Virgin and Child with St Anne*. Da Vinci also worked as a builder of fortresses and devoted himself intensely to scientific tasks. He dissected cadavers, wrote an essay on the anatomy of the human body and illustrated it with drawings. He performed experiments on flight, observed the flight of birds, examined the laws of air and water currents and did botanical and geological experiments. His many drawings, the studies of the movement of the human body, naturalistic observations, designs of buildings and technical projects all prove his universality.

NICCOLÒ MACHIAVELLI (1469 – 1527)

Defender of »raison d'état«

As a historian Niccolò Machiavelli was the greatest chronicler of his home town of Florence. As chief secretary of the republic of Florence (1498–1512), he was a confirmed advocate of the republican system, in which he saw the best chance of personal development for citizens. The Roman republic, which had placed the common good of all citizens before personal good, served as a his model, as he elaborated in his *Thoughts on Politics and Government* (*Discorsi*). The analysis of his own time led to him to penetrating but discouraging insights on the rules of politics. Thus his famous writing *The Prince* (*Il Principe*) reads: »The ruler who is best able to act like a fox has always had the advantage. But whoever has this ability must know how to keep it a secret and must be a skilled hypocrite and swindler.« During his lifetime the writings of Machiavelli were known only to a small circle of intellectuals.

MICHELANGELO BUONARROTI (1475 – 1564)

Caprese is a small village in Casentino, a quiet part of Tuscany off the beaten paths. Here, over 635 years ago, the painter, sculptor, architect, poet and scientist Michelangelo was born. He began his career at the age of 13 as an apprentice in the workshop of the Florentine painter Domenico Ghirlandaio. Along with his affinity to painting he increasingly developed a passion for sculpture. In 1489 the young Michelangelo was accepted by the sculpture academy of the Medici Gardens. In 1494 he left Florence to spend the following four decades travelling between Florence, Bologna and Rome. After that he lived in Rome until his death, with only short interruptions. In Tuscany the work of this great universal artist can be found mainly in Florence, for example in the Galleria dell' Accademia, where the original of the famous *David* is exhibited and in the Uffizi, where his *Holy Family* can be admired.

Universal genius

AMADEO MODIGLIANI (1884 – 1920)

he port city of Livorno is the home of the painter and sculptor Modigliani. After studying art in Florence and Venice he lived mostly in Paris from 1906, where he met Picasso and other contemporary artists. He started sculpting through his acquaintance with the Romanian sculptor Brancusi. He developed his unmistakable style under the influence of Cubism. His portraits typically depict oval faces, long necks, eyes slightly out of position and lifeless, contorted bodies. Like many of his artist colleagues Modigliani lived his life apart from bourgeois standards. Marked by illness, alcohol and drugs, he died of a cold at the age of only 36 on 25 January 1920.

Livorno's most famous son

GIANNA NANNINI (BORN 1956)

Italy's most famous female rock singer was born on 14 June 1956 in Siena. She wrote her first song at the age of 14 and in order to earn money she worked in her family's traditional confectioner's shop while studying piano. At the age of 19, immediately after graduating

Rock singer

from secondary school, she was accepted by the faculty of philosophy in Milan, performed as a singer in bars and got her first recording contract. Her first LP appeared in 1976. After the hit *America* in 1980 her name was known all over Europe. Gianna Nannini's trademark is her powerful, somewhat rough voice. Her music, in which she often advocates human rights, solidarity and liberty, ranges from hard rock to Italian folk songs to sensitive ballads.

IRIS ORIGO (1902 – 1988)

Historian and Tuscan by choice

Many people have adopted Tuscany as their home, but Iris Origo is one who also commemorated the region in literature. Her preferred subject was the medieval history of Tuscany, to which she dedicated two books: *The Tuscan Saint*, a monograph on Bernardino of Siena, and *In the Name of God and Business*, a study on the merchant Francesco di Marco Datini. She was a well-travelled historian of Anglo-American descent, who married Marchese Antonio Origo in 1924 and moved with him to the estate La Foce near Montepulciano. She lived there until her death in 1988 – also during the Second World War. Iris Origo and her husband supported the partisans and prisoners of war who escaped German captivity. In her diary she recorded this period in detail (▶MARCO POLO Tip p. 42).

PETRARCH (FRANCESCO PETRARCA; 1304 – 1374)

One of the founders of humanism

On the transition from the Middle Ages to the Renaissance a figure of enormous significance appeared: Francesco Petrarca, poet and scholar, lover and researcher of classical antiquity, and thus one of the founders of humanism. His family lived in Avignon, the residence of the popes at that time, because of his father's occupation. Francesco studied law. He soon became famous, travelled and gained influence as the friend of Cardinal Colonna. A key experience not only for him but also for the attitude of an entire age was to climb Mont Ventoux in 1336, the first known ascent of a mountain for its own sake in modern times. Later Petrarch withdrew to his estate near Avignon and devoted himself to his literary work. From 1362 he lived in Italy again.

PINOCCHIO

The story of the long-nosed marionette that came to life has been a hit for generations, both as a novel and as a film – most recently in 2002 by Roberto Benigni. The funny long-nosed figure comes from the pen of Carlo Lorenzini, who wanted to remain anonymous and thus named himself Carlo Collodi after his hometown. The theatre critic and founder of the satirical journal »Il Lampione« (The Lantern) first wrote the Pinocchio stories as a serial novel for the »Giornale per i Bambini«, a children's magazine. In 1878 the episodes were collected into a novel and published under the title *The Adventures of Pinocchio*. Translated into more than 80 languages today, the book has become a classic of children's literature.

Legendary wooden marionette

GIACOMO PUCCINI (1858 – 1924)

During his own lifetime the composer Puccini became a music legend and was celebrated by critics and audiences alike. His moving melodies were adored by the middle class at the end of the belle époque and have retained their fascination to this day. As scion of a respected musical family from Lucca, he became organist of the churches in Lucca at the age of 14. When he was present in 1876 in Pisa at a performance of Verdi's *Aida* he resolved that he too would compose operas. He passed the entrance examination for the conservatory in Milan with honours in 1880. From 1884 he was the protégé of the famous publisher Giulio Ricordi. His private life was more complicated, as he fell in love with Elvira Gemignani, a married woman from Lucca, who followed him to Milan. The relationship was made legal only 19 years later. In 1893 the opera *Manon Lescaut* brought his breakthrough, in 1896 *La Bohème* followed, in 1900 *Tosca*, and in 1904 the touching love story *Madame Butterfly* made him world famous. Most of Giacomo Puccini's operas were composed in his art nouveau villa Torre del Lago. Puccini is buried in the chapel next to his study.

MARCO ⊕ POLO INSIGHT

?

Puccini outdoors

Since the maestro himself wanted his operas to be performed outdoors, his friends took up the idea. For over 50 years the Puccini Festival has been held in Torre del Lago on a stage by the sea in July and August.

ENJOY TUSCANY

What are the Tuscan culinary specialties? Where are the best places to stay? What are the Super-Tuscans and where do the best festivals and events take place? Read it here!

Accommodation

From Simple to Luxurious

With more than 12,500 accommodations, Tuscany is one of the best developed and most popular tourist destinations in Europe. The spectrum ranges simple, inexpensive private accommodations to luxurious city hotels or country villas with all modern comforts.

The high prices also show that this is one of the most popular holiday regions of Italy. It is possible to negotiate quite low prices in hotels on the coast in the low season. But apart from that there is no limit to the prices and quality of hotels, holiday houses and flats. The price of a holiday house can go up to €3,000 during the high season. An exclusive **Saracen watchtower** in the Maremma Nature Park is offered for €9,000 per week (information at www.italhaus.com).

High-priced

An accommodation tax has been introduced in Florence that is pro-rated based on the number of stars the accommodation has. It is calculated per person and can be paid at the reception. It is expected that this tax will also be introduced in other cities.

Accommodation tax

On holidays, in the summer months and in general in Florence, Siena, Lucca and Pisa booking early is advisable. In most of the other cities it is only necessary during the high season.
Higher priced hotels often offer better current rates on their websites. Special offers can often be negotiated right at the reception desk. It pays to compare with local reservation sites at home as they often offer special rates and convenient booking. Travel agents also often have inexpensive hotel prices with and without travel packages.
There are many pre- and post-season discounts. Asking about half or full pension can sometimes also save money (mezza pensione / pensione completa).

Booking

Insider Tip

Hotels and alberghi (albergo = guesthouse, pension) in Italy are officially divided into five categories, from luxury hotels with five stars to simple accommodation with one star. Beyond that there is also smaller, unclassified accommodation of an acceptable standard. The number of stars only gives limited information on the actual comfort and prices of the house, which can vary greatly depending on the season and region. Thus the prices in the summer on the coast or in

Hotels and alberghi

Beautiful rural setting: a small simple room with a garden terrace – the best conditions for a good night's sleep

Quiet Rest

Turismo Religioso is booming – and often it is connected with an active holiday outdoors that promises recuperation on foot, by bicycle or on a horse. The EU Council of Ministers supports the transnational projects of the European pilgrimage routes »Cammini d'Europa«. Part of the motivation is to help economically weak areas back on their feet.

The Catholic organisation Accoglienza religiosa in Italia registered just about 3,000 overnight accommodations in 2011– for non-Catholics as well. Tuscany alone has 228 monasteries, hermitages, convents and retreats being used as farms or holiday homes. Its website www.hospites.it is a treasure chest for anyone who would like to enjoy this form of holiday.

Monasteries are not hotels; they have **»house rules«**, which vary: sometimes only men or women are allowed to stop, sometimes only married people, sometimes only groups, sometimes only individuals. The large Casentino monasteries open their doors to both sexes and have a good infrastructure; thre are dormitories for youth groups, but also single and double rooms with bathrooms. And heating – like in La Verna.

A Monastery Bar

Anyone who stays overnight at La Verna in the guest refectory or in the Foresteria will also find a bar where espresso, mineral water, alcoholic beverages or monastery specialities are sold. These »monastery bars« are however never located in the secluded living quarters of the monks where the rules of the order are followed strictly. In La Verna's restaurant three meals of very good quality are served daily at reasonable prices. The six Franciscan monks who live in the monastery as well as their clerical guests and the senior citizens who live here also join in these meals: La Verna is a monastery, hostel and highly-valued retirement home at the same time.

Doors Locked

Daytime visitors as well as overnight guests should bear a few rules in mind. Noise, even from children, is disruptive; standards of dress should be respected. Refrain from smoking and respect mealtimes, which are signalled by bells. Spiritual retreats, times of meditation, fasting or holidays should be respected. The **closing times** are the biggest difference to other accommodations. At 9 p.m. sharp the doors are locked in La Verna – except for the courtyard door. This last entrance is locked at 10 p.m. sharp! Then silence rules. But this last hour of chatting under a starry sky is the most impressive of the day for many people. Guests may only break the silence on Thursdays between one and two a.m. – for devotions in the Cappella delle Stimmate, where Saint Francis is supposed to have received the stigmata. At 7 a.m. sharp the door to the monastery courtyard is opened; the other outer doors are opened at 8 a.m.

Though monasteries are not hotels guests should not expect ascetic frugality

Due to the strict closing hours many Tuscany holiday-makers prefer to stay in the nearby village, thus nullifying the question whether monastery guest houses are too much competition for secular accommodations. The village profits is the unanimous opinion. But the unbeatable advantage to staying in the monasteries is the **deep, sound, restorative sleep**, the good air, the pleasant quietness, wonderful walks through the surrounding monastery forests and in part also the reasonable rates.

A Selection of Monasteries

All Tuscan religious provinces offer this form of hospitality. Bice stays are offered by the Foresteria in Monastero di San Girolamo in San Gimignano, in the Abbazia Santa Maria di Rosano in Pontassive, in Agriturismo La Chiusa in Pratovecchio or in Sant' Antimo in Montalcino, for example.

Information online:
www.laverna.it
www.hospites.it
www.istituti-religiosi.org
www.turismoreligioso.eu/ospitalita_toscana.htm
http://static.repubblica.it/viaggi/pdf/monasteri-italiani/monasteri.pdf (religious hostels listed by the newspaper La Repubblica)
www.ora-et-labora.net/monasteriitaliani.html, www.osb-international.info (staying with Benedictines)
www.monasterystays.com (Australians tested many of the 500 monasteries and convents in Italy.)
www.camminideuropa.eu (European pilgrim's ways)
www.orpnet.org (pilgrim's office in Rome)

Florence for a double room are up to three times as high as in the interior. Many hotels on the coast are only open from April to October. Since most guests stay for more than one or two nights, special rates are offered for stays of at least three nights..

Albergo diffuso

Albergo diffuso refers to accommodations that are managed from a central reception where keys to a room or flat can be picked up for a house nearby. These alberghi are usually located in remote mountain villages and consist of renovated historic houses.

Bed & breakfast

Urban areas offer alternative B & B opportunities. Bed & Breakfast Italia offers everything from a room with use of a bath to accommodation in renowned historic buildings, rooms with the greatest comfort level, only for women or with pets.

Agriturismo

Agriturismo can best be translated as »holiday in the country« and is very popular. One third of all accommodations in Tuscany are in agriturismo. Its success story began a quarter of a century ago with the first accommodations on farms south of Siena. Today more than 4,000 registered fattorie, poderi or country villas entice with fresh air and good sleep for the whole family. Meanwhile about 60% also have a restaurant or package lunches; many offer bikes, mountain bikes and excursions as part of their programme, or even riding lessons or trail riding excursions. Along with swimming pools there are also many kinds of wellness packages in connection with local thermal spas; many an agriturismo has long since become a country luxury oasis. The classification goes from one ear of grain for basic accommodation and service to three ears of grain (spighe). More ears do not mean more comfort, rather better rural quality.

Camping and caravaning

Most camp grounds in Tuscany are situated along the coast and on the island of Elba but can also be found in the interior and near almost all larger cities. On Elba alone there are more than 30 camp sites, some of them extremely pleasant and beautiful. The relatively high cost of accommodation in Italy also applies to camping: the average price for a tent and two people is 20 euros per night. Information on camping can be obtained from the Italian Camping Union. Wild camping is not allowed. Anyone travelling in a caravan may spend one night parked at the roadside, in a parking lot or rest stop if it is not specifically prohibited.

Youth hostels

Youth hostels in Tuscany offer an relatively inexpensive alternative. An international youth hostel identity card is necessary to stay in a youth hostel. Reservations are highly recommended in the high season. Along the old pilgrimage routes most religious accommodations offer inexpensive but spartan places to stay.

Recommended addresses

Price categories
Double room per night
€€€€ over €150
€€€ €100 – €150
€€ €70 – €100
€ up to €70

INFORMATION/BOOKING
General
www.alberghidiffusi.it/it/alberghi/
regione/toscana

AGRITURISMO
Agriturist Toscana
Via degli Alfani, 67
I-50121 Firenze
Tel. 055 28 78 38
www.agriturist.it
www.agriturist.toscana.it

Federazione Coldiretti
Toscana/Terranostra
Via della Demidoff, 64/D
I-50127 Firenze
Tel. 055 324 5655
www.toscana.coldiretti.it
www.terranostra.it

Turismo Verde Toscana
Via Iacopo Nardi 41
I-50132 Firenze
Tel. 055 233 8911
www.turismoverdi.it

BED & BREAKFAST
Bed & Breakfast Italia
Corso Vittorio Emanuele II 282
Rome
Tel. 06 687 8616
www.bed-and-breakfast.it/en

CAMPING
Confederazione Italiana
Campeggiatori
Via Vittorio Emanuele II 11
I-50041 Calenzano/Firenze
Tel. 05 588 2391
www.federcampeggio.it

YOUTH HOSTELS
Associazione Italiana
Alberghi per la Gioventù
Via Cavour 44, I-00184 Roma
Tel. 06 487 1152
www.travel.it/hostels
www.aighostels.com

Children in Tuscany

For Young Tuscany Fans

Italy's birthrate is the lowest in Europe. No wonder since the number of marriages is decreasing and the average age for getting married is increasing. The average age of women is 30 and of men is 32 when they get married. But Tuscany, as well as all of Italy, is considered to be very friendly to children.

This can be seen in the number of offers for children of holiday-makers. For example, there is never any question of obtaining a child's bed in a hotel room at a reasonable price. The number of trattorie and restaurants with cheaper children's portions is growing. There are various activities available for making a family holiday a success: starting with bike tours in and around Lucca, for example (▶p. 300), to visits to the numerous nature parks. The new ecological museums with educational nature trails and programmes for visitors are interesting for the whole family. The specially illustrated children's books available in the parks' gift shops are helpful for visits to the parks and museums. Along with the sea and beach holidays with children can also be spent at the (usually expensive) amusement parks with roller coaster rides along the coast.

Family-friendly destination

Public transportation and the Firenze Card offer **discounts**. Reduced family tickets for museums, parks and recreational centres are generally not available, but **free admission** for small children and 50% discounts for older children up to the age of 18 are common. Incidentally, EU citizens over the age of 65 often have free admission – a good deal for grandparents with their grandchildren!

Inexpensive tickets

Children love Daniel Spoerri's Giardano (garden) in Seggiano (www.danielspoerri.org; ▶p. 336), the surprising tone installations (e.g. tram noises) in the Chianti Sculpture Park near Gaiole (www.chiantisculpturepark.it; ▶ p. 204) or the Giardano del Suoni (Garden of Sound) by the sound artist Paul Fuchs in Boccheggiano near Montieri (www.paulfuchs.com; ▶p. 325).

Something special

The Florentine **museums** are child-friendly; several museums have made special preparations for children and the Associazione Musei dei Ragazzi di Firenze makes history, art and culture come alive through children's games. The Museo dei Ragazzi in the Palazzo Vecchio is recommended especially and the following museums also

Florence for children

Mythical fantasy creatures in the Giardino del Tarocchi made for unusual explorations

cooperate in this ambitious child- and youth-friendly museum pro-gramme: Capella Brancacci in Santa Maria del Carmine, Museo Stib-bert, Museo Firenze com' era (Florence as it used to be) as well as the Museo Leonardiano near Vinci.

Palazzo Strozzi offers very good educational **workshops and guid-ed tours** – also in English – for families with children on weekends, and during the week for older children (www.palazzostrozzi.org; ▶p. 264, family ticket). The **Bottega dei Ragazzi** in the MUDI (chil-dren's workshop for 3- to 11-year-olds, www.istitutodeglinnocenti.it/mudi; ▶p. 273) receives very high marks. Dante Moruzzi in Mondo Bimbo near Piazza Libertà (Via Madonna della Tosse, tel. 055 553 2946, www.mondobimbogroup.com) offers a **kindergarten** for 2- to 6-year-olds. Climbing to the top of the cathedral dome or the Giotto campanile are always worthwhile, as are visits to parks or a not-so-cheap dive into the Piscina Bellariva Nannini (Lungarno Aldo Moror 6, tel. 055 678 841; www.fiorentinanuoto.net) or the Nannini indoor pool (Via Ripoli 70).

Tips for kids

Giardino dei Tarocchi
About 15km/9mi east of Orbetello near Garavicchio
April 1 – Oct 15 daily 2.30 pm – 7.30 pm
Admission: €10.50
www.nikidesaintphalle.com
Colourful fantasy park – the Tarot garden by Niki de Saint Phalle (▶p. 341) is a treat for children. In a huge park eccentric fabled creatures live in a fantasy land.

Parco di Pinocchio
About 13km/8mi east of Lucca in Collodi
Feb 27 – Nov 1 daily 8.30 am – sunset, Nov 2 – Feb 26 Sat., Sun. 9 am until sunset
Admission: Feb 27 – Nov 1 €11, otherwise €10, discounts for chil-dren and senior citizens; www.pi-nocchio.it
Every child knows the long-nosed rascal! Pinocchio's amusement park lies between Pistoia and Luc-

ca in a side valley (▶p. 314). Chil-dren can play here in a labyrinth, explore the pirates' grotto or climb on the corsair's ship, walk along the whisper trail or take a drawing or mask-making course.

Parco Prehistorico Peccioli
about 30km/18mi east of Livorno in Peccioli
Via dei Cappucini
April 1 – Aug 31 daily 9 am – 7 pm, otherwise 9 am – 6 pm
Admission: €4
Tel. 058 763 6030
www.parcoprehistorico.it
Near Pisa 22 dinosaur sculptures from veloci- to oviraptor are wait-ing.

Parco »Selva del Buffardello«
San Romano in Garfagnana
All year round daily 9 am – 7.30 pm
Admission: from 1 m height €10,

from 1.40 m height €16
Tel. 347 711 0433
www.selvadelbuffardello.it
Parents must accompany their
children to this adventure park,
which is open all year round.
There is an acrobatic treetop
course and seven other parcours
for small and big adventurers.

Florence –
»Musei dei Ragazzi«
Florentine museums are generally
very child-friendly, and more and
more of them are taking part in
the ambitious project »Musei dei
Ragazzi di Firenze«, which offers
creative activities to introduce children to history, science, art and
culture in a playful way (www.mu-
seiragazzifirenze.it). The following
are recommended: Museo per Ragazzi (▶p. 250), Museo di Storia
della Scienza (▶p. 256), Museo
Stibbert (▶p. 280) and the pecu-
liar wax figure museum La Specola (▶p. 261).

SMS Museo d´ Arte per
Bambini
Siena
Complesso Museale Santa Maria
della Scala
Piazza del Duomo 2
March 17 – Oct 15 daily 10.30 am
– 6.30 pm, otherwise until 4.30
pm
Free admission
Tel. 057 746 517
www.comune.siena.it/
bambinimus

The museum is devoted exclusively to children up to 11 years old.
Here small children are introduced
to art and its history through theatre performances and workshops. The children are taught to
look at paintings and to »read«
pictures. Too bad that the instruc-
tion is in Italian!

Treno Natura
Visione del Mondo –
Agenzia Viaggi
Via Camollia 130
Siena
Tel. 05 77 20 74 13
http://trenonatura.terresiena.it
From April to November a trip on
the »Treno Natura« through the
Sienese countryside is especially
entertaining for children. Old en-
gines or steam locomotives are
used. The route goes through the
Crete, Val d'Orcia, around Monte
Amiata. There is also an Etruscan
train to Chiusi and trains from
Grosseto to the truffle market in
San Giovanni Val d'Asso.

Parco Zoo Poppi
daily 9 am until sunset
Admission: €7
www.parcozoopoppi.it
In Poppi in the Casentino there is
a zoo dedicated solely to European fauna. There are bobcats, foxes, donkeys, wolves, among others. The 2km/1.2mi path is
manageable even for small children (▶p. 172).

Feast after Feast

It is almost impossible to take a vacation in Tuscany without encountering a festival. Between the Arno and Monte Amiata most of the festivals are religious; the calendar is full of them and they are very attractive.

Along with Christmas, Easter and Pentecost the festivals for the national patron saints Francis of Assisi and Caterina of Siena are very important. Each village celebrates the feast day of its **patron saint**. The carnival in Viareggio, the most popular Tuscan carnival, also has religious connections.

Most of the **village festivals** take place in the fall, usually in the form of thanksgiving or harvest festivals with the presentation of local products like truffles or chestnuts. The olive oil and wine festivals are always worth a visit; the new olives and wines can be tasted and delicious local dishes can be sampled there.

There was a suggestion that national holidays like Republic Day (June 2) be moved to Sundays – as part of recent austerity measures in order to create more working days – but nothing definite has been decided yet.

Medieval festivals are also very popular. These include ones that are famous and have centuries-long traditions like the Palio in Siena. The Bravio delle botti in Montepulciano also has a medieval touch: wine-barrels weighing 80 kg (180 lb) are rolled through the streets in a test of strength. On the Giostra del Saracino in Arezzo the wooden Saracen king Buratto is battled on horseback. In Pisa during the Regatta di San Ranieri the city districts compete and in the Gioco del Ponte – also in Pisa – there are hundreds of costumed people and countless horses to admire.

The classical music festivals also have a long tradition, especially the oldest one, the **Maggio Musicale**, which takes place from April to June in Florence. The Estate Fiesolana in Fiesole or the **Puccini Festival** in Torre del Lago and Lucca also attract crowds; the early evening open air classical concerts in the abbey of San Galgano are also very special. Lucca's Summer Festival is practically a must for lovers of rock, classical and jazz music. Pistoia attracts in July with Blues. Among the large number of new Tuscan festivals the concert series in the Teatro del Silenzio in Lajatico (June/July) near Volterra as well

Festivals the year round

Medieval festivals

Festival season, festivals and events

An old poster from the carnival in Viareggio, always one of the most popular festivals in northern Italy

as the Bolgheri music festival (July) have successfully attracted many world class musicians.

Italia Wave, which has been held since 1987 and which developed out of the Arezzo Wave festival for **young talents** continues to be organized by Arezzo, but now it is held nation-wide (www.italiawave. com) and promotes young and new rock bands. The **comic festival** in Lucca (late Oct/early Nov) achieves a sensational number of visitors – comic authors and artists, comic readers and publishers crowd the old city streets.

Torneo dei Butteri

The **Maremma cowboys**, the butteri, meet every year on August 15 in Alberese for the spectakular Torneo dei Butteri, also called the Rodeo della Rosa. Meanwhile a second butteri festivity is being held in Alberese on May 1. The tournament in Alberese is not the only one that is held in honour of the butteri. But this one offers special attractions: skill, strength and endurance of riders and horses are demonstrated in various horse relays. The butteri ride in their typical Maremma saddles, the scafarda, and hold the reigns in one hand while holding the uncino, a one to two-meter long cowboy staff made of macchia wood.

A highlight is the **battle for the rose**. The butteri are divided into two teams – Rosa rossa (red rose) and Rosa gialla (yellow rose) – and under great hue and cry they try to grab the roses that are attached to their shoulders. It is a man-to-man battle with considerable body contact. The team that has collected to most roses wins.

The **classical rodeos** are also crowd-pleasers. Teams of three ridesr each try to catch a calf that is part of a large herd, to pull it to the ground and tie it up. Of course, the whole herd runs and the cowboys are off in hot pursuit. If the time limit, usually one minute, is passed then the calf can be caught by other means as well (information: Visitor Centre Parco Naturale della Maremma, tel. 05 64 40 70 98).

Sports

The Tuscans' favourite pastime is **football**, be it on TV or in the stadium. The **Italian premier league** (Seria A) matches take place on Saturday evening, Sunday afternoon and evening. The only Tuscan premier league team is AC Florence.

The second great love is the Formula Uno, **Formula 1 Grand Prix** events with the cultic Ferrari race cars, and motorcycle racing. One of the most modern race tracks in the world is in Mugello about 30km/18mi northeast of Florence.

Festival calendar

HOLIDAYS

1 January: New Year's Day (Capodanno)

6 January: Epiphany (Epifania)

Easter Monday (Lunedi di Pasqua)

25 April: Liberation Day 1945 from the German army (Anniversario della Liberazione)

Easter Monday (Lunedi di Pasqua)

1 May: Labour Day (Festa dei Lavoratori)

2 June: Republic Day (Fondazione della Repubblica)

15 August: Assumption of the Virgin (Ferragosta)

1 November: All Saints' Day (Ognissanti)

8 December: Immaculate Conception (Immacolata)

25/26 December: Christmas Day/Boxing Day (Natale)

FESTIVALS AND EVENTS

FEBRUARY / MARCH
Carnival parades

Carnival is celebrated expansively in Pisa and Viareggio. The parade in Viareggio is the most famous, with magnificently and imaginatively decorated floats.

MARCH / APRIL
Easter

On Easter Sunday in Florence residents and visitors go to the Piazza del Duomo for »Scoppio del Carro«. An igniter shaped like a dove shoots on a rope from the cathedral altar to a festively decorated cart in order to set it alight – Easter fire alla fiorentina.

The Sagra del Tordo, which is celebrated in October in Montalcino, comes from the time of the thrush hunt

Go, and Return Victorious

This is easier said than done in the Palio, the famous Sienese horse race and Italy's traditional celebration par excellence. For the riders who take this blessing from the district priest risk life and limb on the campo. Without a saddle, with only reins and riding crop, the jockeys cling to the backs of their horses in order to be the first to cross the finish line at breakneck speed and carry away the coveted victor's ribbon.

Even though there is little evidence of the original procedure of the Palio, it is certain that it existed before 1310, the year when the city council officially confirmed the race: it was to take place every year on **16 August** in honour of the Holy Virgin, Siena's patron saint, but also as the symbol of the independent communes. The race on **2 July** in honour of the Madonna di Provenzano has been held only since 1656.

Excited spectators

17 City Districts Compete

In the Palio the 17 contrade of the various city districts of Siena compete. Their name probably comes from the Latin *contrata*, the place where contracts are made. The contrade are the small villages on the hills of the city, which in the 13th century in the face of the general decay of central government joined together into a local administration which would also serve as a defence in times of war. The militia of the contrade were lead by b**anner bearers** (gonfalonieri), whose commander-in-chief was the Capitano del Popolo. The names of the contrade were fixed in 1370. Apart from exceptions (like Torre for the district with the tower of the city hall and Onda with the wavy coat of arms for the persons responsible for the Sienese harbour Talamone) the names are almost all names of animals – eagle, panther, porcupine, turtle, she-wolf or goose. Next to their military and administrative duties the contrade soon took over important decision-making functions: they proposed laws, built streets, chose the heads of the guilds (priori) and organized the militia. Today they still play a role

The daring Contrade, the battle for the coveted victor's flag, rages on the Piazza del Campo at breakneck speeds

in the life of the city and for every Sienese, man or woman, it is a matter of course to belong to a contrada – they are born and remain contradialo even if they move away.

Coveted Flag

The **Palio** (Latin pallium = cloth) is actually the trophy, a silk flag commemorating the Virgin Mary which is designed new every year by an artist. The first unofficial discussions about the race and the training of the riders (fantini), who are mostly Sardinian, begin months beforehand. Four weeks before the start a draw officially decides which of the three contrade will compete in the Palio along with the seven that did not compete in the previous year. Five days before the feast the wooden stands with expensive seats are erected. To watch the race sitting down, it is necessary to order tickets months ahead (through the tourist office). The centre of the piazza (nicchia), which is enclosed for the race with a wooden fence, can only be reached on the Via Malborghetto and has free admission. For the racetrack a special mixture of tuffstone and ochre-coloured sand is poured around the sloping Piazza del Campo to a depth of 20cm/8in and compacted to make a track 7.5m/25ft wide. When the sand is on the piazza the **excitement is at fever pitch**.

The Tension Mounts

The draw for the horses takes place under the supervision of the mayor on the day before the race on the town hall square. The lucky ones can lead a swift *Barbero* to the stable, and the unlucky ones get a tired nag, a *Brenna*, and can only pray for the help of the patron saints. In the afternoon the qualifying races take place, three times around the square. In the meantime all of Siena is decorated with coats of arms and banners of the contrade and anxiously awaits the final moment. On the evening before the Palio the participating contrade hold banquets on their squares, where everyone joins in and where final arrangements are made. Is there a realistic hope of winning the flag of the Virgin? Or if the horse drawn in the lottery has hardly a chance of winning, then it might at least make the race difficult for the rival contrade. On the morning of the race, horse and rider go to the **contrada church for a blessing**. »Va e torna vincitore – go, and return victorious« are the priest's closing words. Then the horses are presented to the mayor at noon, and at 3pm the contrade members assemble in the cathedral square for the **historic parade**. What the city has longed for, imagined and prepared for all year is delayed unbearably at the end. Without any haste, in fact particularly slowly, the residents of Siena move through the streets and alleys toward the Piazza del Campo to the monotone tolling of the bell of the Torre del Mangia. The colourful **Passeggiata Storica**, which reaches the overcrowded campo along Via del Casato, is accompanied by medieval banner throwers, drummers and pipers. At the front are the six staff bearers, and the town flag bearer rides whirling the black and white flag of Siena. Then come trumpeters and musicians, followed by banner bearers of the estates that once belonged to the city republic. They are followed by the three mercantile magistrates and representatives of the most important guilds. Now come the entourages of the ten participating and seven non-participant contrade: one drummer, two flag bearers, one captain, four pages, another banner bearer, a rider on the parade horse and the stable master leading the racehorse for each contrade. The six historic contrade (bear, oak, rooster, lion, sword, viper) which were barred from the race forever in 1675 because of a riot are also represented. The parade can take up to two hours until finally the four Chianina oxen pull the decorated **triumphal wagon with the Martinella bell and the trophy** past the cheering crowd. Banners are thrown into the air one last time before the bell is silenced around 8pm, the horses trot nervously out of the inner courtyard of the Palazzo Pubblico and line up in the order that was drawn by lot amidst louder and louder cheers.

Decision in Seconds

Suddenly everything happens quickly. The rope (canapo) falls, the crowds roar and the spectacle takes its course. The horses have to circle the slanted oval piazza three times, and take about 100 seconds to do so. In the second round at the latest there is usually a spectacular and often dangerous fall at the notorious **Curva di San Martino**, which is padded with mattresses for this reason. Then one more round at breakneck speed until the first horse crosses the finish line, with or without a rider, to the frenetic shouts of the crowds. The first spectators are already joyfully climbing over the barriers, pulling the winner from his horse and car-

rying him with the Palio on their shoulders in triumph to the thanksgiving Te Deum, on **2 July** in the Provenzano church and on **16 August** in the cathedral. After a mere fifteen minutes the campo is almost empty, while the streets of Siena are quickly decorated with the colours of the winning contrada and everyone gathers around outdoor tables for an exuberant and opulent feast. **The head of the winners' table is reserved for the winning horse!**

Fascinating performance with flags at the beginning of the Palio

Giostra del Saracino in Arezzo is a battle on horseback against the wooden Saracen king

MAY
Giostra del Archidado
Traditional archers' festival with historic costumes. At the end of May elected representatives of the various parts of **Cortona** compete for a 15cm/6in dice, the so-called Dado.

JUNE
Giostra del Saracino
On the third Sunday in June the four city districts of **Arezzo** compete in the battle against the symbolic Saracen king Buratto. The prize is the »golden lance«.

Regatta di San Ranieri
Rowing regatta on the Arno between the four parts of **Florence**, annually on 17 June in honour of the patron saint of Pisa. The rowers compete in historical costumes. On the last Sunday in June the Ponte di Mezzo is transformed into the site of the Gioco del Ponte, a colourful competition between historically costumed representatives of the northern and southern banks of the Arno.

Calcio in Costume
Ball game in historical costumes on the Feast of St John (June 24) on the Piazza Santa Croce in **Florence**. in which the four city districts compete against each other. There is a parade beforehand with representatives of the guilds and the Uffizi flag spinners.

JULY
Palio delle Contrade
▶MARCO POLO Insight p. 90

Giostra dell'Orso
On 25 July on the cathedral
square of **Pistoia**: a festival in
honour of St James. The four
teams representing the four city
districts face off in a competition
on horseback (▶p. 381).

AUGUST
Bravio delle botti
Bravio delle botti is a horse race
just like the Palio in Siena, which
has taken place on 29 August in
honour of the patron saint of
Montepulciano, San Giovanni
Decollati, since 1372. Today it is
no longer carried out on horseback, but with 80kg/176lb barrels,
which are rolled down the main
street by representatives of the
different parts of the town. Beforehand there is a colourful parade with more than 200 knights
and noble ladies, banners and
weapon-bearers.

Opening of the hunting
season
On the second Sunday in August
every year the hunting season is

opened in **Montalcino**. The best
archers of the quartieri (quarters)
compete – a foretaste of the Sagra del Tordo, the larger festival
which is held in October.

Torneo dei Butteri **Insider Tip**
Equestrian competition of the
butteri (cowboys) in **Maremma**.
On 15 August you can get an impression of the skills of the
»Maremma cowboys« in Albarese
(▶p. 316).

SEPTEMBER
Giostra del Saraceno
This competition on horseback in
Arezzo is repeated on the first
Sunday in September (see June).

OCTOBER
Sagra del Tordo
The Thrush Festival in **Montalcino** comes from the time when
thrush were hunted. A parade of
festively costumed knights and ladies of the castle proceeds to the
Fortezza where the best archers of
the quartieri (quarters) compete.
A festive meal crowns the Sagra
del Tordo where the caught
thrush are served.

Food and Drink

Cucina toscana

The worldwide spread of Italian cooking means that Italian food is eaten and the ingredients for an Italian meal are available almost everywhere. However, food cooked locally by local chefs always tastes better.

A typically Tuscan cuisine, the Cucina toscana, has developed, which can claim to have played a large role in the worldwide fame of Italian cooking. It also influenced Caterina de Medici's establishment of fine French cuisine. Tuscan food was originally not courtly, however, rather it was **hearty country cooking**. It loves fresh and high quality local ingredients – garden vegetables, herbs, legumes, olive oil, chicken, rabbit, pork, fish and lots of beef. Many of the recipes have hardly changed over centuries

Hearty rural cooking

Every province has its culinary speciality, be it melons or spinach (Val di Cornia), onions (Certaldo), pine nuts (San Rossore), small chick peas (Valdarno), artichokes (Empoli, Livorno), red potatoes (Pratomagno, Casentino) or cherries from Lari (19 varieties!). Pienza and the province Grosseto (Ricotta) are especially known for cheese. And Tuscan ham would be unthinkable without Sienese pigs (Cinta Senese).

Regional specialities

Foodstuffs are valued highly in Tuscany. Ingredients like olive oil or wine are often protected, usually organically grown or processed and marked as such for sale. Products with the **seal DOP** (Denominazione d' Origine Protetta) include e.g. saffron from San Gimignano, honey from Lunigiana, Tuscan ham and salami alla cacciatore (hunter's style) as well as the cheese varieties Pecorino Romano and Pecorino Toscano. The mark **IGP** (Indicazione Geografica Protetta) can be found on basic ingredients like the marble-white bacon lardo di collonata or chestnuts from Monte Amiata. Even the sweet riccarelli biscuits from Siena are protected.

Tuscan ingredients

The appreciation for food goes even further – nothing gets thrown away, not even old bread. On the contrary: it is the main ingredient in many dishes that are not all part of the Cucina povera, poor man's cooking, but rather from a farm tradition.

LONG MEALTIMES

Italian **breakfast (colazione)** is often limited to cappuccino, espresso or caffè (a strong espresso) with baked goods. But hotels are gener-

Eating habits

Tuscany sometimes offers unusual places to eat

? *Price categories*

Restaurants
(price for a main dish)
€€€€ over €25
€€€ €18 – €25
€€ €12 – €18
€ up to €12

ally prepared for the habits of their foreign guests and offer a more ample breakfast buffet.

The cheerfully familiar, often hours-long session with an opulent lunch from 12.30/1pm or dinner (from 8/8.30pm) is »sacred« in Tuscany. **Lunch and dinner** always consist of several courses. They begin with an appetizer (antipasto), followed by the first course (primo) with pasta or soup and a second course (secondo) with a meat or fish dish. Vegetables (contorni) and salads are ordered separately. Many Italians begin with a salad, too. They finish with cheese (formaggio), a piece of cake or another sweet (dolce), half-frozen sweet (semifreddo) or ice cream (gelato). For that matter: Tuscany is a paradise for people with a sweet tooth. No meal without a sweet highlight before fruit, grappa or espresso call!

In restaurants Extended meals in restaurants are never cheap in Tuscany, but often three-course menus, lunch or daily specials are offered at a **reduced price**. Value-added tax (Iva) is always, service (servizio compreso) is usually included. Often there is a cover charge (pane e coperto) for bread and place settings. 5–10% of the bill (or round up to the next round figure) is generally expected as a **tip**. In bars or cafés an extra coin on the bar makes the service faster. Service at the table (al tavolo) is almost always more expensive.

FROM ANTIPASTI TO GRAPPA

Antipasti Tuscan ham (prosciutto toscano) is delicious and saltier than Parma ham. Tuscan salami (salame toscano) is spicy and prepared with large pieces of fat and peppercorns. **Crostini**, small slices of bread grilled with a topping, are also very popular – the classic topping is a tasty, warm paste made of chicken liver, sardines, onions and herbs in white wine. Finocchiona looks at first like a large salami, but is younger and tastes of the fennel seeds used to make it.

Primo **Pappa al pomodoro** is a tempting paste made of bread and tomatoes, with fresh basil and olive oil. One fantastic cold summer dish is **panzanella** (▶p. 102/103), a salad made of hard bread soaked in water, ripe tomatoes, onions, sometimes cucumbers, seasoned with olive oil, basil, pepper and salt. **Ribollita** is a thick soup that has simmered for hours and is brought to boil again before it is served; the ingredients vary with the region, but Tuscan kale always plays an

After a sumptuous meal people love to sit together for hours

important part, and white beans are mostly included, too. **Zuppa di pane** or **pancotto** is bread soup with tomatoes, garlic, basil and olive oil. **Farinata** is a soup made of chick pea flour. A rich variety of various pasta shapes and recipes, which change from season to season and one region to another, can be added.

Fagioli (white cooked beans) are a classic side dish and are seasoned with olive oil and pepper. **Fagioli all'uccelletto** is a soup made of beans and tomatoes with sage. Local fresh vegetables (verdure) like spinaci (cooked spinach leaves), quickly sautéed in hot garlic-olive oil, or zucchini chunks fried in olive oil taste best. Two especially tasty dishes are **fiori fritti** and **carciofi fritti**, zucchini flowers and artichoke quarters in bread dough, fried in olive oil.

Contorni (side dishes)

Arrosto misto is generally rather dry, a platter of various types of fried meats (chicken, rabbit, guinea fowl, pork chops, beef etc.). The famous Florentine T-bone steak (**Bistecca Fiorentina**) usually comes from Argentina today – seldom is it a genuine Chianina cow raised in Tuscany. Pieces of rabbit dipped in bread dough and fried in olive oil (**coniglio fritto**) are often served with carciofi fritti. **Arista** is spicy oven-roasted pork with rosemary, **cinghiale in dolce e forte** is a sweet-and-sour wild boar stew cooked in Chianti, with celery, rosemary, pine nuts and raisins (▶p. 103).

Secondo

Cheese (formaggio)

The best Tuscan cheese (formaggio) is sheep's cheese (**pecorino**) from southern Tuscany. Fresh (fresco) and matured (stagionato) pecorino of excellent quality are sold in the shops in Asciano, Pienza, Montepulciano and Montalcino.

Bread (pane)

Bread features in almost every Tuscan meal. It is eaten with ham or cheese, with antipasto, even with pasta, meat, vegetables – but not for breakfast. And the bread is unsalted. **Pane toscano** is baked without salt – apparently since the 12th century as the result of boycott quarrels between Pisa and Florence. Dante said: »The foreign bread really tastes salty.« Fortunately most bakers take pity on foreigners and offer one kind of bread with salt (pane salato). Specialities are square bread Prato (Bozza Pratese), 2kg/5lb loaves from Montegemoli (Pisa province) and the Tuscan flat loaf (castagnaccio toscano), made of chestnut flour, olive oil, raisins and pine nuts.

A Tuscan delicacy: Pecorino cheese

Sweets (dolci)

Almonds are one of the most important common ingredients in Tuscan pastries. They are vital in one of the best known Tuscan sweet products, the **cantuccini** of Prato, the pretty almond biscuits which are said to taste best when dipped in Vin Santo. The almond biscuits bruti ma buoni (»ugly but good«) also come from Prato. Castagnaccio, baked from fresh, roasted chestnut flour, a tasty flat bread, is at home in all of Tuscany. Almost every restaurant and every pastry shop (pasticceria) sells **torta della nonna** (grandmother's tart) made of shortcrust pastry, vanilla cream, pine nuts and almonds. But every larger town has its own dolce, which the residents are very proud of. For Lucca it is **buccellato** (»soldier's bread«), an egg and yeast dough with orange peel, aniseed and raisins; in Volterra **cavallucci**, round honey cakes with nuts, candied fruit and aniseed; in Montalcino **ossi di morto** (»dead men's bones«), a dry, flat biscuit made of egg whites and hazelnuts; in Poggibonsi **pan co'santi**, sweet bread with sultana raisins and nuts; in Lamporecchio (near Vinci) **brigidini**, paper-thin, crispy aniseed waffles, and in Siena the legendary **panforte**, similar to gingerbread with almonds and candied fruits.

Ice cream (gelato)

Not everything called gelato tastes good. Gelati that live up to their name are only a few hours old. So the best ice cream comes from ice-cream shops (gelateria) that make their own (produzione propria) and have a fast turnover.

Drinks

Anyone who doesn't want to drink wine with their meal can order beer or mineral water. To conclude a meal everyone in Italy drinks **caffè espresso**. Among foreign travellers to Italy **cappuccino**, a strong coffee with lots of hot milk topped with the famous milk foam, is much more popular. There's nothing better than a cappuccino during an early morning stroll through town. But beware: if you order cappuccino after lunch, you will be marked down as a tourist at first sight. Italians only drink it in the morning. And another thing: drinking coffee standing at the bar (al banco) is cheaper than when seated at one of the small tables (al tavolo).

A grappa to finish off

Grappa is the proper conclusion to a rich meal. Nothing comes after it, except perhaps a cigar. Grappa has to be strong and dry and pleasantly fruity. However, good grappa is rare in Tuscany because the culture of distilling is centred on northern Italy. Tuscany actually has only one first-class grappa distiller: Giovacchino Nannoni in Paganico (not far from Montalcino). Nannoni distils for many wine producers in Chianti and in Montalcino. His spirits are found not in his own name but in those of the winegrowers (for example Altesino, Gabbiano, Nittardi, Mastroianni, Monte Vertine, Poggio Antico, Ornellaia or Verrazzano). If in doubt look for the names of well-known northern Italian spirits.

Typical Dishes

Tuscan specialities tend to be hearty: lots of meat, also fish and seafood, the inevitable pasta – and many dishes based on bread that are now delicately prepared.

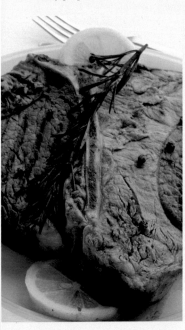

Bistecca alla fiorentina: There are supposed to be 830 recipes for the larger-than-your-plate sized steak, which can weigh up to 1.5kg/3.3lb and which is cut from the short loin of a Chianini cow. Bistecca, which is three fingers thick, got its name from English beefsteak and the Medici festivals in honour of San Lorenzo when huge portions of grilled meat were distributed to the people. It is grilled on both sides over a low flame for 3-5 minutes – and it's done as soon as it can stand on the narrow side! This test is important. Traditionally it is served bloody (al minuto) on the inside. It is never seasoned, but it should always be served with fresh lemon juice. Side dishes are usually a salad and sometimes beans. A strong red wine (Chianti, Morellino di Scansano) is also a must.

Pappa al Pomodoro: The pop singer Rita Pavone made this Cucina povera classic tomato soup or sugo world famous in the 1960s. The recipe includes old unsalted Tuscan bread, olive oil extravergine of course, tomatoes, a little garlic, basil, broth, salt and pepper. Pappa al Pomodoro is also delicious when served cold!

Cacciucco alla Viareggina: This classic dish from Viareggio, a spicy fish soup, is made of Mediterranean fish, squid, mussels, olive oil, garlic, chilli, white wine, tomatoes, slices of white bread, salt and pepper. The combination of fish and cooking tomatoes was first discovered by members of the Jewish community in Livorno. Of course, Cacciucco alla Viareggina tastes best when it's fresh!

Panzanella: This cold poor man's dish tended not to be known north of the line Viareggio – Lucca – Florence. Old bread, soaked in water (for this reason also called »pan molle«), red onions, basil, oil, vinegar, salt are the main ingredients of this popular appetizer. There's no limit to embellishments like cucumber, mint, tomatoes, rocket etc.

Cinghiale in Umido: Wild boar stew is a culinary must, not only in Casentino or the Maremma. The meat is marinated 2-3 days in carrots, celery, garlic, rosemary, olive oil and white wine vinegar before it is fried, seasoned again with the marinade and white wine. Tomato paste and pureed tomatoes are added. In Chianti there is a sweet and sour variation: cinghiale in dolce e forte is made with pine nuts and raisins.

WINELAND TUSCANY

A more traditional wine region than Tuscany is hard to imagine – at least in Italy. Some Tuscan wines are world famous, others are real insider tips, and others again don't need to be considered.

White wines
Even though Tuscany is known mostly for red wine, its white wine tradition is much older. However, white wines have maintained their position only in a few regions like Montecarlo and San Gimignano. The coast near Livorno and around Pisa has interesting white wines from the local Vermentino grape, but the Trebbiano grape, which is still the dominant white variety, hardly yields satisfactory quality. Most of the successful new white wines are thus based mainly on Sauvignon and Chardonnay.

Red wines
The main variety for all traditional Tuscan red wines is Sangiovese in its various forms. Canaiolo is used often in Chianti; the growers aim to gain a more intense flavour from this grape. Colorino is added for colour, Malvasia Nera for a milder flavour. In areas directly influenced by the sea (the provinces Livorno, Pisa and Grosseto) Ciliegiolo mixed with Sangiovese or cultivated separately produces unique and remarkable red wines. Since Tuscany has a very broad range of microclimates – from fertile ground close to a warm coast to stony ground at a cool 500m/1,640ft in Chianti Classico or Rufina – many foreign varieties have been acclimatized here in recent decades. Cabernet Sauvignon and Merlot are the latest trend; more rarely are Pinot Nero and Syrah also grown.

How to judge?
There are several levels of quality in Italian wine according to the most recent wine law of 1992. It begins with **table wine** (Vino Rosso or Vino Bianco, without year or place of origin); the next class of table wines gives the **place of origin** (for example Vino Rosso Toscano) and the best class contains the **DOC and DOCG wines** (controlled and guaranteed place of origin). DOC and DOCG wines are always analysed and tasted before being sold. A new law, which has only partially been applied, controls and guarantees the declaration of sub-zone, commune, location, micro zone, wine and vineyard on the label.

The more exact the declaration, the stricter are the quality controls expected of the wine. Of the average 300 million litres (80 million US gallons) of wine produced in Tuscany annually almost 40% are labelled with a controlled origin (DOC and DOCG) – compared to Italy as a whole (about 17% DOC or DOCG) a high proportion.

Super Tuscans
Certain **outstanding wines** that have achieved cult-status are called Super-Tuscans; they began conquering the wine market before the

There are many opportunities to taste wine in Tuscany

1990s. They were created out of the restricitve regulations for the wine classification DOC, which requires, for example, that Chianti wine must contain 70% Sangiovese grapes at the most and at least 10% of local grapes. Wine designers who were interested in creating top products using other combinations and who wanted to counter the Chianti flood that has been on the market since the 1970s with other quality wine were relegated to the lowest wine class »table wine« (vino da tavola). The first of these **designer wines** is the vintage 1972 **Sassicaia** from Tenuta San Guido vinyards in **Bolgheri** as well as the vintage 1971 **Tignanello** from Marchese Piero **Antinori** (Santa Cristina, Val di Pesa), both marketed in 1978. The wine law of 1992 made it possible to use the simple categorization for superior table wine IGT (indicazione geografica tipica) for these wines as well. It applied until 2009 and was then replaced by the new EU wine market regulation IGP (indicazione geografica protetta, protected geographical calssification), but it may still be used for traditional reasons. In order to **boost sales** the term »super Tuscan« has been extended in part to include other Tuscan top wines like certain Brunello vintages, since it »only« stands for outstanding quality and is not protected.

From the 1980s and 1990s other top quality products followed, starting with the current star, **Ornellaia**, also from **Bolgheri**, which has

In an enoteca in Montalcino

developed into the new Tuscan wine eldorado. Also at home in Bolgheri is Masseto, but Solaia, Solengo or Guado al Tasso have many fans worldwide too. The prices for these connoisseur wines are breaking all records. 13 bottles of a special **art edition** of Ornellaia, vintage 2008, called »El' Energia« and designed by the artist Rebecca Horn, was sold on May 19, 2011 at an auction in the Berlin New National Gallery for a total of €130,000. Along with ten double magnums (3l/6.3pt) and two imperials (6 l/12.6pt) one salmanazar (9l/18.9pt) was sold for an epic €40.000. Normal 0.7-litre bottles of Ornellaia or Sassicaia from 2008 were offered in 2011 in Bolgheri for €140, the 2006 vintage was priced at €170. A Masseto from Ornellaia, vintage 2005, can cost up to $300 in the USA, a Solengo 2004 more than €70. So it's fine that new creations like »Le Difese« from Tenuta San Guido vineyards (Bolgheri) or a simple and very good Rosso di Bolgheri are sold for much less (€30 or less). The good to very good vintages currently include Brunello 2001, 2004, 2006 and 2008.

Meanwhile the next wine boom is already on the horizon. New **organic wines** are being created in many places; they are trendy and have no trouble conquering the market. Worth watching is the Morellino di Scansano made of organically grown grapes.

Above all in Chianti, but also in other wine regions many wine-growers sell their products direct. The signposts to wineries are easy to find – cantina aperta (open cellar), degustazione vini (wine tasting), visita cantina (visit the cellar) or vendita diretta (direct sales) show the way. But it is a mistake to think that buying direct is cheaper: the prices at the wineries are often higher than in the shops (**enotece**) in the surrounding area!

Where to buy?

CLASSIC WINE REGIONS

In Tuscany there are 6 DOCG as well as 11 DOC regions. DOCG are Brunello di Montalcino, Carmignano, Chianti (along with local regions Colli Aretini, Colli Fiorentini, Colli Sebesi, Colline Pisane, Montalbano, Montespertoli and Rufina), Chianti Classico, Vernaccia of San Gimignano as well as Vino Nobile of Montepulciano. DOC classifications are on Ansonica of the Costa dell' Argentario, Barco Reale of Carmignano, Bianco of Valdinievole, Bianco from the Empoli region, Bianco of Pitigliano, Bianco Pisano of San Torpè, Bolgheri with the addition that Bolgheri Sassicaia 1994 is to date the only Italian vineyard with DOC honours, Candia of Colli Apuani, Capalbio, Colli dell' Etruria Centrale region as well as Colli di Luni.

▶MARCO POLO Insightp. 200

Chianti

In ancient times Montalcino was already famous for its (surprise!) white wine. This is not unusual since red wine is a relatively new invention in the history of wine. In the mid-19th century a certain Clemente Santi recognized the advantages of the Tuscan **Sangiovese** variety. Against the customary practice of processing various kinds of grapes together into wine, his grandson Ferruccio Biondi-Santi cultivated Sangiovese separately and called this robust wine, which was rich in tannin, **Brunello**. It was only over 100 years later, in the 1970s, that Brunello became a fashionable wine and fetched top prices. In Montalcino everyone wanted to be a Brunello producer, and today there are more than 200. The Brunello that comes from lower sites in the south of Montalcino is heavy, dark and rich in tannin, while the wines from higher sites and those north of the town are marked by dense colour, elegance, high acidity and fruity character. If €20 for a bottle of Brunello seems too much, there is a more affordable alternative: the younger, somewhat lighter and more rustic Rosso di Montalcino is mostly a good buy!

Montalcino

The **wine »scandal«** that the magazine »L' Espresso« uncovered in 2008 concerning possibly cut Brunello vintage 2003 wines was probably only half a scandal. While grapes from Sicily or southern Italy were added to wines intended for the US market in order to create a rounder tasting experience, these were immediately removed from the market. But the financial damage remains high – without reason: in 2011 cheap Brunello wines vintage 2005 even appeared in the shelves of a German discount supermarket.

The wines: Brunello di Montalcino DOCG (type of grape: Sangiovese, also called Santo Grosso; prescribed storage time: 4 years, of this 3 in a wooden barrel, riserva 5 years). Rosso di Montalcino DOC (type of grape: Sangiovese; prescribed storage: 1 year; wood barrel aging not required). Other wines: Moscadello DOC (sweet desert wine), various white and red Vini da Tavola and – today more rare – Chianti Colli Senesi DOCG.

Montepulcia-
no

As a red-wine region Montepulciano is considerably older than its successful neighbour Montalcino. A good Vino Nobile is neither worse nor better than a Brunello or a Chianti Classico, just different. Maybe it is even the most approachable of the three Sangiovese classics from Tuscany. Its acidity is mostly embedded in a thick cushion of fruit and the tannin is balanced by strength and fullness. The main problem is the bottlers of Vino Nobile today: only a few can still be considered reliable. When it succeeds, the Nobile is a friendly, warm and lovable wine, which generally offers very good value. The situation with the affordable Rosso di Montepulciano is even more heterogeneous; stick to the well-known names.

The wines: Vino Nobile di Montepulciano DOCG (type of grape: Sangiovese, also called Prugnolo, Canaiolo; prescribed storage time: 2 years in a wooden barrel, riserva 3 years). Rosso di Montepulciano DOC (type of grape: like Vino Nobile; prescribed storage time: 1 year, wood not required). Other wines: Vin Santo (dessert wine), white and red Vini da Tavola, Chianti Colli Senesi DOCG.

Carmignano

The modest village of Carmignano crowns the top of the Montalbano ridge of hills west of Florence and was always considered to be part of the city's zone of influence. Even though Montalbano could not devote large, connected areas to winegrowing because of its topography, its wine has numbered among the best and most expensive Florentine red wines since the 14th century. It ought to be mentioned that the amount of Cabernet in a Carmignano does not reflect modern fashion, but has been usual since the 18th century. Its admirers love its smoothness and elegance.

The wines: Carmignano DOCG (type of grape: Sangiovese, Cabernet / 15%, Canaiolo / 15%; prescribed storage time 20 months, of which 1 year in a wooden barrel, riserva 2 years). Other wines: Chianti Montalbano DOCG, Barco Reale DOC (light red wine), Vin Santo DOC.

The rough, clefted Sieve valley east of Florence produces red wines with body and acidity. Rufina wines are mostly very strong and equipped with a steely acidity; they are valued for their durability. The region was forgotten except for two or three quality producers, but in recent years has again been producing wines that can take their place alongside other Tuscan wines. High above the Sieve valley, in the mini-region Pomino (the only producer is Frescobaldi) an extraordinary white and a red with individual character are produced. **The wines:** Chianti Rufina DOCG (type of grape: Sangiovese, Canaiolo; prescribed storage time: 8 months, riserva 3 years). Pomino Rosso DOC (type of grape: Sangiovese, Merlot, Cabernet, Canaiolo; prescribed storage time: 1 year). Pomino Bianco DOC (type of grape: Pinot Bianco, Chardonnay, Trebbiano).

Rufina and Pomino

The historic Badia a Coltibuona wine cellar in Chianti

LESSER-KNOWN WINE REGIONS

Colli Fiorentini
The original zone Colli Fiorentini includes a broad area to the south and east of Florence and would even be much larger if the Florentines had not given a large part of their Colli to the prestigious Chianti Classico. As region of origin the Colli Fiorentini are very heterogeneous and seem to result more from a political compromise than from an appraisal of growing conditions. However, a handful of winegrowers in this part of Tuscany have retained their individuality and aim to produce real top-quality red wines – some as Chianti, some as Vino da Tavola.

The wines: Chianti Colli Fiorentini DOCG (types of grapes: Sangiovese, Canaiolo), Chianti DOCG (types of grapes: Sangiovese, Canaiolo), red Vini da Tavola.

Montecarlo
This wine with a melodious name comes from the warm, green hills of Lucca. The growing region is very small and the wines have not always been worthy of attention. But recently it has been exciting to follow the development in quality of some of the growers' red and white wines.

The wines: Montecarlo Bianco DOC (type of grape: Trebbiano among others), Montecarlo Rosso DOC (type of grape: Sangiovese, Canaiolo).

Red grapes – the basis for many noble wines

California is the name of a village on the so-called Etruscan coast Coast south south of Livorno, and the speedy development and type of wine of Livorno found there indeed seem to be Californian. Until a few years ago the hinterland of Florence's favourite beach was a winegrowing no-man's-land. But there was one prominent exception: the famous Sassicaia of the Marchese Incisa. In 1994 this »ringleader of the Tuscan Vino da Tavola revolution« was given a legal status and since then has very properly called itself **»Bolgheri DOC Sassicaia«**. Only in the recent past were the Ornellaia of Lodovico Antinori and the Grattamacco of Meletti-Cavallari added, and very recently Piero Antinori with his Guardo al Tasso. But a considerable number of winegrowers in the DOC regions Bolgheri, Montescudaio and Val di Cornia are following suit and will soon be talked about. The warm coastal climate is proving to be very suitable for Cabernet and Merlot, which are the dominant element of the majority of wines here. The wines do not have the vegetable aromas sometimes evident in the bad years of the Cabernets of central Tuscany, or the often bitter tannins of the Merlot and Cabernet vintages from Friuli.
The wines: Bolgheri DOC (white, rosé and red), Montescudaio DOC (white and red) and Val di Cornia DOC (white, rosé and red).

The region of Morellino di Scansano comprises about 58,000ha/ Morellino di 143,000ac in southern Tuscany between the rivers Ombrone and Al- Scansano begna. This includes the entire community of Scansano (to which the wine owes its name) as well as parts of the communities of Manciano, Magliano in Toscana, Grosseto, Compagnatico, Semproniano, Montemerano and Roccalbenga. Softly rolling hills with bright colours and an intensive light characterise this landscape. The average elevation lies between less than 100m/330ft to more than 500m/1600ft. The ground varies greatly and the region is marked by a clearly Mediterranean, warm and sunny climate. Summer is usually dry, fall is mild with generally not very intensive precipitation, which becomes even less in January and February and then regular again in spring. There is rarely any frost. Morellino di Scansano, which received DOC classification in 1978, should contain at least 85% Sangiovese (called Morellino in this region) and at the most 15% of other red grapes or recommended or allowed varieties like Alicante, Ciliegiolo, Colorino, Merlot, Cabernet etc.

Once there was a delicious wine, which farmers kept in small Vin Santo amounts in their attics in wooden barrels for five, eight, even ten years. The wine was **very sweet and strong** and was served to guests as a special honour. The farmers would send a bottle of the **»holy wine«** to influential people on holy days when they needed favours. But they would never have stooped to selling their Vin Santo for money. Times have changed, and a caricature of what was once

A Culinary Miracle

We can envy the Tuscans for many reasons: the mild climate, good wine, food, their lifestyle, the rich culture. But maybe their olive trees are the biggest reason to be envious. Without olives something would be missing from the Tuscan landscape, and Tuscan cooking would also lack one vital ingredient: olive oil.

Olives contain a high-quality oil which can be extracted through simple cold pressing. It is the only oil that can be consumed without any treatment. It may be surprising to learn that Tuscans regard wine as a normal foodstuff. But olive oil is much more important to them. They appreciate the work that goes into making just one litre, because they know how little the trees bear and that it takes many years for them to yield fruit at all. Every Tuscan has »his« oil press (frantoio), where he gets his year's supply around Christmas time. Consumption is high: an Italian family of four uses one litre a week.

Harvested by Hand

Many experts consider Tuscan olive oil to be the best of all. The climate and soil quality are vital, as well as the dense network of **oil presses**, which make it possible to press the olives immediately after harvesting and also to choose the time and method of harvesting. The quality of the oil depends on the ripeness of the olives when they are harvested. In the Tuscan hills the harvest usually begins in early November and runs until Christmas. At this time the olives are not yet ripe and taste best. The difficulty comes from the fact that the green, red-green or black-red olives have to be picked by hand because they still cling to the branches and can only be persuaded with difficulty to fall into the **nets** that are spread out below. Beating the trees would damage the olives and the exposed oily flesh would lose its quality and fine taste by starting to oxidize and ferment.

To the Press – as Quickly as Possible

The worst thing for the quality of the oil would be to leave the olives lying on the ground or in the nets. Ideally, olives should go to the press 48 to 72 hours after being picked. The less time they spend in jute sacks, crates or spread out on a wooden or terracotta floor, the less free oleic acids they will develop and the more of their **fruity taste** will remain. In the frantoio the leaves are removed, the olives are washed, ground and pressed. Some swear by heavy old millstones and intermittent pressing, while others are convinced of the superiority of modern mechanical mills and continuous centrifugal pressing. Both methods produce high-quality oil, provided that attention is paid to strict cleanliness in the traditional method, and that the tempera-

Olives are collected in nets during the harvest

tures are not set too high in the modern process in order to extract more oil.

Strict Laws

Attributes like »**cold pressed**« and »**first pressing**« sound good but are only meant to increase sales. They say nothing about the quality of the oil. According to European Union regulations **Olio d'Oliva Extravergine** (»extra virgin olive oil«, the highest quality level) must be cold-pressed from fresh olives and may not contain more than 1% of free oleic acids. The same applies to **Olio d'Oliva Vergine** (»virgin olive oil«), but with a maximum level of free oleic acid of 2%. **Olio**

d'Oliva (olive oil) is a mixture of refined and virgin olive oil (max. 1.5 % free oleic acids). Olive oil is getting to be more and more popular and it has almost more benefits for health than in terms of taste. Apart from the fact that it is easy to digest and has a high content of **vitamin E**, olive oil also reduces the risk of heart attacks. While polyunsaturated fats such as those in sunflower, maize or soy bean oil reduce both LDL cholesterol and HDL cholesterol in equal measure, the **oleic acids** in olive oil reduce only the harmful LDL cholesterol. So enjoy olive oil, and do some- thing for your health at the same time ...

a fine wine can be found in every supermarket. The production of authentic Vin Santo is highly complicated. And how could it be other than enormously expensive, after being pressed from dry grapes, stored for years in small barrels and thus concentrated to a fraction of the original amount? An encounter with a really great Vin Santo – and that happens rarely – is an unforgettable experience, as hardly any other sweet wine can attain its variety in taste, its depth and harmony. Recommended producers with highly concentrated, in some years unforgettable Vin Santo are Avignonesi (Montepulciano), Capezzana (Carmignano), Isole e Olena (Barberino / Chianti Classico), Montellori (Fucecchio), Paterno & Corzano (San Casciano / Colli Fiorentini), Poliziano (Montepulciano), San Giusto a Rentennano (Gaiole /Chianti Classico) and Selvapiana (Rufina).

Selected winegrowers

CHIANTI: BARBERINO
VAL D'ELSA
Isole e Olena
Località Isole 1
Tel. 05 58 07 27 63
Fax 05 58 07 22 36

Castello di Monsanto
Via Monsanto 8
Tel. 05 58 05 90 00
www.castellodimonsanto.it

Casa Emma
San Donato in Poggio
Tel. 05 58 07 22 39
www.casaemma.com

Le Filigare
Via Sicelle 35
Tel. 05 58 07 27 96
www.lefiligare.it

CHIANTI: CASTELLINA
IN CHIANTI
Castellare in Castellina
Località Castellare
Tel. 05 77 74 2903
www.castellare.it

San Fabiano Calcinaia
Località Cellole
Tel. 05 77 97 92 32
www.sanfabianocalcinaia.com

CHIANTI: GAIOLE
IN CHIANTI
Badia da Coltibuono
Località Badia a Coltibuono
Tel. 0 57 77 74 61 10
www.coltibuono.com

Castello di Cacchiano
Località Monti in Chianti
Tel. 05 77 74 70 18
www.chianticlassico.com/en

Capanelle
Località Capanelle 13
Tel. 0 57 77 45 11
Fax 05 77 74 52 33
www.capannelle.it

Rocca di Montegrossi
Località Monti in Chianti
I-53013 Gaiole in Chianti
Tel. 05 77 74 79 77
www.roccadimontegrossi.it

CHIANTI: GREVE
IN CHIANTI
Castello di Querceto
Via Alessandro François 2
Tel. 05 58 59 21
www.castellodiquerceto.it

Castel Ruggero
Via Castel Ruggero 33
I-50011 Antella
Tel. 05 56 49 94 23
www.castelruggero.it

Viticcio
Via San Cresci 12/A
Tel. 055 85 42 10
www.fattoriaviticcio.com

MAREMMA
Tenuta dell'Ornellaia
Via Bolgherese 191
I-57022 Castagneto Carducci
Tel. 05 65 71 811
www.ornellaia.com

MONTALCINO
Tenute Silvio Nardi
Località Casale del Bosco
Tel. 05 77 80 82 69
www.tenutenardi.com

Siro Pacenti
Località. Pelagrilli 1
Tel. 05 77 84 86 62

MONTEPULCIANO
Rendola
Località Pian d' Asso
Torrenieri
Tel. 05 71 40 97 50
www.rendola.com

MORELLINO DI SCANSANO
Fattoria Le Pupille
Località Istia d'Ombrone
Piaggie del Maiano 92a
I-58040 Grosseto
Tel. 05 64 40 95 17
www.fattorialepupille.it

Shopping

Shopping Heaven

Like all of Italy Tuscany is an El Dorado for fans of souvenirs. Shoes, clothing, household items, jewellery, pasta or wine: weekly and speciality markets, shopping centres and streets, boutiques and outlet centres spoil for choice in often unusually good quality.

Shopping heaven

Be careful when buying fashion or other imitations. There are fines on the purchase of »**fakes**« – for the buyer! And they can be up to €10,000!

Pitfalls

Visitors who like to preserve their holiday memories with something culinary will be spoiled for choice by the huge selection of tasty foods and delicious local products. Gourmet products and other fresh foods are available in great selection in weekly markets, which are still an important institution in daily life in Tuscany.
Tuscan **wines** come first, above all the top vintages of Chianti Classico, Brunello di Montalcino and Vino Nobile from Montepulciano. Tuscan **olive oil** is also famous (►MARCO POLO Insightp. 112), as are the **cheeses**, especially the various kinds of pecorino, the air-cured wild boar ham, other **sausages, truffles and dried porcini mushrooms**. Nibblers will love the countless **pastries and cakes**, including the famous Sienese panforte and the Luccan chestnut bread or the sweet temptations from Chocolate Valley (►p. 132).

Culinary souvenirs

The region is famous for exquisite fashion and beautifully made leather products – from shoes to belts and bags to wallets or gloves – but also for fine **accessories**, wonderful fabrics and jewellery. Especially in Florence, Siena, Pisa or Lucca the well-known **labels** have their own shops. The factory outlets in Prato and the Valdarno (Empoli) are famous for bargains.

Fashion from Armani to Zegna

Marble products from Carrara or Pietrasanta and alabaster work from Volterra are among the most popular souvenirs. High quality ceramics can often even be bought directly from the workshop. In Arezzo, Pisa or Pietrasanta there are good antique markets. Tuscany is also known for its outstanding wrought-iron work (e.g. knives from Borgo San Lorenzo and the Mugello), basketry, artistic glassware and designer furniture.

Kitsch or art?

Anyone not satisfied with the creations of Tuscan fashion icons has a large selection of fabric to make his own clothing

White and Velvety

Alabaster is to Volterra what marble is to Carrara. The processing of the white stone has provided jobs for the city since time immemorial – and any number of souvenirs for the tourists.

Alabaster has always been popular with artists, as it is so easy to work. In the course of history it has been used for many things: in the ancient Orient, for instance, white alabaster was used for containers or statuettes; the coarser, greenish alabaster was used in Assyria for large reliefs, steps, basins and the like. Vessels, lamps and canopic jars were the most popular objects in ancient Egypt, and in Roman times it was used most often for vases, urns and reliefs. The much-praised alabaster work of Volterra flourished from the 6th until the 1st century BC under the **Etruscans**, who used this attractive natural stone along with tuff and terracotta to produce urns. After production all but stopped at the end of Roman rule, and the more resistant and precious ivory was more in demand in the Middle Ages, the processing of alabaster only began again during the Renaissance. The first artisan school for alabaster was started by Inghirami-Fei in the late 18th century. By the middle of the 19th century there were more than 60 workshops which increasingly used alabaster for mass production. Today's selection in the around 1,000 alabaster shops lies somewhere between art and kitsch.

Insider Tip

One special shop in Volterra is Opus Artis, Piazza Minucci 1. Here Giorgio Pecchioni sells alabaster and »Etruscan flutes«, alabaster drums, ocarinas and horns. Pecchioni flutes are used for classical and rock concerts – Ian Anderson from the band Jethro Tull loves them, as do his audiences. A visit to Signore Pecchioni's alabaster workshop is highly recommended, Via A. Cinci 22 (Tel. 0 58 88 67 87, www.alabastrosonoro.com).

Alabaster figures in Volterra

An alabaster workshop, in which tourists can see how the white material is processed

A Type of Plaster

Alabaster is a hydrous calcium sulphate, a crystalline, fine-grained variety of plaster. Four different kinds can be found near Volterra. The white-grey **bardiglio** has many colour nuances and structures and is opaque; it is mined, and was used by the Etruscans for funeral urns. **Pietra a marmor**, twice as expensive and milky white with less structure, is extracted in surface mining near Siena and Volterra. **Scaglione** is translucent and slightly marbled. It is mined near Castellina Marittima in shafts up to 300m/1,000ft below ground and costs three times as much.

But the ultimate alabaster is the transparent **alabastro agatha**, a light-yellow to dark-brown stone with a very fine structure which occurs near Volterra and Siena and costs about four times as much as bardiglio. Anyone who is uncertain and wants to test whether an object is genuine alabaster can test it like this: try scratching it with a fingernail. Unlike artificial materials, alabaster can easily be scratched.

Sports and Outdoors

Swimming, Hiking, Biking

A Tuscan holiday does not have to be cultural. The uniquely beautiful landscape invites hiking, strolling and bike tours, and to water sports along the coast. Tuscany can be explored on foot on pilgrimage routes, on horseback along wine routes, classically on a Vespa scooter over gentle hills and along wonderful cypress-lined roads or it can just be enjoyed in a wellness spa.

THROUGH TUSCANY ON A BIKE

Biking is the most popular sport in Tuscany. No weekend passes without groups of well-equipped amateur cyclers hitting the roads on their racing bikes for longer tours. Moutains and slower hill stretches are ideal for beginners who are trying to step into the shoes of the great Tuscan biking heroes or who just want to do something for their physical fitness. The most famous Tuscan cycling legend is **Gino Bartali** (1914 – 2000), who won the Tour de France twice and the Giro d' Italia three times. In 2006 a **bicycle museum** was opened in Gino Bartali's birthplace Ponte a Ema near Florence, which is also dedicated to sports cycling in Tuscany. The museum organizes 60 – 110 km (36 – 66 mi) long day tours into the Chianti region. Stars like the Tuscan-born Mario Cippolini or Francesco Casagrande and especially the two-time world and Olympic champion Paolo Bettini from the village Bibbona near Bolgheri see to it that biking remains extremely popular.

> **? MARCO POLO INSIGHT**
>
> *Gino Bartali ...*
>
> ... combined his innocuous bicycle training in Mussolini times with courier trips for the resistance movement against the German occupation and thus took part in saving several hundred Jews. The film »The Assisi Underground« is a tribute to his activities.

Museo del Ciclismo »Gino Bartali«: Via Chiantigiana, 177, Ponte a Ema (Bagno a Ripoli/Florenz), Fri 9.30am – 1pm, 3.30pm – 7.30pm, Sat 9.30am – 1pm, closed Sun – Thu and Aug; admission: €3.50; www.ciclomuseo-bartali.it

In 2013 Tuscany hosted the cycling world championships for pros and amateurs. The **amateur routes** are open for recreational cycling. Biking routes around Tuscany can be found at www.turismo.intoscana.it/site/en/cicloturismo/.

Cycling World Championships

Wellness is a »hot topic« in Tuscany with its many hot springs

Tours through Tuscany

Of course it's possible to discover Tuscany on side roads as well – alone or on a guided tour. Main roads (Via Aurelia, Via Cassia) should be avoided for safety reasons. The **L' Eroica route**, which is divided into four units (38km/22mi, 75km/45mi, 135km/81mi or 205km/ 123mi; information: www.eroica-ciclismo.it), and the **Sentiero della Bonifica** (planning/accommodation tips, download PDF brochure: www.sentierodellabonifica.it) are especially attractive and among the 50 top bike tours worldwide; the latter runs along drained sections of the Canale Maestro della Chiana in four sections from Chiusi to Arezzo.

> !
>
> **MARCO ⊕ POLO TIP**
>
> *Take a Vespa!* **Insider Tip**
>
> On a Vespa through Tuscany – it doesn't get more classic than this. Versiliana Viaggi rents Vespa scooters: Via P. E. Barsanti 63/65, Pietrasanta, tel. 0 58 43 65 41, www.versilianaviaggi.it

The Parco Ciclistico del Chianti makes the 400km/240mi trail network in **Chianti** a paradise for mountain bikers as well. Along with L' Eroica the tour »Chianti Classic« is a hit; information: www.parcociclisticodelchianti.it (website under construction). The **province of Siena** has developed a complete network of bike trails (http://inbici.terresiena.it). Day trips for mountain bikers await at **Monteriggioni**.

Along the **Etruscan Riviera** as well as around Bolgheri and Paolo Bettini's birthplace Bibbona hundreds of cyclists are out on weekends. The **Maremma** poses a special challenge with the 366km/219mi-long Grand Tour (information: www.cicloturismoinmaremma.it). Mountain tours in the Apuan Alps and the Apennines are more intended for pros. Finally: in **Casentino** there are at least 6 tours (www.casentino.it).

Lucca

Cycling holiday-makers are especially fond of **Lucca** with the nearby Garfagnana. Lucca's old city can be explored on an **e-bike**; the demand for multi-day tours continues to grow and exceed the supply (www.luccatourist.it).

Florence

Around Florence is the **Anello del Rinascimento**, which includes Valdarno and Valdisieve. Start and finish of the 172km/103mi-long route that was developed for mountain bikers in two variants is Castello di Calenzano near Prato (www.turismo.intoscana.it).

Versilia coast

The Versilia coastline between Forte dei Marmi, Pietrasanta, Lido di Camaiore and Viareggio is great for bikers as it has in part well-developed bike trails.

PILGRIMAGE, HIKING, TREKKING

Hiking and trekking opportunities are booming, not least because of the revival of the **Via Francigena**, whose northern part runs through the ►Alpi Apuane. It can be hiked in sections or in guided tours, e.g. from San Miniato or Monteriggioni near ►Siena. The two variationas of the old Etruscan trail from ►Volterra to Fiesole (Via Volterrana) have also been integrated into the 450km/270mi long network of trails belonging to the Via Francigena (www.associazioneviafrancigena.com, www.turismo.intoscana.it).

Along with many round routes in the Apuan Alps, in the Apennines and at Monte Amiata the **pilgrimage route in the footsteps of Francis of Assisi** (►Bibbiena · Casentino) is interesting and can easily be combined with visits to monasteries (www.camminodiassisi.it, www.caifirenze.it). The **pilgrim's card** (carta credenziale/modulo richiesta credenziali) or pilgrim's credentials, in which all important waystations are stamped, is in hot demand. They can be requested online from the Assoziazione Via Francigena. After arriving in Rome the Vatican's pilgrim's office on St. Peter's Square (Opera Romana Pellegrinaggi) accepts them and gives the pilgrim a certificate.

Information about longer hiking tours (trekking) is available from the Italian Alpine club (Club Alpino Italiano). Around 1985 the ten-section-long round route **Garfagnana Trekking** with start/finish in Castelnuovo di Garfagnana was developed (info/route: www.alpiapuane.com). Hiking recommendations, mountain bike tours, climbing locations and riding trails in English and Italian can be found at www.parks.it/parco.alpi.apuane/Eiti.html.

Overnight stays in bivouacs and mountain cabins (rifugi), in B&Bs or vacation on a farm (agriturismo) are organized in cooperation with the Italian Alpine club CAI.

SEASIDE HOLIDAYS

Beaches

Most of the Tuscan Mediterranean beaches are flat and have fine-grained sand; the coastline around Piombino and Populonia as well as around Monte Argentario is rocky. Beach holidays-makers are mostly attracted to the beaches on the Versilia coast at Forte dei Marmi, Lido di Camaiore and Viareggio. **Elba** and **Isola del Giglio** are also very popular while less frequented areas are the Riviera degli Etruschi between Livorno and Piombino as well as the coast of the Maremma, whose most beautiful beaches are Punta Ala and on the side of the Monte Argentario facing the sea.

Watersports

Along the Tuscan mainland coast there are lots of opportunities for sports: swimming, beach volleyball and beach soccer, badminton, surfing, kite-surfing or snorkling are available between Viareggio, Talamone and the Monte Argentario Peninsula.

Elba and Isola del Giglio attract sailors and divers. Numerous **sailing and diving schools** offer courses in several languages.

Stylish Spas

Along with the beauty of the beaches along the azure Tyrrhenian Sea and the gentle nature around crystal clear moutain lakes, cool streams and waterfalls in the Casentino or the Appenines more and more visitors to Tuscany are discovering the advantages of the thermal spas.

About 30 locations make Tuscany to the Italian region with the most thermal baths. Once Etruscan kings and Roman statesmen relaxed here; celebrities handed

Hard to top: wellness swim in the natural pool at Bagni di San Filippo

each other bath towels here. Federico Fellini recognized that the spa ambience restored body and soul in his movie »8½«. Spafinder website found the Europe's best spa resort in Tuscany – no wonder then that Tuscan tourism pays special attention to »termalismo« and spoils guests in many places with rare essential oils and raindrop massages.

Pleasure with a Past

The Etruscans already discovered the myriad blessings, the physical and emotional release that comes from enjoying the bubbly waters flowing from volcanic rock; they even memorialized their passion on grave monuments. They left the Romans with enviably beautiful locations in the midst of healthy nature, which they had decorated with temples and altars. The art of building aqueducts brought thermal joys to urban centres as well. The thermal springs close to Pisa (San Giuliano Terme) and Florence (Fonte Antica, Fonte Celeste) still bear witness to this tradition, which did not even stop during the bathing-phobic Middle Ages. The free »light therapy« of the Tuscan sun have always been in competition with the natural healing powers of the water and first class, high quality foods for the health of the guests. The enjoyment of art and culture like only Tuscany has to offer should not be left out: aesthetic relaxation like Mathilde of Canossa enjoyed in the thermal baths of Versilia. Stylish wellness also attracted Renaissance popes and nobility.

Health

Today **Montecatini** with its stylish old hotels, spa houses and parks, **Monsumano Terme** and **Chianciano Terme** head the list of Tuscan wellness and thermal spa pleasures. But it doesn't always have to be marble. The small but fine facilities at Bagni San Filippo, **Bagno Vignoni or San Casciano dei Bagni** offer restorative, stylish Tuscan rehabilitation – even with insurance benefits. Unusual healing methods can be found here as well as organically structured natural medicine. But the goal is always the same. Antistress programmes that restore inner balance and outer beauty, physical fitness and holistic wellbeing – in steaming grottos, splashing hot springs cascades or terraces.

Thermal baths

Terme di Montecatini
Montecatini Terme
Viale Verdi 41
Tel. 05 72 77 84 18
www.termemontecatini.it
Very formal, elegant state spa – the largest in Tuscany and one of the most famous in Europe

Terme di Saturnia
58050 Saturnia
Tel. 05 64 60 10 61
www.termesaturnia.it
Singularly beautiful natural pools, open for a relaxing swim free of charge

Terme di Bagno Vignoni
San Quirico d'Orcia
Piazza del Moretto
Tel. 05 77 88 73 65
www.termedibagnovignoni.it
Idyllic spa with a large 15th-century pool. A small natural pool below Bagno Vignoni is free of charge.

Terme di San Filippo
Castiglione d'Orcia
Loc. San Filippo 23
Tel. 05 77 87 29 82
www.termesanfilippo.it
Outside the tiny spa town in a wooded valley is the charming waterfall Fosso Bianco. The warm water is an inviting place for a swim.

Terme di Chianciano
Chianciano Terme
Via delle Rose
Tel. 057 86 81 11
Tel. 8 48 80 02 43 (call centre)
www.termechianciano.it
Modern, popular spa, famous for its thermal springs

Bagni di Lucca
Piazza San Martino 11
Tel. 058 38 72 21
www.termebagnidilucca.it
Open April until 20 Nov Ancient spa, very popular in the belle époque among intellectuals, artists and the aristocracy.

Surfer's paradise at Versilia coast

AND THEN THERE'S ...

Riding

There are also **riding schools and stables** (maneggi) in the Tuscan hills, especially the Maremma. Information is available at www.turismo.intoscana.it (Turismo equestre).

Tuscany can be explored on horseback along various **riding trails**. The more than 10 possibilities for riding tours in the Maremma Nature Park are the most spectacular. The multi-day tours along the 23 tuscan wine routes and the riding trails (ippovie) are especially worthwhile, e.g. the 210km/130mi-long **Via dei Cavalleggeri**, which is divided into six sections, through the provinces Grosseto, Livorno and Pisa (information: http://eventi.intoscana.it/ippovie/scheda_Cavalleggeri.pdf). **Monte Amiata** can be circled on the upper (L' Anello A – alto, 30km/18mi) and on the lower riding trails (L' Anello B – basso, 80km/50mi; information: http://eventi.intoscana.it/ippovie/scheda_Amiata.pdf).

The **Ippovia di San Jacopo** leads through Pistoiese and is connected to the Via Francigena. This trail through the **province of Siena** is 175km/105mi long in all and divided into three separate routes (25, 60, 90 km (15, 36, 54 mi) in length; Ippovia Terre di Siena: http://eventi.intoscana.it/ippovie/scheda_Siena.pdf).

Its **39 golf courses** make Tuscany one of the top European golf destinations. The national golfing federation Federazione Italiana di Golf has a list of all locations.

MARCO POLO TIP

Golf for all the senses   Insider Tip

No true golfer should miss the pleasure of indulging in his hobby at the slightly undulating Punta Ala golf course! The 18-hole course lies high above the sea. There is a breath-taking view from the 7th tee and from behind the 9th green. However, even experienced golfers may find themselves distracted here (Via del Golf 1, tel. 05 64 92 21 21, fax 05 64 92 01 82, www.puntaala.net/golf).

TOURS

Five suggestions for exploring Tuscany on winding roads and picturebook landscape to cultural highlights and to unknown sites off the main roads.

Tour Overview

The suggested tours are as varied as Tuscany itself. Some lead to cities and towns that offer any amount of art and culture, others go through unique landscape. Better bring enough time along to try evverything out!

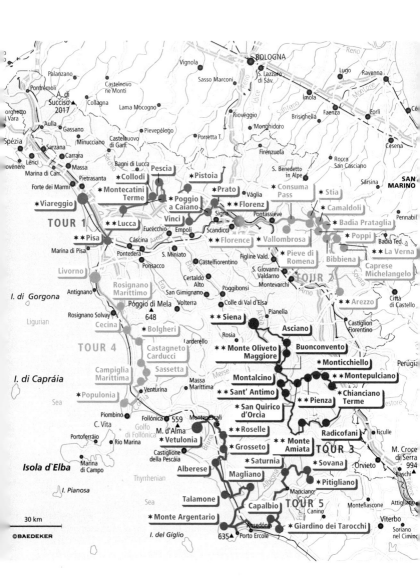

Travelling in Tuscany

The right means of transport In Tuscany most holidaymakers still travel by car. There are reasons for this: as the train system does not cover every town, many places can only be reached by car. However, it is not impossible to travel through Tuscany by train (▶Arrival ▶Transport) – provided you are not too short of time and accept the fact that not every town is accessible.

Beaches and culture For those who want to enjoy the beaches and swimming in Tuscany, the coast and the islands are the right destination, of course. In Viareggio and most places along the Versilia coast, however, the prices are high. The best place to combine the beach with the art is the northern part of the coast, where cities like Pisa, Lucca, Pistoia or even Florence are in easy reach of the coast via the motorway. So it's easy to stay along the coast and make day trips to the cultural highlights.

For nature lovers Nature lovers might feel more at home on the coast south of Livorno, the so-called Etruscan Riviera with its long beaches and backdrop of pine forests. There are no quick motorway connections into the hinterland in southern Tuscany, and excursions to Chianti or Siena take a long time on winding roads.

Florence and Siena with Chianti in between are the **heart of Tuscany** both geographically and in view of their importance – and thus come top in terms of accommodation prices, too. What to do? It is easy to reach Florence from Prato, due to the good motorway connections, and visitors to Siena can easily find accommodation further to the west or south, for example in a town along the SS 2 motorway.

If you are looking for a rest, the **»border regions« of Tuscany** are most suitable: Casentino and Pratomagno in the north-east, Garfagnana in the north-west, Maremma in the south-west or the area around

! *Sweet nothings* **Insider Tip**

In Pisa the dream tour for sweet-lovers begins to the Tuscan »Chocolate Valley«, with the name borrowed from California's Silicon Valley. Top pasticceri are located in the four »P cities« (Pisa, Pontedera, Pistoia, Prato). In Pisa, for example, is the chocolate paradise De Bondt (Lungarno A. Pacinotti 5, www.debondt.it), in Pistoia at Bruno Corsini (Piazza San Francesco 42, www.brunocorsini.com) all »Chocolate Valley« dreams come true, and almost all chocolate temptations between Pisa and Prato are collected by Marilena Pratesi in her shop Le Gelosità also in Pistoia (Via Roma 28). As far as sweets and cakes go Luca Mannori in Prato (Via Lazzerini 2, www.cioccolateriamannori.com) is the perfect conclusion of the Chocolate Valley Tour.

Monte Amiata in the south. These parts of Tuscany still offer rural and reasonably priced accommodation that is often suitable for holidaymakers who want to stay longer.

From the Coast to Florence on Side Roads

Tour 1

Start and finish: from Viareggio to Florence
Length: about 180km/108mi
Duration: 3–7 days

The seaside resort Viareggio is the starting point for this route, which touches Pisa, Pistoia and Florence, three of the most beautiful Tuscan cities. Modern art, Puccini's inspiring home, maginificent country homes, sophisticated spas and even Pinocchio are the attractions on this tour.

The seaside resort ❶*Viareggio with its Art nouveau villas and traditional old hotels is worth a whole day if you want to see everything worth seeing – not to mention going for a swim! Art lovers should definitely see the Galleria di Arte Moderna e Contemporanea (GAMC) with its high class 20th century art while carnival lovers should check out the Museum in der Cittadella del Carnevale. Opera fans can make the pilgrimage to nearby **Torre del Lago** where **Puccini** composed his works in his villa by the sea. His home is now a museum and his works can be experienced in the Grande Teatro »Giacomo Puccini« on the seashore in front of a breathtaking backdrop.

Old seaside resort and carnival town

In ❷**Pisa, a good 20km/12mi away, the legendary Leaning Tower, cathedral, baptistery and Camposanto are waiting on the square of miracles, as are the worthwhile historic centre on the banks of the Arno river and the university quarter. The street for shopping and strolling is the famous Borgo Stretto. Art is ubiquitous in Pisa: the most significant collection is in the National Museum, contemporary art can be admired in the Palazzo Blu in spectacular special exhibits, Pisan cultural life pulsates in the new Centro Espositivo San Michele degli Scalzi (Centro SMS) at the municipal park Parco delle Piagge.

More than just the Leaning Tour

In ❸**Lucca do not miss out walking on the city wall, visiting the cathedral San Martino and the National Museum in the Villa Guinigi or meandering along Via Fillungo. And here's something else for Puccini fans: the favourite café of the opera composer, who was born

A total work of art

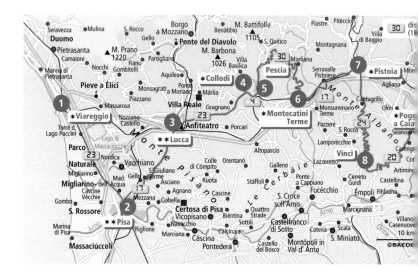

in Lucca, is in the Via Fillungo and his birthplace is open to the public. Friends of modern art should not leave out the Lu.C.C.A Museum. On Piazza Santa Maria, where the tourist information office is located, Cicli Bizzarri (www.ciclibizzarri.net) offers unique bicycles and Antonio Poli (www.biciclettepoli.com) normal ones, which can be rented for day trips.

Pinocchio's birthplace

The SS 435 goes on to **④ *Collodi**, birthplace of the long-nosed wooden puppet Pinocchio. Collodi is particularly attractive for families as the site of Pinocchio Park, which presents the corsair's ship and sculptures of the talking cricket, »Murder« and a carabiniere (constable). The highlight of the nearby Giardino Garzoni is the butterfly house. The Taverna dei Miracoli offers a convenient place to stop for a pizza. If you're interested in citrus trees then turn off the SS 435 heading south and visit the Giardino degli Agrumi in Castellare di Pescia (www.giardinodegliagrumi.it). A little further to the southwest stop at the Fattoria Il Poggio (Via San Piero 39, www.fattoriailpoggio.com) and try the top class DOC wine from Montecarlo. In **⑤ Pescia** the medieval Piazza Mazzini is an inviting place to stop and stroll.

Montecatini Terme

From Pescia follow the panoramic road via Vellano and Marliana to Montecatini Terme – it runs through beautiful landscape with green valleys similar to parts of Switzerland and thus called »Svizzera pesciatina«. After taking a look at the spa area of the world famous ther-

mal spa ❻ **Montecatini Terme** take the rack railway to **Montecatini Alto** for a spectacular view; the cars Gigio and Gigia are an attraction for children as well. Paolo Bargilli sells the world-famous Montecatini wafers, which taste best with an ice cream (Cialde di Montecatini, Viale P. Grocco 2, www.cialdedimontecatini. it).

In order to enjoy ❼ **Pistoia** for a whole day without a car, park along the city wall or on the Parcheggio Cellini and take shuttlebus M. Piazza della Sala and Piazza del Duomo with the San Zeno cathedral, campanile, baptistery and Palazzo Pretorio should no more be missed than the Museo Civico, San Giovanni Fuorcivitas and Sant' Andrea. For something more unusual take the tour Pistoia Sotterranea (Below Pistoia) Ospedale del Ceppo. The café in the hortensia cloister at the Museo Marini (Corso Silvano Fedi 30, www.fondazione-marinomarini.it) has officially been declared a stress-free zone and is a good place to relax after hours of sightseeing.

Pistoia

From Pistoia it is only about 40km/25mi on the autostrada to Florence. A small detour through the hills to Vinci. The hamlet **Lamporecchio** lies on the way. It is famous for the sweet **brigidini** (www.verobrigidino.it), which can be found at every Tuscan festival. The cart business with the sweet made of eggs. flour, sugar, salt, vanilla and anis seed grew into a veritable industry. At the Pasticceria Carli (Via Gramsci 31) they are still made in the traditional fashion.

At the gates of Florence

In ❽ **Vinci**, the birthplace of the famous Leonardo, along with the Museo Leonardiano the Piazza dei Guidi, which was designed by Mimmo Paladino, and the sculpture path are attractions. A hiking path, also for cyclers, leads to Leonardo's birthplace 3km/2mi away. ❾ **Poggio a Caiano** has Italy's only museum for still life art and it is housed in one of the most beautiful Renaissance villas of the Medici family. Anyone who still has the time to stop in ❿ **Prato** should not miss the Castello dell' Imperatore, Santo Stefano cathedral with its Filippo Lippi frescos and the Centro per l' Arte Contemporanea Luigi Pecci (www.centropecci.it) with its sculpture park. For shoppers there is the outlet centre. The end of the route is then ⓫ **Florence**, where the most significant Tuscan cultural highlights area waiting.

Tour 2 **Through the Casentino**

Start and finish: from Florence to Arezzo
Length: about 120km/90mi
Duration: 2–3 days

The Casentino, headwater region of the Arno, is a forested
mountainous area with remote monasteries and small towns
that see few visitors. Only in the south of the Casentino, in the
art city of Arezzo, does the route return to the tourist track.

To the
mountains!

Leave ❶**Florence** on the eastern route (SS 67) towards Pontassieve, where medieval stone bridges cross the Sieve before it flows

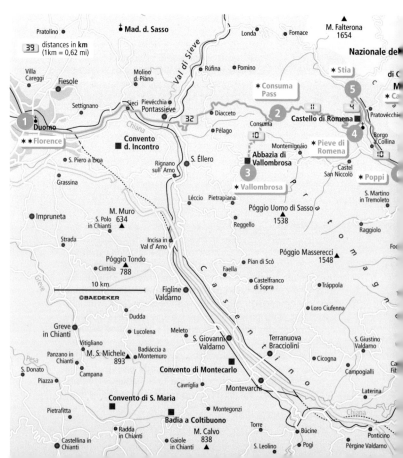

into the Arno. Then follow the winding SS 70 up to the ❷ *Consuma Pass**. At 1,060m/3,478ft elevation there is a fantastic view of a fascinating mountain world.

From the Passo di Consuma it is easy to make a detour to ❸ *Vallombrosa Monastery**, which lies secluded in the Reserva Naturale di Vallombrosa. Walk along the chapel path or simply enjoy the cool air at the pond. The monastery apothecary shop sells gourmet food, cosmetics, massive wooden crosses, small madonnas and tiny angels.

Monastic peace and quiet

On the other side of Passo di Consuma continue on the winding SS 70 towards Poppi. About 10 km/6mi beyond Passo di Consuma a country road branches off from the SS 70 towards Pratovecchio and Stia. Along the road, in the middle of wonderful scenery lies the medieval ❹ *Pieve di Romena**, where especially the chapel with depictions from the life of St Peter should definitely not be missed. Dante Alighieri already visited the neighbouring Castello di Romena and described it in his *Divine Comedy*. The castle was restored by Ottaviano Flamini as part of the eco-museums of the Casentino and can be toured.

Romantic jewel

❺ *Stia** has a small, very pretty old town. A visit to the old wool factory, which now houses the Museo dell' Arte della Lana – Stia is a traditional location of wool manufacturing and its wool products are known well beyond the region. When you get hungry: Ristorante Falterona gli Accaniti (Piazza Tanucci 9) is excellent.

Typical Casentino town

A mere 14km/8mi away, ❻ *Poppi** is a typical Casentino town with a beautiful old city where the arcades immediately catch the eye. The castle tower rises up above the centre. Just like the Castello di Romena the castle in Poppi was built by Count Guidi in the 13th century. It was the seat of the noble family that ruled the Casentino in the Middle Ages. The castle and the Poppi zoo are also good places to visit with children.

To the monks of Camaldoli

The imposing monastery ❼ ***Camaldoli** is the mother house of the Benedictine Camaldolese order. It goes back to an early 11th century monastery that was founded by the Augustinian Order. The drive up into the quiet of the Eremo di Camaldoli, with 20 monk's cells that each have its own garden, is nicer because it leads away from the business below. Clear, icy cold mountain spring water bubbles from a tap above a tiny basin at the gate to the hermitage. The eremo was added by Saint Romuald of Camaldoli after the monastery was built – the newly built monastery was too noisy for already him.

Pilgrim paths

If the weather is good the beautiful road via Passo Fangacci (1233m/4068ft) to Badia Pratraglia is worth the drive; if not continue on the road through the health resort town of Serravalle. In ❽ **Badia Pratraglia** the old abbey church is worth seeing. The village might soon wake up out of its beauty sleep since the Francis of Assisi pilgrimage route already leads through it. In 2012 the pilgrimage route Via Teutonica was added with funding from the EU. Pizzeria La Foresta opposite the church in Badia Pratraglia is a good place to eat. ❾ **Bibbiena**, the industrial heart of the Casentino, is also located on the Via Teutonica. It is not very touristy but the old city is worth seeing. The theatre museum presents the history of ancient and Baroque theatre in Europe; silk costumes and wigs are also displayed (www.cittadelteatro.it). In the Teatro Dovici world premiers of operas that heave never been performed are staged.

Franciscan pilgrimage site

From Bibbiena take the SS 208 (about 25km/16mi) to the beautifully situated pilgrimage site ❿ ****La Verna** with the Cappella delle Stimmate. The monastery was founded by St Francis of Assisi, who according to tradition received the wounds of Christ here on Sept. 14, 1224. Many pilgrims come to La Verna on Sept. 14 every year. It is possible to stay and to eat at the monastery for a reasonable price.

Michelangelo's birthplace

A detour from Chiusi della Verna to the birthplace of Michelangelo in ⓫ **Caprese Michelangelo** is worthwhile. Until 1875 Chiusi della Verna claimed that Michelangelo was born there but when a birth certificate was found it became clear that he was born in Caprese. In the little known but thoroughly charming village everything revolves around the other important Renaissance artist next to Leonardo da Vinci. There is a museum complex of several houses, the Michelangelo library and several copies of his sculptures.

To Arezzo

A route leads through charming scenery across the Catenaia Massif via Chitignano to Rássina. From here the SS 71 winds through the Arno valley to ⓬ **** **Arezzo**. Among many other attractions, the frescoes of Piero della Francesca in San Francesco church should not be missed.

In the Heart of Tuscany

Tour 3

Start and finish: circular tour starting from Siena
Length: about 150km/90mi
Duration: 3 days

Siena is a good starting point for exploring south-eastern Tuscany. This route passes through one of the most beautiful classic landscapes in Tuscany, through pretty towns like Pienza and the world-famous wine town Montepulciano, as well as the spa Chianciano Terme. Take lots of time to enjoy this tour.

Plan a couple of days for ❶**Siena– the city is full of important art historical buildings and is also a seductive shopping town.
On the way to Asciano herds of sheep enliven the stark beauty of the *Crete Senesi that is formed by wind and heat. The town of ❷ Asciano is a centre for the production of pecorino cheese. The Mercationo delle Crete takes place every second Sunday; along with organic foods crafts are sold at the stands. Gourmands who are interested in Tuscan black gold may decide to make a detour in the next part of the tour to Italy's first truffle museum in the castello of San Giovanni d' Asso (www.museodeltartufo.it).

Starting point is Siena

About 8km/5mi beyond Asciano the monastery of ❸**Monte Oliveto Maggiore, the headquarters of the Olivetans, appears behind tall cypresses. The medieval Benedictine abbey was built in the early 14th century and soon became the spiritual and cultural centre of the region. There are famous **frescoes** to see in the cloister with scenes from the life of Saint Benedict of Nursia. The shady terrace of the La Torre Bar at the entrance serves refreshments and offers monastic serenity.

Monte Oliveto Maggiore

The romantic little brickworks town ❹Buonconvento, which was surrounded by a brick wall in the 14th century, is an important junction on the busy Via Cassia; On every last Sunday of the month farmers and other producers from the region meet for the Mercato Agricolo della Filiera Corta. »Chilometro zero« (zero kilometres) is their motto – the cheese, honey, oil and wine are local products that are sold here in the market in accordance with their motto.

Brickwork gem

The well-tended vineyards of ❺*Montalcino already show that very noble wines are ripening here. The dark red Brunello di Montalcino is the top wine label of Tuscany, and the medieval town is like an open wine market. Price tags of up to €400 for the expensive, dark red luxury label are not to be missed. The Brunello vineyards offer winetasting, as well as a very worthwhile glass museum.

Expensive wines

Sant'Antino
in serene
landscape

From Montalcino go to the abbey church of ❻∗∗**Sant'Antimo**, one of the most beautiful and largest Romanesque country churches of the region, located in magical quiet at the end of a valley, surrounded by meadows and olive groves. Sant'Antimo was one of the most important and richest Tuscan monasteries in the high Middle Ages. Gregorian chanting can be heard as part of the devotions and masses celebrated in the church.

Enroute to Monte Amiata a visit to **Daniel Spoerri's sculpture garden** is worth the stop; his own works and the works of other international artists are exhibited on his park-like grounds. Spoerri also offers accommodations and food in his »Non solo Eat Art« Restaurant (www.danielspoerri.org).

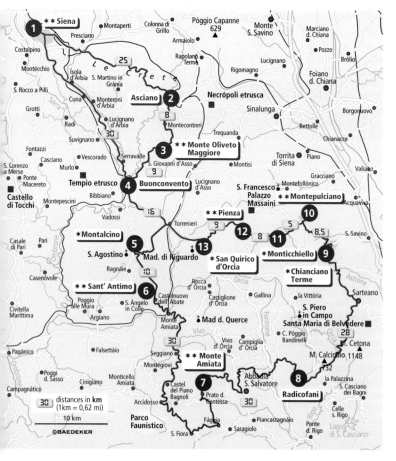

In the distance the 1738m/5735ft-high peak of ❼****Monte Amiata** Monte
can be seen, an extinct volcano, which often remains covered with Amiata
snow until late spring. The mountain road to the peak goes through
pine, mixed and mountain forest up to Alpine altitudes. Winding
roads, now passing through forests of chestnut and beech, lead to the
town of **Abbadia San Salvatore**, which lies below the interesting
abbey that gave the town its name. Its five-aisle crypt from pre-Romanesque times is impressive. Anyone who wants to stay in Abbadia
San Salvatore will find good accommodations in the Hotel Kappa
Due – K 2 (www.hotelk2.net); in the evening the Monte Amiata beer
»Bastarda Rossa« tastes especially good.

The road to Radicofani is extremely winding, but it offers a beautiful In the middle
view of the sparsely populated hills. Farms on hilltops with narrow of nothing:
roads leading up to them characterize the picture. The only larger Radicofani
town is ❽**Radicofani** a little above the old Roman road Via Cassia
and which can be seen from far off thanks to its tall castle tower.
Around 1296 the brigand Ghino di Tacco caused a lot of excitement
here, Dante banned him immediately to purgatory (Canto 6, 13-15).
Amiata sausages and hams are produced by master butchers Alfideo
Rossi (Via Roma 37, www.macelleriarossi.it) and Sandi (Via Renato
Magi 5a, www.macelleriasandi.it)

❾***Chianciano Terme**, the largest spa in Tuscany, is now a sophis- Wine and
ticated wellness resort. Surprisingly the city, which does not seem wellness
very appealing at first sight with its large hotel complexes, has a pretty old town.
What Chianciano is for visitors to the spa, ❿****Montepulciano** is
for wine lovers. Vino Nobile di Montepulciano is well known and it
can be tasted at Consorzio del Vino Nobile. Anyone who didn't just
come for the wine will find one of the most beautiful and best preserved old Tuscan towns.

The next gem is ⓫***Monticchiello**, which can be considered to be a What to see
medieval complete work or art. It gets its fame from the annual street around
theatre festival in the summer, the Teatro povero, which was started Pienza
by people in the village in the 1970s and in which the villagers are the
actors. There is also a museum on the history of this unusual theatre.
⓬****Pienza** about 8km/5mi away is a must: acompletely planned
Renaissance town that rises above the incredibly beautiful hilly landscape. Along with the almost neighbouring San Quirico d´Orcia it
has been added to the **UNESCO world cultural heritage** list. Park at
no charge in Via della Circonvallazione below Piazza Pio II, where
the cathedral, Palazzo Borgia and Palazzo Piccolomini are located.
The second most important thing in Pienza, after culture, is cheese.
Its **Pecorino** is considered to be one of the best in Italy and can be

! *Take a break?* **Insider Tip**

On this tour there are many places to drink a cappuccino outdoors, but one of them is worth a detour: right next to the entrance to the tiny mountain village of Monticchiello there is a bar (La Porta) with a terrace on the old fortified walls.

bought at Le Bontà di Pio (Corso Rossellino 6, www.lebontadipio. com). A famous cheese festival is held in September.

A last delightful town on this tour is ⓭ *San Quirico d'Orcia with a wonderful Italian garden and a Romanesque church with any number of figures to study on its main doors. Return to Siena on the SS 2.

Tour 4 Just Follow the Coast

Start and finish: from Livorno to Populonia
Length: about 120km/75mi
Duration: 2-3 days

The Riviera degli Etruschi, the Etruscan Riviera, stretches from Livorno to Piombino – a strip of land replete with history, which gets its name from numerous archaeological finds from the Etruscan period. Long stretches of coastline alternate with rich green Mediterranean macchia, pine forests and areas of swamp.

Livorno   It's best to arrive in ❶ **Livorno** the night before starting on this tour. The city quarter Venezia Nuova invites strolling or visiting a bar or restaurant. On the next day there's time for a visit to the synagogue and the central market hall is an absolute must with a great fish market and a kosher butcher. Families will also enjoy the aquarium and taking a boat ride on the Medici Canals.

Via Aurelia (SS 1) leaves town heading south and at first runs parallel to the coast. This most striking section of coastline to ❷ **Rosignano Marittima** is about 25km/15mi long. The old mountain village on a hilltop with a castle towering over it is about 3km/2mi from the coast and is visible from afar. It offers a broad view of the coast and the flatter region to the south.

Continue on and take time to stop at *beach at Vada, which is considered to be one of the most beautiful on this section of coast. ❸ **Cecina** is only a few kilometres to the south. In the village of La Cinquantina nearby in the Villa Guerrazzi is an archaeological museum with fascinating prehistoric and Etruscan-Roman finds. The coastal town of Marina di Cecina is much more touristy than Cecina and has a beautiful beach and a water park.

Drive east up to Montescudaio. Signs point out the »Strada del Vino« (wine route) and small winegrowers who sell wine and usually also olive oil at acceptable prices in Montescudaio. The panoramic road passes the villages of Guardistallo and Casale Marittimo and leads to the medieval Bibbona, then on to the growing region of the famous Ornellaia wine. Just before ❹ ✶ **Bolgheri** look out for the unique **cypress-lined avenue** stretching more than 5km/3mi from the church of San Guido, across the SS 1, straight into the town. Every Italian knows the famous lines of the poet and Nobel prize winner Giosuè Carducci (1835 bis 1907) »Davanti a San Guido ...«, which described and immortalized Bolgheri. The

village is clean and tidy, decorated with flowers. Advice on wine, tasting and cellar tours in English as well as accommodations in Agriturismo businesses are offered by Consorzio La Strada del Vino e dell' Olio Costa degli Etruschi (Loc. S. Guido 45, Tel. 05 65 74 97 68, www.lastradadelvino.com).

On the road to ❺ **Castagneta Carducci** lies the sophisticated winery Ornellaia (Via Bolgherese 191, www.ornellaia.com). The poet Carducci lived in Carducci and gave the hamlet its name; his former residence is now a museum with a literary park. The ubiquitous olive oil, to which the Strada del Vino e dell' Olio is dedicated, is the sub-

Ancient mountain villages

ject of the Museo dell' Olio. The taverna »Il Glorione« serves good food.

The tour winds along through dense forests of holm oak and chestnut to ❻ **Sassetta**, a village that should not be missed, is ideal for a longer stop. The region is ideal for interesting hiking and trekking tours, but nikers need to be in good shape. Motorists can park at the small parking lot by Pizzeria Maria Pia and walk uphill to the village on foot. There are often concerts on the Piazzetta della Chiesa in the summer.

A truly beautiful section of the wine route leads to the magnificent medieval town of **Suvereto**, which goes back to before the year 1000 The picturesque ❼＊**Campiglia Marittima** towers majestically above the sea and the surrounding countryside. In the archaeological museum an »ArcheoCard« or »Passepartout« is available for all of the surrounding museum parks.

Drive through the lower Cornia valley to the small town of ❽＊**Populonia**, the final stop of the tour. One of the most important Etruscan

There's nothing like it: Tuscan landscape with gentle hills

necropolises of Tuscany can be explored here – the archaeological park **Parco Archeologico Baratti e Populonia** covers more than 80 ha/197 acres on the mountain ridge above the Gulf of Baratti. The view of the gulf from here is unique. Plan in half a day, better a whole day, to visit the archaeological park. Information on the huge round graves or slag heaps from the iron foundries can best be gained from a guided tour. In the information centre about 400m/1300ft from the museum parking lot in San Cerbone there is a small bar with wooden benches and an acceptable menu.

MARCO ⊕ POLO TIP

! Podere SS. Annunziata II Insider Tip

Just before the chic seaside resort San Vincenzo this family farm produces soaps, salamis, ricotta cheese, organic products and olive oil. Guests of the B&B (7 apartemnts) can also use the pool and the restaurant, which serves barbecue and pizza baked in a stone oven (Via del Castelluccio 142, tel. 05 65 70 21 44, www.ssannunziata.it).

The best way to end a day like this is on one of the pine tree-lined **beaches** of the gulf: the Etruscan coast offers all of the advantages that the life- and water-loving Etruscans enjoyed 2,500 years ago.   Beaches

Hot Springs and Old Necropolises

Tour 5

Start and finish: from Vetulonia to Pitigliano
Length: about 150km/90mi
Duration: 2-3 days

Etruscan burial sites, a restful, protected natural landscape, swimming on Monte Argentario peninsula or in the springs of Saturnia, and old towns on tuffstone cliffs are the attractions along this -route.

Before the director, Dr. Simona Rafanelli, unlocks the doors to the archaeological museum of ❶*****Vetulonia** the day could begin with a cappuccino breakfast in the Vecchia Cantina opposite the museum, which Fosco Barberini runs. There is even a small garden. Audio guides help you explore the legendary treasure of jewellery or the recently discovered link between the Etruscans and Sardinia. Thanks to the exhibit items that were returned from Florence the world of the Etruscans come to life. The high point of the exhibit comes last: a gold scarab ring discovered in 2007. The excavations below the sleepy mountain village are also worth looking at: about 10,000 people once   Following Etruscan footsteps

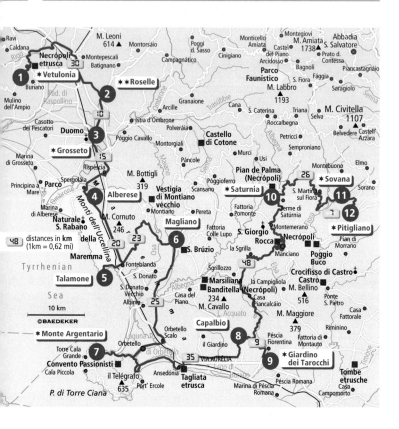

lived around the villa of Medea. Excavations continue here. The huge round graves of the necropolis are especially worth seeing, above all the **Tomba del Diavolino**.

In the
Maremma

Plan some time for ❷**✶✶ Roselle** as well – at least half a day – to view the remains of ancient Rusellac. The Etruscan site Rusellae was taken by the Romans in the early 3rd cent. BC. Parts of the 7th cent. BC city wall can still be seen.

❸**✶Grosseto** is the capital of the flat Maremma. It developed in the Middle ages from a castle on the Via Aurelia, which connected Pisa with Rome. The tidy, bicycle-friendly provincial capital, whose old city is surrounded by fortifications with bastions, is booming and growing. With the aquarium and the newly remodelled MuseoLab there are two more attractions.

»Traffico Limitato«, i.e. no more than 250 vehicles per day, is the rule on the narrow country road to ❹**Alberese** and the marina of the same name as Albarese is in the **Parco Naturale della Maremma**. This last refuge of free-roaming cattle and horses also includes a bird sanctuary and the coast. Hiking trails cross the natural pasture, macchia, swamp and coastal landscape.

At the extreme south the nature reserve borders on the popular fishing and bathing village of ❺**Talamone**, which has the whole spectrum of accommodations from campgrounds to the cliff hotel Capo d' Uomo; it is a surfer's and snorkler's paradise. Paolo »il Pescatore« Fanciulli, an ecology activist known from TV appearances, organizes boat tours to the fishing grounds followed by Jeep excursions with campfires and meals; they start from Talamone.

Continuing on to ❻**Magliano**, and into the heart of the southern Maremma (Maremma Alta), pasture land with special charms. The lightly rolling plain rises over 100m/328ft only in a few places. With a little luck you will see longhorn Maremma cattle. Magliano is surrounded by an almost intact medieval city wall; the Renaissance panel »Madonna del Latte« in the Chiesa della Santissima Annunziata a little outside of town is worth seeing. It is one of the Maremma's most important works of art. Trattoria Aurora (Via Chiasso Lavagnini 12/14) with its pretty summer garden is a good place to stop for lunch.

Home of long-horn cattle

A quiet country road leads on to Orbetello and from there to the beautiful ❼*****Monte Argentario** peninsula, which is popular with locals and tourists alike for its beaches in little bays, yacht harbours and former fishing villages. Mainly wealthy holiday-makers take refuge on Monte Argentario. Susanna Agnelli, granddaughter of the founder of Fiat and mayor of Monte Argentario from 1974 to 1984 prevented mass tourism hotels from being built here. Today there are even ads for »organic beaches« on the way to **Porto Santo Stefano**, the peninsula's central community.

Monte Argentario

The medieval town wall of the pretty town of ❽**Capalbio** is a pleasant place to take a walk. With a little luck there will also be an interesting art exhibition in the Capalbio castello.

On the border to Latium, Niki de Saint Phalle's fantastic sculpture park ❾*****Giardino dei Tarocchi** is a special experience. Between 1979 and 1997 the artist created her own fantasy landscape here with imaginative figures modelled on the figures on tarot cards.

Capalbio, Giardini del Tarocchi

Via La Sgrilla and Manciano it takes half an hour to get to ❿*****Saturnia**, which claims to be the oldest known thermal spa in Italy. It looks back on almost 3,000 years of spa tradition; here the Etruscans dis-

Saturnia: luxurious »dolce far niente«

Magic moments – when light transforms the landscape

covered »dolce far niente«. Today it offers wellness like a raindrop massage in the Blackrose Spa of the Terme di Saturnia, Europe's largest thermal spa resort – plan in some time for wellness. Anyone who prefers outdoor wellness should follow the signs to the Cascate del Molino – here the waterfalls and sinter pools with steaming sulphuric water are open for everyone at all times.

Tuffstone towns: Sovana and Sorano

From Saturnia the road winds through a bizarre tuffstone landscape radiating in green, grey and olive tones, one of the most beautiful parts of Tuscany. The Etruscan ⑪ **＊Sovana** is an idyllic elongated village with a massive ruined castle. Nearby is an extensive Etruscan necropolis; marked paths lead to the most important burial chambers, especially **Tomba Ildebranda**. The neighbouring **Sorano** stands gracefully on a rugged cliff above a craggy karst landscape. The tuffstone cliffs at the edge of Sorano hold 3rd and 2nd cent. cave-like burial vaults.

The final part of the route through the Etruscan-Roman border region is ⑫*Pitigliano** with a fantastic location on a long rock spur, where the houses rise from the green countryside like a sculpted crown. The rock cellars under the town are still used to store Bianco di Pitigliano. Stroll through the old city and visit Palazzo Orsini and the former Jewish ghetto.

MARCO ⊕ POLO TIP

Unique creations with esprit **Insider Tip**

Very beautiful ceramic plates, candle holders and vases with unusual decoration are sold by the potter Roberto Polidori in Pitigliano (Via Roma 156, Tel. 05 64 61 54 94, tel. 05 64 61 93 30, www.robertopolidoriceramista.it).

SIGHTS FROM A TO Z

There is lots to discover in Tuscany: not only highlights like Florence and Siena, but also pretty little villages and peaceful landscapes with rolling hills and colourful poppy fields.

** Alpi Apuane · Garfagnana

— ✴ E/F 3–6

Provinces: Massa-Carrara (MS), Lucca (LU)

Most of the fascinating mountains of the Apuan Alps in northwestern Tuscany has been a national park since 1985. Between the Apennines and this massif lies the Garfagnana, a mountain valley with isolated plateaus, chestnut forests, wild rivers and caves.

Mountain range The name of the mountain range, which runs parallel to the Appenines and the coast, comes from the Ligurian Apuan people and was first used by Giovanni Boccaccio. **Monte Pisanino** is the highest mountain (1,947m/6,425ft), but Monte Cavallo, Sagro, Tambura and Pizzo d'Uccello are also only just below 2,000m/6,600ft. The Apuan Alps are highly attractive to hikers, bikers, mountain bikers, horseback riders and cave explorers; a variety of guided tours is available. For hikers the **Via Francigena** (Frankish pilgrimage route) is especially exciting. Two different versions of it have run through this area since the 6th/7th cent. and it was revived recently (▶p. 122).

L'Orto Botanico »Pietro Pellegrini« In Pian della Fioba above Massa a small version of the Apuan Alps can be seen in L'Orto Botanico »Pietro Pellegrini«. The 3ha/7.4ac large garden at an elevation of 850 – 950 m (2,800 - 3,100 ft) shows native flora and artefacts from Roman times (3rd/2nd cent. BC).

❶ May – Sep daily 9am – 12pm, 3pm – 7pm; www.parcapuane.it/ob

* CASTELNUOVO DI GARFAGNANA

Heart of the Garfagnana The heart of Tuscany beats in Castelnuovo (population 6,100) in the Serchio Valley. Especially during carneval, the patronal festival of Sts Peter and Paul on June 29 and on Thursday mornings during the »Mercato dei banquetti« a visit is worthwhile. The rocca, literature prizes and the »Sentiero dell' Ariosto« path around the fortress of Alfonso II are reminiscent of the poet Ludovico Ariosto, the author of *Orlando Furioso*, who was an official in the erstwhile provincial capital in 1522 – 1525.

From Piazza Umberto I go up to the entrance gate to the fortified old city with its castle that was reconstructed during the Renaissance. The street on the right behind the city gate leads to the cathedral square with a nice view of the forested slopes in the background. **Sts Peter and Paul Cathedral** was built starting in 1504 on a previous,

Alpi Apuane · Garfagnana

INFORMATION
Castelnuovo di Garfagnana
Pro Loco:
Via Cavalieri di Vittorio Veneto
Tel. 05 83 64 10 07
www.castelnuovogarfagnana.org

Turismo Garfagnana/
Centro Visite »Alpi Apuane«:
Piazza delle Erbe 1
Tel. 05 83 64 42 42
www.turismo.garfagnana.eu/en

Barga
Piazza Angelico 3
Tel. 05 83 72 34 99
www.comune.barga.lu.it

EVENTS
MAGIX: »Festival della magia e dell' illu-
sionismo« (magic festival): one day each
year in Aug./Sept.; antique market in
Barga (every 2nd Sun/month).

WHERE TO EAT
Osteria Vecchio Mulino €€
Castelnuovo di Garfagnana
Via Vittorio Emanuele 12   **Insider**
Tel. 05 83 621 92   **Tip**
www.vecchiomulino.info

Closed Mondays. Rustic osteria that is
part of the Slow Food movement. Andrea and Cinzia Bertucci cook Mamma
Rosa's recipes, sell spicy cheeses and local products like giant mortadella that
they cut into cubes for customers to
sample or traditional salamis like mondi-
ole (made from mortadella), biroldi, go-
lette and pancetta.

Osteria I Macelli €
Borgo a Mozzano
Via di Cerreto
Tel. 0 58 38 87 00
www.trovalucca.info/osteriaimacelli
Closed Wednesdays
Tasty Garfagnana cooking, good service
and competent advice from Lara and
Samuele. In the historic centre, just a
few steps from the Devil's Bridge.

WHERE TO STAY
La Pergola €€
Barga, Via San Antonio 1
Tel. 05 83 71 12 39
www.hotel-lapergola.com
Family hotel with 30 pretty rooms and a
terrace for sunning. There are also 5
apartments for up to 4 people that are
rented by the week.

Norman building (10th cent.). It has a beautiful crucifix (*Christo
Nero*; 15th cent.) and a terracotta group *St Joseph and Two Angels*,
which is attributed to the school of della Robbia or Andrea del Verrocchio. On the town square, Piazza delle Erbe, a tourist information
office Turismo Garfagnana sells hiking maps and local products (potato bread, chestnut flour, mushrooms) and organizes stays in mountain cabins. Biologists offer one-day or longer tours, also for bikers
and on horseback.
The **Parco dell' Orecchiella** in San Romano di Garfagnana with an
enclosure for bears, wolves, deer, wild boar, a natural history museum and a botanical garden is nearby.

Parco dell' Orecchiella: June 15 – Sep 15 daily 9am – 7pm, Apr 1 – June 14 and Sep 16 – Oct 31 Sat and Sun 10am – 5pm; admission: €2

Castiglione di Garfagnana
In Castiglione di Garfagnana, 5km/3mi north-east of Castelnuovo, Luigi Pellegrini's collection in the Don Luigi Pellegrini Ethnographic Museum is housed in a fomer pilgrim's hospice that has been documented from 1110 on; it presents an overview of the traditional costumes, utensils and tools of the Garfagnana.

❶ Via del Voltone 14, June 1 – Sep 30 Tue – Sun 10am – 1pm, 2pm – 6.30pm, July/Aug also on Mon, Apr 1 – May 31 only until 4.30pm, Oct 1 – Mar 3 Tue – Sat 9.30am – 1pm, Sun 10am – 1pm, 2pm – 4.30pm; admission: €2.50; www.sanpellegrinoinalpe.it

* Ponte tibetano
On the charming Lago di Vagli at the foot of the Monte Pisanino the opening of the Ponte tibetano was announced in 2011. The Tibetan hanging bridge made of ropes, wood and steel is with its 200m/660ft one of the longest in the world. It crosses about 4m/13ft above the lake. About 1.6 mil. Euros were spent to make a view of **Fabbrica di Careggine**, which sank under the water level of the reservoir in 1953. A transparent glass dome is planned to make it possible to look to the bottom of the lake. It can be seen every ten years – last in 2005 – when the lake is drained for cleaning – an eerie sight which draws many visitors.

* BARGA

The very worthwhile cathedral San Cristoforo, Palazzo del Podestà or the Balduini, Pancrazi or Angeli palaces testify to the wealth of the former silk weaver city (population 10,000). In the Middle Ages Lucca, Pisa, Florence and the house of Este (Modena) fought over this strategic fortress. The city gates, especially the Porta Reale with the city coat of arms showing a barca (ship), are witnesses of these times. Teatro dei Differenti is used every year for jazz and opera festivals. Walk through the centro storico to the **cathedral**, where the Piazza Arringo offers a wonderful view of Barga and its surroundings. The noteworthy feature on the plain Romanesque façade of the church is the 12th-century portal with a detailed relief depicting a grape harvest. Inside the church the **marble pulpit** (2nd half of the 13th century) is the main attraction. It is set on four marble pillars of which one stands on a crouching bearded man and two on lions. At the end of the main aisle is a statue of St Christopher from the high Middle Ages.

**Grotta del Vento
The detour from Barga (about 9km/6mi) to the Grotta del Vento near Fornovolasco in the Parco Naturale delle Alpi Apuane is worthwhile. The dripstone cave, which can be explored to a depth of 2.5km/1.5mi,

The view from the terrace in front of the cathedral of Barga over the rooftops goes to the nearby peaks of the Apuan Alps

with bizarre stalactites and stalagmites along an underground river, is the main tourist attraction of the Garfagnana. The various routes through the grotto take from 1 to 3 hours.

❶ Apr 1–Nov 1 daily Route 1: 10am–12pm, 2pm–6pm; route 2: 11am, 3pm, 5pm; route 3: 10am, 2pm; Nov 2–Mar only Mon–Fri only route 1, Sat and sun all routes, www.grottadelvento.com; admission: €9 (route 1), €14 (route 2), €20 (route 3)

BAGNI DI LUCCA

Bagni di Lucca is a spa on the Lima River, a tributary of the Serchio, that is very popular among Italians. Legend has it that an underground volcano between Bagni Caldi and Ponte a Serraglio warms the steamy waters in the Grotta Grande and Grotta Paolina, which was named after Napoleon's sister, to 40 – 47°C (105 – 115°F). In fact the thermal waters, which are rich in sulphates, bicarbonates and calcium, come from the Sorgente »Doccione«, which has temperatures up to 54°C/130°F. Matilde of Canossa visited the spa in the 11th century. Bagni di Lucca flourished during the Belle Époque: Shelley, Byron, Puccini, Mascagni and Henry James all took the waters here. Heinrich Heine commemorated his visit in 1829 in his *The Baths of Lucca*.

Spa with tradition

MARCO POLO TIP

A wild mountain region **Insider Tip**

In Botri, about 13km/8mi north of Bagni di Lucca, lies the entrance to a rocky canyon, part of the Riserva Naturale dell'Orrido di Botri. Two-hour and four-hour guided tours into the canyon are offered (from Jun. 15–Sept. 15, Sat, Sun beginning at 9.45am). Hiking boots necessary, a helmet is provided, take along a change of clothing. Information: Loc. Ponte a Gaio, Montefegatesi, www.orridodibotri.toscana.it

The Centro Benessere has offered a large palette of beauty and wellness treatments since 2008. The spas offer skin treatments, antirheumatic and antistress treatments, wellness and well-being. Steam baths, almond oil massages, fango, balneo and aroma therapies, chocolate or Golden Breast treatments are all available (www.bagnidiluccaterme.info/en).

In the through the lower Serchio valley in * **Borgo a Mozzano**, the spectacular 37m/40yd arch of the **Ponte della Maddalena**, the landmark of the Garfagnana, has spanned the river since the 12th century. The unusual stone bridge is also called the devil's bridge by local people – probably because it was a masterpiece of engineering in its time which could only be understood as a work of the devil. Thanks to Matilde of Canossa the first bridge was built in the 11th cent.; the current one goes back to the 14th cent. In the early 16th cent. it was named the Magdalene Bridge after a nearby oratory. The statue »Maddalena in terra« from the Della Robbia school that stood there is now in the church of San Jacopo.

** Arezzo

✦ I 14

Province: Arezzo (AR)
Altitude: 296m/971ft above sea level
Population: 100, 200

It was no coincidence that Roberto Benigni used the squares and streets of Arezzo for the setting of his film *Life is Beautiful*: the old city centre is among the most beautiful in Tuscany. For art lovers there is another reason to visit the provincial capital on the edge of the broad plain of the Val di Chiana: the frescoes of Piero della Francesca in the church San Francesco, which can be viewed again after a restoration that took fifteen years.

History   Umbrians and Etruscans settled the hill with its fertile surroundings. The city belonged to the league of twelve main Etruscan centres. Under the Romans Arretium was founded in 294 BC as a military stati-

Arezzo

INFORMATION
Piazza della Libertà 1
(Atrium of the Palazzo Comunale)
Tel. 057 54 01 945
www.arezzoturismo.it

Tourism Info Arezzo Turismo:
Logge Vasari 13
Emiciclo Giovanni Paolo II
San Sebastiano (Via Ricasoli)
Museo Casa del Petrarca
www.arezzoturismo.it

PARKING
Free parking at Piazza Pietri. Take the escalator to the old city.

EVENTS
Giostra del Saraceno
On the first Sunday in September eight representatives of the four parts of the city compete in a horse tournament, first documented in 1593, which is not without danger. Armed with lances they fight the wooden king Buratto of the Saracens. Pity the rider who gallops too long – he feels the long arm of the turning figure. The winner gets the »golden lance«. The event is repeated on Giostra di San Donato, the third Sunday in June (www.giostradelsaracino.arezzo.it).

WHERE TO EAT
❸ Antica Osteria l'Agania €€
Via Mazzini 10
Tel. 05 75 29 53 81, www.agania.com
Closed Mondays. Popular trattoria in the historic centre of Arezzo with typical Tuscan dishes, for example panzanella (bread soup) or ribollita (bean soup).

❶ Buca di San Francesco €€€
Via San Francesco 1, Tel. 057 52 32 71

Closed Monday evenings and Tuesdays. Charlie Chaplin and Salvador Dalí were pampered in this 14th-century palazzo.

❷ La Lancia d'Oro €€€
Piazza Grande 18 / 19
Tel. 05 75 21 033
Closed Sunday evenings and Mondays and in November. In the warm season this restaurant is unsurpassed, as it has tables outdoors under the shaded loggias of Vasari. Maurizio and his team serve traditional food, fresh pasta, a very good selection of wine (Tignanello, Brunello, Rosso di Bolgheri). Specialities: Filetto di manzo (with Chianina beef) or pears with truffles and potato soufflé on a saffron sauce as antipasto.

WHERE TO STAY
❶ Hotel Graziella Patio €€€€
Via Cavour 23
Tel. 05 75 40 19 62, www.hotelpatio.it
A Tuscan palazzo in the old city with 7 individually decorated rooms and suites named Utz, Baalbek, Arkady or Cobra Verde – inspired by the well-travelled author Bruce Chatwin.

Villa Burali
Gorello di Policiano
Tel. 05 75 97 90 45, Fax 05 75 97 92 96, 11 rooms
Notable 18th-century stately home, about 7km/4mi outside of town on the SS 71. The restaurant is highly recommended.

❷ Hotel Arezzo Badia di Pomaio €€ – €€€
Localitá Pomaio 4
Tel. 05 75 37 14 07
www.hotelbadiadipomaioarezzo.it

New hotel in a restored monastery from 1645 at an elevation of 650m/2,100ft, right at the gates of Arezzo. With pool and a good restaurant in a vaulted room. Dinner can be served outdoors.

❸ B & B Tarussio
Via Isonzo 41

Tel. 05 75 90 10 35, 33 94 44 84 68
www.bbtarussio.it
White, early 20th cent. villa located only 150m/500ft from the railway station, the Tarussio is a good alternative to the more expensive hotels of the old city. It has parking and internet access.

Arezzo

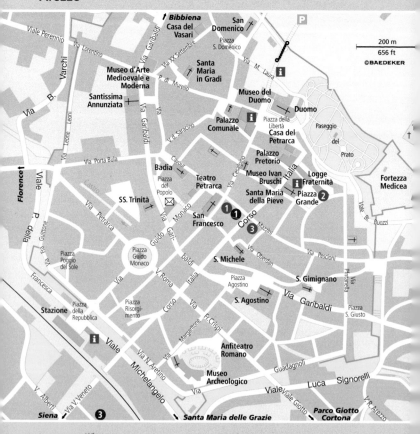

Where to eat
❶ Buca di San Francesco
❷ La Lancia d'Oro
❸ Antica Osteria l'Agania

Where to stay
❶ Graziella Patio
❷ Badia di Pomaio
❸ B & B Tarussio

 escalator

on on the Via Cassia. During the republican period a forum, theatre and baths were built. Arezzo became famous in the Augustinian era for of its foundries and coral-coloured lacquered vases. From 1098 elected consuls ruled the city republic, which was able to stand up against Florence and Siena. Only in the battle of Campaldino (1289) was the former Ghibelline city, loyal to the emperor, defeated by the Florentines. In 1337 Arezzo was sold to Florence for 40,000 guilders and submitted to it from then on.

** SAN FRANCESCO

❶ Apr 1 – Aug 31 Mon – Fri 9am – 6.30pm, Sat 9am – 5.30pm, Sun 1pm – 5.30pm; Sep 1 – Mar 31 until 5pm; frescos, by appointment: tel. 05 75 35 27 27; admission: €6; www.pierodellafrancesca.it; max. 25 visitors at a time, visits limited to 30 min.

The massive mendicant church of San Francesco stands in the heart of the old city, where Via Cesalpino intersects Via Cavour, which expands to an oblong square with pretty street cafés – including the famous Caffè dei Costanti. The unassuming, undecorated exterior of the church does not betray the world-class work of art hidden inside, which has been given new brilliance after a long restoration period. The church was begun in 1290 and finished in 1377 in the Tuscan Gothic style. The side chapels were added in the 15th century, the campanile in 1600. Above the entrance a round window by Guillaume de Marcillat portrays Pope Honorius III, who approved the order of St Francis. The 53m/174ft-long, aisle-less interior is remarkable for its murals. When the large Baroque altars were removed at the beginning of the 20th century remarkable frescoes by Spinello Aretino and his pupils came to light, including the *Meal with the Pharisee* (around 1440) by Parri di Spinello as well as the *Mystic Marriage of St Catherine*, the *Baptism of Jesus* and the *Annunciation* by Spinello Aretino himself, who also painted a cycle on the life of St Michael in the right choir chapel and a crucifixion group in the left choir chapel. The *Annunciation* in the Capella Tarlati is attributed to Luca Signorelli, the depiction of the *Life of St Bernardino of Siena* (around 1460) on the right-hand wall and the *Legend of St Anthony of Padua* (around 1480) in the left side chapel are by Lorentino d'Arezzo.

A highlight of western art is the restored frescoes on the legend of the cross by Piero della Francesca (1420–1492) in the **Cappella Bacci** (main choir chapel). The frescos can only be seen up close by appointment (prenotazione) and at a fee.

**Fresco cycle by Piero della Francesca

The commission to paint the chapel was given in 1447 by the wealthy merchant family Bacci to the Florentine Bicci di Lorenzo. He painted the triumphal arch wall (*Creation to Last Judgement*) and the dome of the choir (*Doctors of the Church*) up to 1452. After his death Piero della Francesca continued the work on behalf of Giovanni Bacci. It was completed in 1464. The main master of the Italian early Renaissance took up the *Legenda Aurea*, which was composed in 1275 and narrates the fate of the cross of Christ. With this cycle he created one of the most expressive works of Italian Renaissance painting. The story goes from the death of Adam to the Persian War (7th century). The order of the pictures is not chronological – unlike the following description.

Right-hand wall, top: After Seth planted a tree branch on the grave of his father Adam at the direction of the archangel Michael, the shoot of the hope of salvation grew there.

Right-hand wall, middle: The kneeling Queen of Sheba recognized the sacred wood and prophesied that it would be the instrument of Christ's suffering. The handshake of the Queen of Sheba and King Solomon, wearing the hat of a Roman Catholic cardinal and the papal garments of the patriarchs of Constantinople, symbolized the unification of the church of the circumcision and the church of humankind to the people of God.

Facing wall, right, middle: With a great effort three men carry the wood to Jerusalem for the building of the temple. There are no scenes from the New Testament. Neither did Piero della Francesca depict the crucifixion, since there was a 13th-century crucifix in front of the altar at that time already, which was included in the fresco cycle.

Facing wall, bottom right: Before the decisive battle against Maxentius (312), the Roman emperor Constantine dreamt of the sign of the cross, under which he would be victorious. Using sophisticated light effects that include the choir windows as a source of light, Piero della Francesca here created **one of the first night scenes in European art**.

Right-hand wall, bottom: At Ponte Milvio Constantine – riding a white horse and carrying the cross – defeats Maxentius, who dies in the Tiber River.

Facing wall, bottom left: An angel tells Mary that she will die and ascend to heaven; the victory palm that the angel carried symbolized the incarnation of the Son of God.

Facing wall, middle left: Judas the Levite, who was tortured in a well, showed Helena, the mother of the emperor, the place where the true cross was buried.

Left-hand wall, middle: Three crosses were found on Golgotha but only the sacred cross could raise a dead person; Jerusalem in the background is actually Arezzo.

Right-hand wall, bottom: Chosroe II conquered Jerusalem in 614, stole the cross and had it made into a throne for himself, but the Byzantine emperor Heracleios won the cross back in a battle and con-

demned the defeated Persian king to death in front of his empty
throne. Next to the shredded Moorish flag, the victorious banners of
the crusades (white cross on red background) and the flags of the
Holy Roman emperor wave in the
centre of the picture; the green flag
with a mystical bird postulates unity
and love.
Left-hand wall, top: Heracleios
brought the cross back to Jerusalem.
Adam's shoot bore fruit; the believers worshipped him. Two prophets
conclude the cycle on the facing wall,
top left and right.

Insider Tip

MARCO POLO TIP

Biglietto Cumulativo

The combination ticket »Biglietto
Cumulativo« for San Francesco/
Cappella Bacci, the Archaeological
National Museum, Museo Statale
di Arte Medieavale e Moderna
and Museo di Casa Vasari is valid
for two days and costs €12.

Galleria Comunale d' Arte Contemporanea on the Piazza San Francesco buys modern art through the »Premio Arezzo« art award and
organizes worthwhile temporary exhibitions in the church of
Sant' Ignazio (Via Carducci) and in Palazzo Chianini Vincenzi.

Galleria
Comunale
d' Arte
Contempora-
nea

AROUND PIAZZA GRANDE

Piazza Grande, the steeply sloping main square of Arezzo, with stately old houses with opportunities for browsing in antique shops and
second-hand bookshops, is the most beautiful square in the city. The
semicircular choir of the church Santa Maria della Pieve is an attractive architectural feature. To the right are the Renaissance façades of
the Palazzo del Tribunale and the elegant Palazzo della Fraternità dei
Laici, both built in the 17th–18th centuries, while the north side of
the square is dominated by Vasari's loggias with restaurants and cafés
under the shady arcades of the loggias.

****Piazza
Grande**

The most important and also oldest church in the city is the parish
church Santa Maria della Pieve, simply called »la Pieve«. It already
stood in the 12th century, was rebuilt after being destroyed in the
13th century and modernized in the 16th century by Vasari. The façade faces the Corso d'Italia and was built in front of an older one in
the 13th century; unlike most churches it is not aligned with the
nave. In the dwarf galleries above the entrance the number of columns increases with every storey, which gives the impression that the
building tapers. A look up to the five rows of double windows of the
campanile explains why this elegant torre, which was built around
1330, is called the »tower of one hundred holes«. The interior of the
church has an austere clarity. Under the elevated presbytery, which
was begun before 1200 and is the oldest part of the church, is the
crypt with a reliquary bust of St Donatus, Arezzo's patron saint. The

*** Santa Maria
della Pieve**

The arcades of the Piazza Grande: a beautiful place to enjoy a cappuccino

gilded silver bust, set with gems, is dated 1346. The polyptych of the Virgin above the altar, which was painted by the Sienese Pietro Lorenzetti starting in 1320, is noteworthy. Notice also the font in the baptistery under the tower with three relief scenes from the life of John the Baptist (around 1333).

❶ Mon – Sat 8am – 1pm, 3pm – 7pm, Sun until 6.30pm

Museo Ivan Bruschi The medieval Palazzo del Capitano del Popolo, Corso Italia 14, opposite the entrance of Santa Maria della Pieve was the home of the collector Ivan Bruschi, whose art collection with works from the 7th cent. BC to the present are on display here.

❶ Apr 1 – Oct 31 Tue – Sun 10am – 6pm, Nov 1 – Mar 31 Tue – Sun 10am – 1pm, 2pm – 6pm; admission: €5; www.fondazionebruschi.it

Palazzo della Fraternità dei Laici Adjoining the Palazzo del Tribunale is the Palazzo della Fraternità dei Laici, built by the charitable order of lay brothers Santa Maria della Misericordia in the 14th and 15th centuries. Its façade was begun by Baldino di Cino and Niccolò di Francesco in Gothic style and completed by Bernardo Rossellino in the Renaissance style. The belfry was added by Giorgio Vasari in the middle of the 16th century. In the palace museum climbing the tower is especially worthwhile. There is also a very interesting astrological clock from the 16th century.

❶ Mon – Sun 10.30am – 5.30pm (admission every 60 min.); admission: €4

The Palazzo delle Logge was also built to plans by Vasari, between 1573 and 1581 on the north side of Piazza Grande. It imitates ancient architecture. In front of the palazzo is a copy of a so-called petrone, a medieval pillory.

Palazzo delle Logge

Not far north of the church Santa Maria is Palazzo Pretorio. Originally built in 1322 out of three patrician houses, the palace was altered considerably in the 15th and 16th centuries. In the past the palazzo was used by the judicial administration; today it houses the public library. The façade bears numerous coats of arm of the podestà and commissars of the 15th to 18th centuries.

Palazzo Pretorio

The Casa del Petrarca (no. 28), presumed to be the birthplace of the poet Petrarch, is part of the same building block on Via dell'Orto. Francesco Petrarca (Petrarch) really was born in this street but the house was built in the 17th century, almost completely destroyed in World War II and rebuilt in 1948. Today it is the seat of the famous Accademia Petrarca di Lettere, Arti e Scienze, which guards the memory of the great humanist and has awarded the coveted Petrarca Prize for Literature since 1974.

Casa del Petrarca

❶ i Apr 1 – Oct 31 daily 10.30am – 6.30pm; Nov 1 – Mar 31 Mon, Tue, Thu, Fri 11.30am –3.30pm, Sat/Sun 10.30am – 4.30pm; admission: €4; www. accademiapetrarca.it

Until the 13th century the cathedral of Arezzo stood outside of the city walls on Piota Hill where St Donatus was martyred and buried in 304. When the people of Arezzo demanded in 1111 that the bishop's seat be moved into the city a riot started and the medieval church was destroyed. In 1277 the building of the cathedral was begun on the site of the former Benedictine church San Pietro Maggiore at the urging of Bishop Guglielmino degli Ubertini. Work was not completed until the early 20th century.

*Duomo

In compliance with the rules of the mendicant orders the **interior** of the pillared basilica is plain. The main attraction is the wonderful large-scale stained glass by the French Dominican monk Guillaume de Marcillat (1467–1529) in the south aisle. Also worth seeing is the tomb of the Arezzan pope Gregory X (died 1276) and the burial chapel of Ciuccio Tarlati dating to 1334. The main altar holds the richly decorated late Gothic marble funerary monument with the relics of St Donatus. In the north aisle Piero della Francesca painted an impres-

> **! Seek and find**   Insider Tip
>
> MARCO POLO TIP
>
> Arezzo is a mecca for antique lovers – all year round thanks to its many shops, but especially on the first Sunday of the month when the big antique market is held on Piazza Grande.

sive fresco with a depiction of the Magdalene (1459). After a miracle by the Virgin Mary the chapel Madonna del Conforto (Madonna of Consolation) was built between 1796 and 1817 at the northern aisle. The cathedral museum (Museo del Duomo) in the former sacristy shows goldsmith work and an early Romanesque crucifix from the 11th century.

❶ **Duomo:** daily 7am – 12.30pm, 3pm – 6.30pm

Passeggio del Prato, Fortezza Medicea

After visiting the cathedral take a walk through the park of the Passeggio del Prato to the modern monument to Francesco Petrarca. The large park extends to the Medici fortress, which stands on 13th-century foundations. Cosimo I commissioned Giuliano da Sangallo in the mid-16th century to extend the fortifications and to give it a new wall and bulwarks. There is a fine panoramic view from the top.

Palazzo Comunale

A massive medieval tower marks the Palazzo Comunale west of the cathedral. Today it is the city hall. It was built in 1333 as the office of the head of the guilds. After 1384 it was the residence of the administrative commissars from Florence, who also had the façade decorated with their coats of arms. In Palazzo Comunale there is a permanent exhibition of more than 1,000 objects from the Casi Collection from the fields cinema and computer, calculators, TV and mechanical music machines.

❶ Tue, Thu, Sat and 1st Sun/month 10am – 5pm; admision: €3; www.faustocasi.it

WESTERN OLD CITY

San Domenico

The plain, aisle-less church of San Domenico on the square of the same name was donated by the Tarlati di Pietramala family in 1275. It was completed shortly after 1300. The most valuable decoration was returned to its place in the apse in 2001: the crucifix by Cimabue dated 1265, ***Crucifix by Cimabue** an early work by the famous artist which shows Byzantine influence. But with its image of a suffering Christ it is also a pioneering work. It is also worth taking a look at the frescoes by Arezzan painters, such as the scenes from the lives of St Philip and St James by Spinello Aretino on the entrance wall created around 1390, and the Crucifixion by his son Parri (around 1450). For information on the restoration of the Cimabue cross: www.cimabuearezzo.it.

❶ daily 7am – 1pm, 3.30pm – 7pm

*Casa di Giorgio Vasari

The painter and architect Giorgio Vasari (1511–1574) not only accomplished architectural masterpieces; his **biographies of Italian artists** are among the most important sources for Italian art history.

In 1540 Vasari bought the two-storey house no. 55 in today's Via XX Settembre and painted the rooms (up to 1548). The paintings were intended to depict one thing above all: the glory and importance of the arts. Vasari made use of allegorical images, for example the ceiling painting in the Camera Nuziale, or artists' portraits. The museum also has Vasari's model of the Palazzo delle Logge on Piazza Grande as well as paintings by contemporaries, including Jacopo Zucchi, Perin del Vaga and Francesco Vanni.

❶ Mon, Wed – Sat 9am – 7pm, Sun 9am – 1pm, admission: €2

Allegory of poetry according to Vasari

The elegant Palazzo Bruni-Ciocchi or Palazzo della Dogana (there was a customs house here in the 19th century) in Via San Lorentino was designed around 1450 in early Renaissance style, presumably by Bernardo Rosselino. It was commissioned by Donato, the son of the famous Florentine chancellor Leonardo Bruni. Today the palace houses the **museum for medieval and modern art**. Visitors get an excellent overview of painting in Arezzo until the end of the 16th century, with works by Margarito d'Arezzo, Spinello Aretino and his son Parri, by Bartolomeo della Gatta, Luca Signorelli, Rosso Fiorentino and Vasari. The Tuscan masters of the 17th to 19th centuries include Cigoli, Fattori and Signorini. The museum also has valuable majolica, goldsmith work, ivory carvings as well as coins.

*Museo d'Arte Medievale e Moderna

❶ Via San Lorentino 8; Tue – Sun 9am – 7pm, closed Mon; admission: €4

Steps lead up to the church of Santa Maria in Gradi, built by the Florentine architect Bartolommeo Ammanati (1511 – 1592) on the foundations of a Romanesque church. Along with the bell tower built in 1631, in the interior a terracotta group (Madonna of Mercy) by Andrea della Robbia and the crypt of the original church deserve a look. Only a few steps south-west on Via Garibaldi the Renaissance master builders Bartolomeo della Gatta and Antonio da Sangallo the Elder built the Church of the Annunciation between 1490 and 1520. The portal on the right is part of the previous Gothic oratory on this site, as is the fresco of the annunciation above it (1370). The interior is remarkable for its glass window by Marcillat.

Santa Maria in Gradi and Santissima Annunziata

The second large Renaissance church in Arezzo is the abbey of St Flora and St Lucilla (also called Chiesa di Badia), which was founded

Sante Flora e Lucilla (Chiesa di Badia)

in the 14th century by Benedictine monks from the monastery Monte Cassino. It got its present form when Giorgio Vasari undertook thorough renovations in the late Renaissance style in the mid-16th century. The monumental high altar is also his work (1562). **Andrea Pozzo** from Trento gave an excellent example of high Baroque mural painting in the tromp l'œil dome in the nave (1703): the skilled mixture of perspective, light and shade create an impression of a massive dome.

SOUTHERN OLD CITY

Chimera
In front of the main railway station is the trademark of Arezzo, the wild chimera. The strength of a lion, the cleverness of a snake and the stoic temperament of a goat are united in the demonic fabled creature. The bronze monument is a copy of an Etruscan statue from the 4th century BC, which is in the Archaeological Museum of ▶Florence today.

Anfiteatro Romano
The remains of the amphitheatre (entrance in Via F. Crispi) bear witness to the Roman period. The elliptical construction (1st/2nd cent.) once held between 8,000 and 10,000 spectators. It was 121m/132yd long and 68m/74yd wide. The theatre fell into decay later when it was used as a stone quarry.

*Museo Archeologico Mecenate
The former monastery San Bernardo, which was built in 1547 by Olivet monks on the ruins of the Roman amphitheatre in a part of the stands, now holds the collections of the Museo Archeologico Mecenate. The archaeological museum displays numerous **finds from the Etruscan and Roman periods**, including terracotta decorations from a temple of the 5th century BC, Etruscan reliefs and votive offerings, Roman small bronze figures and mosaics as well as typical Arezzan »vasi corallini«, coral-coloured ceramic vases with terra sigillata decoration which were a popular export item during the imperial Roman period.
❶ Via Margaritone 10; daily 8.30am – 7.30pm; admission: €4

Museo Aziendale Gori & Zucchi (Uno-A-Erre)
In the Uno-A-Erre Museum the history of Italian jewellery-making is shown through 400 objects and the history of the Gori & Zucchi Company from 1926. The works of Dalí, Manzù, Messina and Gio' Pomodoro are especially interesting.
❶ Via Fiorentina 550; Mon – Fri 9am – 5pm; free admission; www.unoaerre.it

Santa Maria delle Grazie
About 2km/1.3mi south of the old city stands the late Gothic pilgrimage church of Santa Maria delle Grazie. According to tradition St

Bernardino of Siena came 1428 to this place, where there was a sacred spring from ancient times. He had the remains of the pagan cult removed and built a chapel. In 1449 the present building was begun in honour of the Madonna of Mercy (Madonna delle Grazie); in 1478 Benedetto da Maiano added a graceful portico. Toward the end of the 15th century Andrea della Robbia created the extravagant main altar with a pietà of marble and terracotta.

Bibbiena · Casentino

✳ G 13

Province: Arezzo (AR)
Altitude: 425m/1,394ft above sea level
Population : 12,750

Bibbiena, located 30km/19mi north of ▶Arezzo on a hill near the place where the Archiano flows into the Arno. It is a good place to start excursions into the Casentino, the mountain range that borders the north-east of the Arno valley, a densely forested but fertile mountain landscape, largely untouched nature and solitude.

The city was probably founded by the Etruscans and was the object of heated conflicts well into the 15th century because of its location. Florence and Arezzo both claimed the valley pass in the extreme north-east of Tuscany for themselves and fought hard-contested battles here. Already in the early Middle Ages small monastic communities were founded in complete isolation in the Casentino. They included the hermit monastery Camaldoli and the famous Franciscan monastery La Verna, today an important place of pilgrimage. West of the Casentine source of the Arno lie the Pratomagno mountains with wonderful chestnut, pine and beech forests.

Embattled city

! *Nightly excursions* **Insider Tip**

MARCO POLO TIP

The cooperative »óros« – its name means »Montagna sacra« (holy mountains) – offers themed excursions to Parco Nazionale delle Foreste Casentinesi (Monte Sacro/ La Verna, Monte Falterona), e.g. night excursions to the park planetarium. Information: Via Rachiana 18, Badia Prataglia, tel. 05 75 55 94 77, www.orostoscana.it

Bibbiena offers no sensations, but a **complete old town,** in which souvenir shops are so far rare. Via G. Borghi runs almost straight to Piazza Tarlati, the high main square with a clock tower and Palazzo Vecchietti Poltri. In the **Palazzo Comunale** is the exhibition **»Paesaggi del Casentino«** (Villages in the Casentino). In the same building the **Museo del Teatro** presents the history of

Sights in Bibbiena

occidental theatre. works by Andrea Palladio, by Baroque stage designers like Niccolò Sabbatini and Giacomo Torelli, silk costumes and wigs are on display. In the **Teatro Dovizi** premieres of operas, which have never been performed and whose scores are kept in the theatre museum, are staged, In the church of San Lorenzo terracottas from the workshop of the della Robbias can be admired.

»**Paesaggi del Casentino**«: Tue – Sat 9am – 1pm; free admission
Museo del Teatro: Tue – Sat 10am – 12pm, 3.30pm – 6.30pm, Sun 10am
– 12pm; free admission; www.cittadelteatro.it

EXCURSION TO CAMALDOLI

Mother house of the Camaldolese Order
Camaldoli Abbey, the centre of the Camaldolese order, lies in the middle of a glorious forest landscape about 20km/13mi north of Bibbiena in the mountains of the Casentino. It was founded at the start of the second millennium in the course of the great western church reform. The members of the order retreated to places that were as isolated as possible. In the Casentino, Count Maldolo d'Arezzo (d. 1027) gave St Romuald and his brothers in faith a piece of land where he built the founding monastery at an elevation of 830m/2,800ft starting in 1012. The house was named Ca(sa di) Maldolo, »House of Maldolo«, after its generous donor. A short while later some monks moved higher up in order to be completely isolated in today's Eremo di Camaldoli. The papal recognition of the order in 1113 the Camaldolese community allowed it to flourish.

Monastero di Camaldoli
The monastery complex today consists of a cloister, convent buildings, pilgrims' hospice (foresteria) and church. The monastery church was built in from 1509 to 1524 in place of a previous church and got its Baroque appearance in the late 18th century. Giorgio Vasari did several paintings for the interior. A visit to the **pharmacy** (16th cent.), a rare surviving example with its hand-carved shelves and laboratory, is a must. The pilgrims' hospice is used for conferences and seminars.

> **Insider Tip**
> *Homemade*
>
> MARCO POLO TIP
> Herbal liqueurs distilled from traditional recipes, varieties of tea, jams and aromatic ointments are only a few of the delicacies to be bought in the monastery pharmacy.

*Eremo di Camaldoli
Shortly after the founding of the monastery St Romuald and a few monks moved higher up to an elevation of 1100m/3600ft in search of even greater solitude. Thus on the »pleasant field« surrounded by woods, the Eremo di Camaldoli, a group of monks' cells with a

Bibbiena · Casentino

INFORMATION
Casentino Sviluppo e Turismo
Via Roma 203
Ponte a Poppi
Tel. 05 75 52 05 11
www.turismo.casentino.toscana.it
www.casentino.ar.it

WHERE TO EAT
Foresteria del Monastero €
Camaldoli, rel. 05 75 55 60 13
www.camaldoli.it
Open 7 days a week. Good food at a
reasonable price is offered here, but reservations are requested (just tell them in
the attached bar of the foresteria). There
is cheap and good accommodation in
the Monastero.

Il Tirabusció €€
Via Borghi 73, Bibbiena
Tel. 05 75 59 54 74
www.tirabuscio.it
Closed Mon all day and Tue noon. The
entrance to this excellent restaurant is in
Via Rosa Scoti opposite Teatro Davizi.
160 wines do honour to the name Tira-
busció (cork screw). Alberto cooks according to the season. Try the prosciutto

(ham) from the grey Casentino pig or
tortelli made from red potatoes from
Cetica!.

WHERE TO STAY
Albergo San Lorenzo € – €€
Poppi
Piazza Bordoni 2 – 5
Tel. 34 84 03 18 11
www.poppi-sanlorenzo.com
Interesting accommodation for art lovers: Works by A.R. Penck, Jean-Yves
Klein and various other arts, some of
them renowned, are displayed on the
walls of the San Lorenzo Art Hotel. The
Romanesque church of San Lorenzo
serves as a gallery and conference room.
The 10 rooms are simple but tastefully
furnished; with a garden and wellness
offers.

Albergo Falterona €€
Stia
Piazza Tanucci 85
Tel. 05 75 50 45 69
Charming little city hotel in an old palaz-
zo. The 23 rooms are tiny, but furnished
tastefully.

church dedicated to the redeemer, was built. The Chiesa del Salvatore
owes its Baroque appearance to renovations carried out in the years
1658, 1708 and 1714. 17th-century frescoes on the walls of the
church show scenes from the life of St Romuald. The **20 monks' cells**
are small huts standing in five rows, each with a small garden. They
can only be seen through a screen. According to tradition five were
built by the founder of the order. Others go back to illustrious donors, like Pope Leo X's cell, where Maria de Medici is supposed to
have lived once, and the cell of Duke Ranuccio Farnese. The modest
cell of St Romuald, with a tiny chapel and study, is reached through
the Foresteria Vecchia.
❶ daily 8.30am – 12.30pm, 3pm – 7pm

EXCURSION TO LA VERNA MONASTERY

**Famous place of pilgrimage

A winding road runs from Bibbiena 26km/156mi up to the pilgrimage site (1128m/3722ft) at the foot of Monte Penna (1,289m/4,253ftft). Hiking trails begin at Santuario and lead into Parco Foreste Casentinesi (www.parcoforestecasentinesi.it). The most famous Italian saint, Francis of Assisi, retreated to the isolation of the Casentino mountains after relinquishing the leadership of the Franciscan order. In 1213 Count Orlando Cattini of Chiusi, who had heard the preaching of the beggar monk, gave La Verna mountain to the saint and his followers. Here the Franciscans lived in simple huts at first. According to tradition Francis received the wounds of Christ here on 14 September 1224, two years before his death. Since then La Verna has been considered a holy place. Large numbers of pilgrims come here, especially on 14 September and 3 October, the day on which St Francis died.

Franciscan monks in front of La Verna Monastery

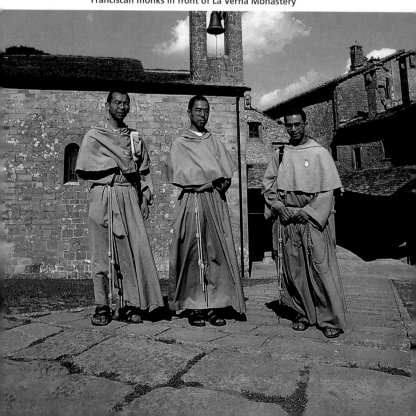

From the parking lot in the woods walk about 400m/1300ft to the entrance of the extensive monastery complex. The path leads to a broad square called Quadrante, from which the most important attractions of the sacred site can be reached. In 1348 at the order of Count Tarlato di Pietramala the building of the large church (Chiesa Maggiore) was begun. It was completed in the early 16th century. The beautiful **terracottas by Andrea della Robbia** are notable: *Madonna with Saints* and *Adoration of the Child* (1479), *Annunciation* (1480), *St Anthony Abbas* and *St Francis and Ascension* (1499). The little adjoining church Santa Maria degli Angeli is older. St Francis himself laid the foundation stone for it in 1216. Inside are some terracotta works from the workshop of the della Robbias, and a memorial for the donor Count Orlando Cattani.

The »Walk of the Stigmata«, decorated with frescoes on the life of St Francis, leads from the Quadrante to a group of chapels with the main attraction, the Capella delle Stimmate (Chapel of the Wounds). Halfway there a door leads into a cleft in the rock where St Francis set up spartan sleeping quarters for himself. In the Stimmate chapel, which was built in 1263, a marble frame in the floor shows the place where Francis is supposed to have experienced the **miracle of the stigmatization**. Ceiling and walls were originally painted with frescoes, which were lost or removed in order to make room for the large altar by Andrea della Robbia (1481). Step out of the chapel of the cross, which lies in front of the Capella delle Stimmate, where a narrow, secured path leads around the cliff – in good weather there is a wonderful view of the Casentino. A beautiful hiking trail leads to the peak of the 1,289m/4,253ft-high Monte Penna.

*Chiesa delle Stimmate

Sanctuary: daily 6.30am – 7.30pm, summer until 21.30pm
Cappella delle Stimmate: daily 8am – 5pm, summer until 7pm
www.santuariolaverna.org

Caprese Michelangelo, 10km/6mi south of Chiusi della Verna, offers wonderful views of the craggy mountain world of the southern Casentino. The town with a population of 1,600 would probably attract no attention if it were not the birthplace of Michelangelo Buonarroti (▶ Famous People). Of course this has only been certain since 1875 when a copy was found of the artist's birth certificate, made for Michelangelo's father Lodovico, at that time mayor of Caprese. It stated that Michelangelo was born in Caprese on March 6, 1475. Chiusi della Verna had also claimed to be the great man's birthplace. Caprese has dedicated **Museo Michelangiolesco**, which consists of several houses, to Michelangelo. In the house where he was apparently born, Casa del Podestà, photographic reproductions of Michelangelo's frescos and a documentary film on the life of the artist are shown, among other things. Palazzo Clusini houses the ticket office,

Caprese Michelangelo

the Michelangelo library and a collection of small Italian sculptures form the 19th cent. In the museum complex and the Corte Alta garden there are 15 plaster copies of Michelangelo's sculptures. The Corte Alta garden meanwhile also displays sculptures by 98 20th cent. sculptors.

❶ June 16 – Jul 31 Mon – Fri 10.30am – 6.30pm, Sat, Sun 10am – 7pm; Aug 1 – Sep 15 daily 9.30am – 7.30pm; Sep 16 – Oct 31 Tue – Sun 10.30am – 6.30pm; Nov 1 – Mar 31 Fri – Sun 11am – 5pm; Apr 1 – June 15 Tue – Fri 11am – 6pm, Sat, Sun 10.30am – 6.30pm: admission €4; www.capresemichelangelo.net/costume/museo

VIA POPPI TO VALLOMBROSA

*Poppi

From Bibbiena follow the Arno valley upstream with its meadows, vineyards and olive groves for 6km/3.5mi to Poppi (population 6,400). From the lower town on the river cross the old stone bridge and go up the wooded hill to the charming upper town with **beautiful old arcades** and a pretty square with the domed 17th-century oratory. A steep ascent leads from the centre of Poppi up to a strong **castle** from which there is a **wonderful view of the hilly landscape of the Casentino**. The powerful Guidi counts had the castle built in the 13th century. The two-storey wings of the building surround an elegant inner courtyard with a boldly curved staircase, wooden galleries and the coat of arms of the Florentine governor on the gatehouse. The castle chapel is well preserved with 14th-century frescoes, which are thought to be by Taddeo Gaddi. The library has precious incunabula and manuscripts. In the Parco Zoo, which can be explored on a 2km/1.2mi-long path, buffaloes, wild boar, bobcats, foxes, donkeys and wolves live on 50ha/125ac.

Castle: daily from 10am, Nov 6 – Dec 25 and Jan 10 – Mar 3 only Thu – Sun; admission: €5; www.buonconte.com

Zoo: daily 9am until sunset; admission: €7; www.parcozoopoppi.it

!

Pilgrimage in the Casentino Insider Tip

The pilgrimage route »Cammino di Assisi« follows the footsteps of St Francis of Assisi from the Emilia-Romagna near Corniolo through the nature park region of the High Casentino and to the monasteries of Camaldoli and La Verna. Then it runs via Caprese Michelangelo, Pieve Santo Stefano and Sansepolcro to Umbria. Stages, hostels and tip for hikers: www.camminodiassisi.it

Castello Romena

Near Romena the Guidi had a hill on the western bank of the Arno fortified with a **castle**, which fell to Florence in 1357. Today the castle is privately owned. It numbers Dante Alighieri, who mentioned it in his Divine Comedy, among its guests. The museum displays archaeo-

logical finds and weapons. Below the castle stands the small Romanesque country church ***Pieve di San Pietro** (around 1150). Inside
the church the **capitals** deserve attention. They are richly decorated
with plants, heads of wild demons and scenes from the life of the
apostle Peter.

Castle museum: July/Aug daily 10am – 7pm, otherwise Thu – Sun 10am
– 5pm/6pm; closed Nov 1 – Mar 15; admission: €3
Pieve di San Pietro: daily 10am – 12pm, 3pm– 6pm
www.pratovecchio.net/romena.htm

Stia is worth a stop for its wonderful atmosphere and harmonious   ***Stia**
appearance around Piazza Bernardo Tanucci. Among the ecological
museums of the Casentino is the **Museo dell'Arte della Lana** in
Stia's old wool factory. In 14 rooms the production of Stia's famous
wool products is described.

Palagio Fiorentino houses a museum to promote modern and contemporary Tuscan and Italian art. The core consists of works from the
private collection of Vicky Galati Indelli, including Marino Marini
and Emilio Vedova. Also included in the 200-piece collection are
works by Remo Brindisi, Pietro Cascella, Primo Conti, Leonardo
Cremonini, Salvatore Fiume, Bruno Innocenti, Mino Maccari, Quin-
to Martini, Giò Pomodoro, Ottone Rosai.

Museo dell'Arte della Lana: Via G. Sertori 2; Sat 3pm – 6pm, Sun
10am – 1pm, 3pm – 6pm. Admission: €3; www.museodellalana.it
Museum in the Palagio Fiorentino: Via Vittorio Veneto 35; June 1 – Sep
30 Sat 4pm – 7pm, Sun 10am – 1pm, 4pm – 7pm; admission: €1

About 13km/8mi west of Romena via the 1,060m/3,478ft-high Con-   ***Passo di**
suma Pass is the lonely forest region of Pratomagno, where nature   **Consuma**
lovers and hikers can find unforgettable scenery. Mountain trails lead
to Monte Secchieta and the Falterona Massif, the headwater region
of the Arno.

From the top of the pass a road to the left leads to the village of Mon-   **Monte-**
temignaio, 8km/5mi to the south. According to tradition its   **mignaio**
Romanesque parish church was commissioned by Countess Matilda of Canossa.

In the early 11th century two monks from Settimo monastery settled   ***Vallombrosa**
as hermits in the lonely forests below Monte Secchieta. In 1028 the
Florentine nobleman Giovanni Gualberto de Visdomi joined them
and a short time later had a chapel built in Valle Ombrosa. In 1038
Gualberto founded the **Vallombrosan order**, which was confirmed
in 1055 by the pope. Gualberto was canonized only 20 years after his
death in 1073. In the 12th century the monastery properties grew
through large donations, and in the 15th century the abbots even re-

ceived the secular title of Marquess of Canneto and Monteverdi. The fortified monastery, which was later plundered, was built in the middle of the 15th cent. At the end of the 16th century the impressive monastery library and the small cloister were added. In the mid-17th century Gherardo Silvani gave the façade its present appearance. In 1866 the monastery was secularized, and monks did not move in again until 1963. The Romanesque monastery church is adorned with frescoes and paintings on the life of the founder of the order. In the left transept the chapel of the founder, Giovanni Gualberto, holds a shrine (around 1500) with an arm relic of the saint. Liqueurs, altar wine, chocolate and cosmetics are sold in the monastery pharmacy.

Reggello Into the valley towards the Arno a stop in Reggello is worthwhile. In the Romanesque church of **San Pietro a Cascia** there is a worthwhile 15th cent. crucifix; in the museum of sacred art »Masaccio« there is the famous **Mtriptych by Masaccio** from San Giovenale (St. Juvenal; 1422).
❶ Via Casaromolo 2a, Loc. Cascia; Tue, Thu 3pm – 7pm, Sat, Sun 10am – 12pm, 3pm – 7pm; June – Sep every first and third Sat of the month also 9pm – 11pm; admission: €3; www.museomasaccio.it

Borgo San Lorenzo · Mugello

✳ F 11

Province: Florence/Firenze (FI)
Altitude: 193m/633ft above sea level
Population: 18,100

Borgo San Lorenzo lies in the heart of the Mugello, a landscape in the north-east of Tuscany where the two artists Giotto and Fra Angelico were born and the Medici had two of their most beautiful country villas built.

About 30km/19mi north of ▶Florence the Sieve meanders through the Mugello hill and mountain landscape. The Mugello Alto has the character of the Apennine mountain range while the landscape around Borgo San Lorenzo in the upper Sieve valley (Val di Sieve) rolls gently and is used for agriculture.

History During the high Middle Ages Borgo San Lorenzo was part of the lands of the **Ubaldini**, who were able to resist the domination of Florence for a long time. The fate of Borgo San Lorenzo was sealed from 1290, when Florence acquired all rights to the Mugello region for 3,000 gold florins. In the mid-14th century the Florentines emphasized their claim by building a fortified wall around the city. The Albizi, the most stubborn opponents of the Medici, occupied Borgo in 1440. 1529/1530 imperial troops built a military camp in Borgo and conquered Florence from here after an eight-month siege.

WHAT TO SEE IN BORGO SAN LORENZO

The main attraction in Borgo San Lorenzo is the Romanesque parish church in Via San Francesco, which was first mentioned in 941 and which has the typical shape of an early Christian basilica without a transept. An inscription with the date 1263 reveals when the Romanesque-Gothic campanile was built. In the 16th century the adjoining monastery was built. The decorations inside consist mainly of panel paintings and terracotta work of the 15th to 17th centuries. The most important of these works is the *Black Madonna* of 1290, which is attributed to the famous Giotto.

*Pieve di San Lorenzo

> **MARCO POLO TIP**
>
> **! Art nouveau in Tuscany?** **Insider Tip**
>
> Sometimes examples of an architectural period can be found exactly where they are not expected. The city hall of Borgo San Lorenzo on Piazza Dante is such a case. The art nouveau decoration from 1931 is by Tito Chini.

The oratory in Piazza Cavour was built between 1714 and 1743 to plans by the Florentine architect Girolamo Ticciati to hold a wooden crucifix which was revered for miraculous works (14th century).

Oratorio del SS. Crocifisso dei Miracoli

In the patrician Villa Pecori Giraldi a little further to the east is the toursit information office, a literary café and the Museo della Manifattura Chini. The most famous offspring of the Chini artist family was **Galileo Chini** (1873–1956), who founded a ceramics factory in Borgo San Lorenzo in 1896 and influenced art nouveau in Tuscany with his decorations.
❶ Thu – Sun 9am – 11am, 3pm – 7pm; admission: €5; www.villapecori.it

Museo della Manufattura Chini

Only two of the five original gates remain in the medieval city fortifications: Porta Fiorentina, which has a rare type of Sienese round and pointed arch, and Porta dell'Orologio, which has a square bell-tower with a clock.

Porta Fiorentina and Porta dell' Orologio

EXCURSIONS INTO THE MUGELLO · VAL DI SIEVE

In Scarperia, 10km/6mi north-west of Borgo San Lorenzo, **the best knives in Italy** are supposedly made. But many people now know

Scarperia

Borgo San Lorenzo

INFORMATION
Comunità Montana del Mugello
Villa Pecori Giraldi
Piazzale Lavacchini
Borgo San Lorenzo
Tel. 055 845 62 30
www.turismo.mugello.toscana.it

WHERE TO EAT
Cosimo de' Medici €€
Barberino di Mugello
Viale del Lago 19
Tel. 05 58 42 03 70
www.ristorantecosimodemedici.com
Closed Sun evening and Mon
Cosimo de' Medici serves excellent Tuscan cooking: fresh pasta, excellent porcini dishes, pappardelle al cinghiale (wild boar), and they also have 150 wines. The chef cuty the bistecca alla fiorentina personally at the table.

Trattoria Il Camino € – €€ **Insider Tip**
Viale Baccarini 38
Marradi
Tel. 05 58 04 50 69
www.ristoranteilcamino.net
Closed Wed
Rita does the cooking, Simona creates excellent dolci (try the il bicchierino) and Mirco recommends the right wine for the Mugello specialities..

WHERE TO STAY
Casa Palmira €€
Via Faentina 4 Loc. Feriolo, Polcanto
Tel. 055 840 97 49
www.casapalmira.it
Stylish rural accommodation with 6 rooms and 2 little houses. The owners, Assunta and Stefano, take especially good care of their guests and organise various courses, workshops and excursions.

Scarperia for a completely different reason: about 1km/0.5mi east of the town is the Mugello racetrack (Autodromo Internazionale del Mugello), a track over 5km/3mi long where international car and motorcycle races have been held since 1974. The massive Palazzo Pretorio (or Castello del Vicario) stands on Scarperia's main square, built in 1306 to plans by Arnolfo di Cambio and once the office of the Florentine vicars, whose stone and majolica coats of arms decorate the outer walls. The knife museum which ***Museo dei Ferri Taglienti** is housed here is an attractive presentation of local craftsmanship – Scarperia was already known as the »city of knives« in the 15th century. A visit to the five still active knife smiths is worthwhile, e.g. Saladini (since 1840) or Berti (since 1895). The Antica Bottega dei Coltellinai in der Via Solferini (since 1970) gives guided tours. Opposite the palazzo is the **Chiesa della Prepositura**, which belonged to the adjoining Augustinian monastery until 1812. The showpiece of the church is a marble relief with a Madonna and Child.

❶ **Museo dei Ferri Taglienti:** June 1 – Sep 15 Wed – Fri 3.30pm – 7.30pm, Sat and Sun 10am – 1pm, 3.30pm – 7.30pm; otherwise only Sat and Sun 10am – 1pm, 3pm – 6.30pm; admission: €3

In the neighbouring town of Sant'Agata (4km/2.5mi) there is a fine example of Romanesque church architecture. The parish church was built almost completely of light stone (pietra alberese). Six slender columns divide the interior into a nave and two aisles and support the wooden roof. The eight-sided baptismal font (1503) is made from a single sandstone block (pietra arenaria).

*Pieve di Sant'Agata

The medieval town 5km/3mi west of Borgo San Lorenzo on the Sieve distinguished itself after the Ubaldini were driven away as the most loyal ally of the Medici. They built two of their most beautiful country villas in the immediate surroundings of San Piero a Sieve in the 15th century and financed the expansion of Bosco ai Frati monastery near the town. In San Piero itself the Medici architects Baldassarre Lanci and Bernardo Buontalenti built the largest fortress of the Mugello, **San Martino**. But no large military battles were fought here. The Medici fortress is privately owned today.

San Piero a Sieve

3km/1.8mi north of San Piero a Sieve lies Bosco ai Frati, one of the oldest monasteries in Tuscany. Monks still live there today and it is open to the public. It was probably settled as early as the 6th century by Latin Basilian monks. The Ubaldini di Soli founded the monastery and turned it over to Franciscan monks in 1206. In 1420 Cosimo de Medici bought the complex. The court architect of the Medici, Michelozzo di Bartolomeo Michelozzi, finished the renovations and expansion of the monastery in 1438. It was converted to Baroque in the 17th century under Ferdinando II de Medici. On the plain façade and inside the church the **Medici coat of arms** (turtle and/or 6 spheres) can be seen several times. Even the gilded main altar (1626) displays the Medici symbols of worldly power. In the small Museo d'Arte Sacra the showpiece is a wooden crucifix by Donatello.

*Bosco ai Frati monastery

❶ Mon – Sat 10am – 12pm, 6pm – 7pm, Sun from 11.30am

This fortified **country estate of the Medici** is accessible from San Piero a Sieve via the SS 65 towards Florence (turn off to the right after about 1km/0.6mi). This well-preserved country estate, which Cosimo il Vecchio built in the middle of the 15th century, stands in a dense cypress wood on a hill. Its fortress-like character with tower and ramparts is reminiscent of the Medici villa in Careggi near Florence. The adjoining garden is a rare example of a late medieval garden. The extravagantly furnished villa and the fabulous park can only be viewed as part of a guided tour.

Castello di Trebbio

Appointments: Tel. 0 55 84 80 88

Another **country estate of the Medici** stands directly on the SS 65 between San Piero a Sieve and Barberino di Mugello. The surrounding meadows, vineyards, orchards and forests give an impression of

Villa di Cafaggiolo

the charming landscape of the time when the Medici court moved here in the summer to escape the city heat – Villa di Cafaggiolo was **the favourite country residence of Cosimo il Vecchio**. Michelozzo began it in 1451, after Castello di Trebbio was completed. In the 16th century the outbuildings of the villa housed a famous ceramic and porcelain factory (not open to the public).

Barberino di Mugello The town of Barberino di Mugello lies by the motorway exit with the same name on the Firenze – Bologna autostrada. The castle on a hill on the north-eastern edge of town belonged to the Ubaldini and the Cattani di Cambiate in the High Middle Ages; the coats of arms of these dynasties can still be seen undamaged in the walls. During the 17th century the Cattani heirs turned the castle into a fattoria (not open to the public).

Villa Demidoff The park Medici-Villa Demidoff in Pratolino with its mannerist figures and the fountain statue of Apennin of Giambologna is very worthwhile.

❶ May/Sep Sat, Sun 10am – 6pm, June – Aug Sat, Sun 10am – 7pm, Oct only first Sat and second Sun 10am – 6pm; free admission

EAST OF BORGO SAN LORENZO

Vicchio The painters **Giotto di Bondone** (b. 1267) and **Fra Angelico** (b. 1395) were born in or near Vicchio. Fra Angelico later entered the Dominican order in Fiesole, Giotto moved to Florence, where he left important works in the Peruzzi chapel and the Bardi chapel in Santa Croce. In Vespignano, halfway between Borgo San Lorenzo and Vicchio, in the house where he is presumed to have been born the **Casa di Giotto** exhibit documents his artistic life.

The famous Florentine goldsmith **Benvenuto Cellini** also lived in Vicchio between 1559 and 1571. He does not appear to have been very welcome since he barely survived a poisoning attempt. On the house where he lived, Casa di Cellini, a memorial stone commemorates his stay. Giotto by contrast is honoured with a larger than life-size bronze statue on the central piazza. The **Museo di Arte Sacra e Religiosità Populare** on Piazza Don Milani displays frescoes from the school of Giotto and terracotta work from the school of della Robbia, among other things.

❶ Casa di Giotto und Museo di Arte Sacra e Religiosità Populare: June 1 – Sep 30 Thu 10am – 1pm, Fri – Sun also 3pm – 7pm, otherwise Sat, Sun 10am – 1pm, 3pm – 7pm; admission: €4; www.comune.vicchio.fi.it

San Godenzo On 8 June 1302 the exiled Ghibelline leader **Dante Alighieri** met the rulers of the Mugello, the Ubaldini, in San Godenzo 20km/12mi east

Harvest time: olives are collected in large nets

of Vicchio in order to make plots against Guelf Florence; their plans failed in the end. St Gaudenzio lived here in the 6th century. Bishop Jacopo il Bavaro founded the Benedictine abbey on his hermit's grave in 1028. Comparisons are drawn between the plain Romanesque columned basilica (in the town) and the basilica of Fiesole as well as San Miniato al Monte in Florence. The furnishings include a Madonna polyptych from the school of Giotto and a wooden statue of St Sebastian by Baccio d'Agnolo (1507). The mummified corpse of St Gaudenzio rests in the crypt.

6km/4mi south-east lies the mountain village of Castagno d'Andrea, the birthplace of the Renaissance painter Andrea del Castagno (1423–1457). The visitor's centre of Parco Nazionale Foreste Casentinesi in Castagno dʻAndrea shows a virtual presentation of his main works. Hiking trails lead up to the 1,654m/5,427ft-high Monte Falterona. On the SS 67 toward Rufina, which follows the course of the Sieve, leads to the largest wine region of the Mugello. Enormous **vineyards in fields and terraces** cover the fertile lower Sieve valley. About 4km/2.5mi before Rufina it is worthwhile to make a detour to the 992m/3,255ft-high Monte Giovi, a charming but also somewhat time-consuming drive on a small country road via Tamburino. The partisans of Mugello, around which heavy fighting raged, retreated to Monte Giovi at the end of World War II: the Gothic Line, the last German defensive line, ran along here. Today the slopes of Monte Giovi are part of a the Casentino forest reserve.

In the centre of this wine region numerous enoteche offer wine for sale along with wine tastings. A walk up to the Renaissance ***Villa di Poggio Reale** (16th century), which is often called a Medici villa, is recommended. It belonged to the Mormorai counts and later to the

Castagno d'Andrea

Rufina

Berardi. The villa houses, among other things, the **Museo della Vite e del Vino**, a museum on wine and varieties of grapes that is well worth visiting.

● Wed, Fri 3pm – 7pm, Sat 9am – 1pm, 3pm – 6pm, Sun 10am – 1pm; admission: €3; http://comune.rufina.fi.it/museo_vite_vino.php

Pontassieve The name of the town at the confluence of the Sieve and Arno comes from the charming, double-arched brick bridge over the Sieve. It was built under Cosimo I in 1555 to plans by his architect Bartolomeo Ammannati.

* Carrara · Massa

✦ E 3

Province: Massa-Carrara (MS)
Altitude: 80m/262ft above sea level
Population : 65,600 (Carrara), 70,800 (Massa)

Carrara is the capital of the marble industry. The city owes not only its worldwide fame but also its name to the white stone: »kar« or »kair« is Celtic and probably means quarry.

Provincial capital Carrara, which spreads out on the western slope of the ►Alpi Apuane and in the south merges almost seamlessly with Massa, capital of the province Massa-Carrara. Massa has more ties with its famous neighbour than just geographical proximity. Both cities belonged to the **Malaspina** family from the 15th to the 18th century and later to the Lunigiana (and thus feel themselves to be part of Liguria rather than Tuscany), and both are characterized to this day by marble quarrying.

History The beginnings of Carrara go back to pre-Roman times. Its first written mention is in a charter of donation of Emperor Otto I to the bishops of the neighbouring city Luni in 963. In the 11th century Carrara fell to Pisa, which got its marble here to build the Campo dei Miracoli. This began its unstoppable rise to become the centre of Italian marble quarrying. In 1322 the town passed to Lucca, in 1329 to Genoa, in 1343 to the Visconti and in 1442 together with Massa to the Malaspina counts.

WHAT TO SEE IN CARRARA

*Old town, Duomo Sant'Andrea The appearance of Carrara is marked by the 19th and 20th centuries. The oldest part lies near the river Carrione, between the building of the Accademia di Belle Arti, **Piazza Alberica**, which is lined by Baroque palazzi, and the cathedral. The cathedral, a marble-clad basilica begun in the 11th and finished in the 14th century, is hemmed in by other buildings on a small square above Piazza Alberica. Its Pisan façade is divided in the lower part by early Romanesque blind arcades, while a rose window dominates the upper part. The **four-storey campanile** was built around 1280 and imitates Ligurian models. The unified Romanesque interior has an open roof and small upper windows that let in hardly any light. The capitals, mostly from the 12th century, stand out, as does the 16th-century marble pulpit with steps made from a single block of marble. In the right-hand aisle is the grave of the city's patron saint, St Ceccardo (15th cent.). Francesco Bergamini created the main altar, and the cross (14th century) in the choir is probably by Angelo Puccinelli. In the left-hand aisle the remains of the former marble top of the main altar can be seen.

The centre of Carrara, city of marble

Carrara · Massa

INFORMATION
Massa
Lungomare Vespucci 24, Marina di Massa
Tel. 05 85 24 00 63
www.massacarrara.turismo.it

EVENTS
Biennale Internazionale di Scultura, Simposio, Marble Week
The biennale takes place once every two years and Piazza Gramsci, Piazza Erba and Via Plebiscito become one large open-air studio. In June sculptors from all over the world meet for the Simposio di Scultura. The Carrara Marble Week was held for the first time in 2011 at the academy of art and on Via Roma. Info: www.comune.carrara.ms.it.

WHERE TO EAT
La Petite Cusine €€€
Via Verdi 4, Carrara
Tel. 058 57 02 26, closed all day Sun and Mon evening (open Mon in August) Pretty little restaurant with light cuisine and outstanding fish dishes.

Venanzio Colonnata €€ – €€€
Località Colonnata
Piazza Palestro 3

Tel. 05 85 75 80 62 Closed Thu and Sun evening (except August) and Dec. 20 – Jan. 25.
Alessio Lucchetti and Roberto Ferlini interpret recipes by the famous Venanzio Vannucci and serve the snow-white lardo (bacon). Filetto al lardo in salsa di Chianti or the house speciality crespelle ai fiori di zucca are especially good.

WHERE TO STAY
Hotel Villa Maremonti €€€€
Viale Lungomare di Levante 51
Massa (Marina dei Ronchi)
Tel. 05 85 24 10 08
www.hotelmaremonti.com
Cultivated hotel in a 19th-century villa with an enchanting garden and pool. Rooms facing the back are quiet, rooms facing the front have a terrace and a view of the sea.

Hotel Michelangelo Carrara €€€€
Corso Carlo Rosselli 3, Carrara
Tel. 05 85 77 71 61
www.michelangelocarrara.it
In Palazzo dei Conti del Medico 28 rooms are stylishly furnished with items from various periods; 6 rooms have a jacuzzi; WLAN, rental bikes.

Accademia di Belle Arti
Anyone interested in meeting young artists will find them here: the academy of art has had its seat in Via Roma in the historic centre, in an old city palace since 1805. It was founded in 1769 by Maria Theresia Cybo Malaspina.

*Museo Civico del Marmo
On the road to Marina di Carrara to the southwest outside of the city centre the **city marble museum** provides information on quarrying techniques since antiquity, among other things.
❶ Viale XX Settembre; May 1 – Sep 30 Mon – Sat 9.30am – 1pm, 3.30pm – 6pm, Oct 1 – Apr 30 9am – 12.30pm, 2.30pm – 5pm; admission: €4.50; http://urano.isti.cnr.it:8880/museo/home.php

AROUND CARRARA

A four-lane road connects Carrara with Marina di Carrara, which is both the world's largest shipping harbour for marble and a modern seaside resort with streets on a grid system and a newly renovated, somewhat sterile city square (Piazza Menconi). The road from Carrara leads straight to the yacht harbour, which forms a buffer between the marble harbour in the south and the stabilimenti, the bathing facilities, which completely block the view of the beach.

Marina di Carrara

South of Marina di Carrara lies the somewhat more charming Marina di Massa, Massa's seaside resort. In the centre old **villas with lush gardens**, palms and jasmine bushes set the scene. Swimming is possible at the somewhat narrow beach of fine-grained sand.

Marina di Massa

A winding road leads to Campo Cecina, a 1,300m/4,265ft peak north of Colonnata, which offers the most spectacular view of the marble quarries of Carrara (signposted from the SS 446). At the top the forest clears and there is a free view down the mountain where the quarries have already cut deep »wounds«.

**Campo Cecina

Do not miss a drive up into the quarries. At present there is still a few hundred around Carrara. Of the quarries that are still in use today, ***Cave dei Fantiscritti** at 450m/1,476ft and the **quarries at Colonnata** at 532m/1,745ft are the largest and most interesting. Both are accessible by car or bus. In Fantiscritti the quarry tunnel Ravaccione Nr. 84, which was dug in 1963 for the Ferrovia marmifera marble train, can be viewed. Minibusses drive 600m/2000ft into the marble cave.

Marble quarries

The danger and difficulty of **life in a marble quarry** can be seen best in **Cava Museo**, a somewhat bizarre open-air museum that has been established in the middle of the quarrying area of Fantiscritti. The techniques of marble quarrying are explained precisely here. There is even a completely furnished workers' hut in the museum. The dedicated initiator and manager of the private museum is **Walter Danesi**, who is there most of the time and is always happy to talk to interested visitors about the quarries and his life's work.

! Insider Tip

Lardo di Colonnata

The fine white bacon is stored according to an old tradition for six months in marble containers before it can be served in paper-thin slices. It tastes best in layers on unsalted Tuscan bread with a glass of Tuscan wine. Try the former »poor man's meal« locally in one of the friendly trattorias. An especially pretty location is the »Larderia Lardarium« of Alessandro Guadagni, which has also been operating pithily under the name of »Lard Rock Café« (Via Fossacava 9).

School children at the Fantiscritti marble quarry

Cave di Fantiscritti daily 11am – 6.30pm, Apr, Sep , Oct Mon – Fri only until 5pm; admission: €7; reservations: Marmo Tour, tel. 33 97 65 74 70, www.marmotour.com
Cava Museo: Dec – Mar Mon – Sat 10.30am – 1.30pm, Sun 11am – 5pm, Apr – Nov daily 9am – 7pm; free admission; www.cavamuseo.com

*Colonnata

Between Fantiscritti and Carrara a very winding narrow road branches off high up to the **workers' village** of Colonnata, where marble was quarried as early as Roman times. On summer weekends and in August the road to Colonnata is sometimes closed because of the high traffic volume. At those times a minibus (navetta) runs back and forth. Colonnata is visited today above all for its culinary specialty, **lardo**.

WHAT TO SEE IN MASSA

*Piazza
Aranci

The most beautiful thing about Massa is the **orange trees**. They stand in two rows around Piazza Aranci in the heart of the old city designed by Alberico I in the 16th century. In the middle of the square a fountain obelisk commemorates the unification of Italy in 1860. The entire south side of the square is taken up by the extravagant Palazzo Cybo-Malaspina, today seat of the prefettura. The inner courtyard with loggia was built in 1665 by Giovanni Francesco Bergamini, who extended an existing 15th-century villa for this purpose. The richly decorated façade was provided by Alessandro Bergamini around 1701.

The late Gothic cathedral that was begun in 1389, then remodelled in Renaissance and Baroque style and gained a classical façade of Carrara marble in 1936. The Cappella del Santissimo Sacramento to the right of the altar, the funeral chapel of the Malaspina, holds fragmentary remains of a **Madonna fresco by Pinturicchio** (late 15th century). The Madonna triptych next to it (around 1460) presumably comes from Bernardino del Castelletto. Devotional objects of the 17th/18th century are displayed in the cathedral museum.

Duomo, Museo d'Arte Sacra

The castle of the Malaspina (La Rocca), one of the most imposing fortresses in all of Tuscany, rises high above the city. A defensive tower already stood here in the 11th century and was fortified with a ring wall in the 13th century. The Counts of Malaspina built the L-shaped Renaissance palace with fine marble decorations in the 15th and 16th centuries.

*Castello Malaspina

❶ Via del Forte 15, Sep 1 – June 30 Sun 3.30pm – 6.30pm, July 1 – Aug 31 Tue – Sun 10am – 1pm, 5pm – 12pm; admission: €5; www.istitutovalorizzazionecastelli.it

✴ EXCURSION TO THE LUNIGIANA

From the Tyrrhenian Sea to the foothills of the Apennines, the varied landscape of the Lunigiana stretches across the extreme north-west of Tuscany and includes the Magra valley and its side valleys. The region gets its name from the city of Luni, which was founded by the Romans. Numerous castles, most of which were built by the Counts of Malaspina, are a characteristic of the area.

*Magra Valley

The first defensive measures for Fosdinovo's imposing castle on Monte Grosso were built in the early Middle Ages in order to control the old road that connected the valleys of the Lunigiana with the coast. In the 13th century the Malaspina family had the existing fortress reinforced. In 1340 the fiefdom passed to Spinetta Malaspina, who had the cylindrical towers with battlements built. The project »Castello in Movimento« (castle in movement) has elevated Castello Malaspina to a cultural centre. Writers and visual artists work here; dance, theatre and writing workshops are held here.

*Fosdinovo, Castello Malaspina

❶ ⓘ Via Papiriana 2, tours (6 people each): Wed – Mon 11am, 12pm, 3.30pm, 4.30pm, 5.30pm and 6.30pm; admission: €6; www.castellodifosdinovo.it

Carrara Marble

From a distance they look like fields of snow –the gigantic steps of the white marble quarries above Carrara, which go up to 1,000m/3,281ft in the massif of the Apuan Alps. No other natural stone is valued as highly as the fine-grained white marble whose name comes from the Greek »mármaros« for »broken stone«. ableiten lässt.

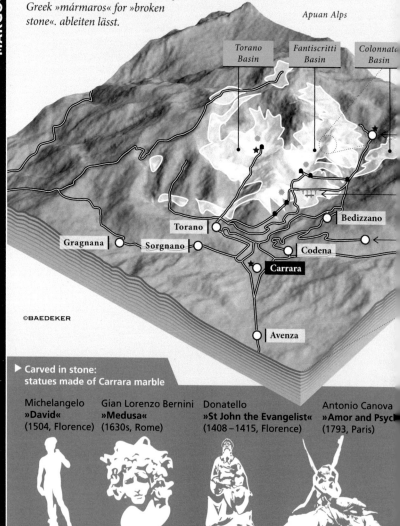

Apuan Alps

Torano Basin · Fantiscritti Basin · Colonnata Basin

Bedizzano

Torano

Gragnana · Sorgnano

Codena

Carrara

©BAEDEKER

Avenza

▶ Carved in stone:
statues made of Carrara marble

Michelangelo
»David«
(1504, Florence)

Gian Lorenzo Bernini
»Medusa«
(1630s, Rome)

Donatello
»St John the Evangelist«
(1408 – 1415, Florence)

Antonio Canova
»Amor and Psych
(1793, Paris)

Transport today and past

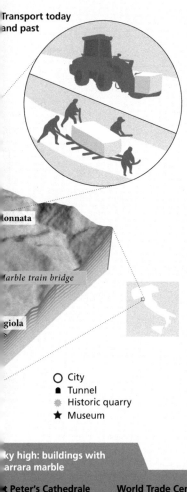

onnata

Marble train bridge

giola

- ○ City
- ■ Tunnel
- ✳ Historic quarry
- ★ Museum

ky high: buildings with arrara marble

▶ Stone masons

Before the industrial revolution stone masons had three tasks:

1 Marmische/ Marmorarii
... broke large blocks of stone out of the quarry walls.

2 Quadratarii
... worked the raw blocks with chisels and made them square.

3 Sectores serrarii
... split the plates.

Today Carrara marble is sawn out of the rock walls with wire saws and cutters. There is probably enough stone in the 150 quarries above and below ground for another 300 years.

| Peter's Cathedrale n Rome 506–1626 | World Trade Center in New York (1966–1973) | Dom in Florence (completed 1436) | Campanile in Pisa (1173–1370) |

Durable and Valuable

From a distance they look like fields of snow –the gigantic steps of the white marble quarries above Carrara, which go up to 1,000m/3,281ft in the massif of the Apuan Alps. No other natural stone is valued as highly as the fine-grained white marble whose name comes from the Greek »mármaros« for »broken stone«.

Chemically seen marble is limestone. The Apuan Alps were covered by the sea more than 200 million years ago. The remains of dead shellfish and organic substances were compressed by the weight of the water and crystallized to an unusually pure limestone. When the African and European continental plates were pushed one over the other 50 million years ago the region sank and the limestone was turned into marble by **extreme pressure** and **high temperatures**. After more millions of years the Apuan Alps were raised up and the marble in the almost 2,000m/6,560ft high massif was exposed.

The main characteristic of the hard, homogenous stone is its **durability**, which stands up to every kind of weather and thus to the ravages of time. Foreign particles change the originally snow-white marble to striped, flame-patterned, spotted, marbled, veined, colourful marble. Traces of metallic salts cause **discolorations** during the creation process: iron oxides causes red colours, iron sulfide blue-black colours, limonite, iron and manganese carbonate and iron hydroxid cause yellow and brown tomes, ferrous silicates produce green tones. Thus in Carrara along with the much praised statuario more than 60 different types of marble are quarried.

White Gold

What nature created in millions of years can only be taken off the Apuan Alps with sweat and tears. The emperor Augustus sent slaves to the marble of quarries of Carrara already in order to get marble for the triumphal arches and manorial villas of ancient Rome. The income of the Ligurian Luni, the centre of marble processing at that time, went down with the fall of the Roman empire in the 4th century AD. In 1185 the marble quarries of Carrara were mentioned as the suppliers of Genua and Pisa, but it only became really famous in the **Renaissance** when sculptors and master builders looked for perfect white blocks here for their sculptures, palaces and churches. Be it Pisani, Bernini, Donatello or Henry Moore, they all wanted the »Tuscan white gold«. Michelangelo would not be denied the right to pick the best stone on site himself for his »David«. But even today star architects are conscious of the representative effect of the valuable stone as in the seat of government in Brasilia or the heavily symbolic marble palaces in the desert sand of Saudi Arabia.

Current estimates claim that the **marble supplies** will last at least another 300 years. The marble industry employs almost 3,500 people, among them 1,200 in 300 quarries. The **price** per cubic meter of average marble is by about 1,000 Euros. A mid-sized sculpted column costs 20,000 Euros and more now.

Iron Chisel and Wire Saw

The first »marmische«, as the workers are called here, made use of natural rock clefts by driving **spikes made of fig tree wood** into them which had been soaked in water, so that the expanding wood would split the rocks. In Roman times **iron wedges** were bored into the rock along the cutting line in order to split it from the mountain. In the middle of the 19th century the 3,000 or so workers in the 600 quarries at that time still won raw marble in this way.

An important improvement was a motor-powered **wire saw** which was introduced in 1885. The annual production then climbed to almost 200,000 t. In this method, which is till used today, a 4mm to 6mm thick spiral wire which is guided over rollers runs in a circular path parallel to the stone layer at a speed of 5 to 6m/5.4 to 6.5yd per second penetrates the stone and carries the actual cutting and sanding material – gravel sand – all the while being sprayed with water. It can cut about 20cm/7.8in into the rock in an hour. The massive, up to 400 t heavy blocks (bancata) are then cut to transport size with diamond saws. Recent efforts to cut marble with laser technology have proven to be too expensive.

Flowing fabric chiselled in stone

A sculptor at work

Work in the marble quarries was always dangerous – it was not without reason that **slaves and prisoners** worked there in antiquity. One of the most dangerous jobs until the industrialization was the transport of the gigantic marble blocks with the help of primitive wooden sleds, which rolled downhill on **wooden poles** that were greased with soap and secured only with hemp ropes. Not rarely were there fatalities when one of the giant blocks got out of control and buried workers underneath it. The buccine horns still sound in the valley today when the marble has claimed another victim.

Around the turn of the century **lifts and cable cars** transported the blocks to a loading ramp. From 1876 to 1891 a 20km/13mi railway was built, which runs over 16 bridges and through 15 tunnels on a partially adventurous route down to the sea.

Today there is **heavy technology** everywhere in the marble quarries; heavy steam shovels lift the up to 25 t heavy blocks on a large truck for transport to the harbour in Marina di Carrara, Marina di Massa and Marina di Pietrasanta. From there the marble is exported into the whole world. But the route to the coast is still very full of bends, narrow and has in places a slope of 20%. One slack moment and the heavy load can quickly become deadly dangerous.

Marble for Everyone

The souvenir shops of Carrara and along the serpentine road to the quarries offer every possible item in marble, form the much copied »David« to tabletops to chess sets and ashtrays.

The **quarries can be visited** without special permission but caution is advised when on the premises. Anyone interested in the history of marble, quarry methods and use should visit two museums: Walter Danesi's outdoor museum in Fantiscritti and the marble museum in Carrara (Viale XX Septembre).

The massive Brunella castle of Aulla, about 15km/9mi to the north, guards the confluence of the Aulla and Magra. The fortress was begun in the late 13th century and expanded at the beginning of the 16th century. It holds a worthwhile museum on the natural history of the Lunigiana, while the adjacent park is an inviting place for a restful stroll.

*Aulla, Fortezza della Brunella

❶ Mar – May, Oct Tue – Sun 9am – 12pm, 3pm – 6pm, park until 6.30pm; June – Sep 9am – 12pm, 4pm – 7pm, park until 7.30pm, Nov – Feb 9am – 12pm, 2pm – 5pm, park until 5.30pm; admission: €3.50; www.fortezzadellabrunella.it

Tours through the cultural park »Grotte di Equi« and the Archeoparco Equi Terme show the spa's attractions; it is known for its chalcolithic finds and its sulphur springs.

Equi Terme

❶ July 1 – Sep 30 Mon – Fri 10.30am – 12.30pm, 2.30pm – 7pm, Sat, Sun 10.30am – 7pm; admission: route 1 €5, route 2 €8.50; www.terredilunigiana.com

Verrucolacastle with its church and Renaissance loggia (15th cent.) was built by 1350. Today it belongs to the sculptor Pietro Cascella whose works are displayed in two halls (only Fri 1pm – 5pm, free admission). Museo della Stampa in Palazzo Fantoni inform on book printing after 1470, exhibits include a prototype typewriter from 1802

*Fivizzano, Castello della Verrucola

❶ tel. 0 58 59 20 75; appt. only

About 10km/6mi north of Aulla lies the sleepy village of Villafranca. The fortress Malgrate is privately owned today and is used for art exhibits. The central element is the medieval main tower. Conversion from a fortress to a residence for the Malaspina began in the middle of the 14th century. In 1641 the Marchesi Ariberti from Cremona took over the fiefdom.

Villafranca, Castello di Malgrate

The **Museo Etnografico** in a former mill explains old crafts such as basket weaving, carving, smith and stonemason work, traditional forms of agriculture (including the use of chestnuts).

❶ **Museo Etnografico:** Via dei Mulini 71, June – Sep Tue – Sun 9.30am – 12.30pm, 3.30pm – 6.30pm; Oct – May Tue – Fri 9.30am – 12.30pm, afternoons by appt., Sun 2.30pm – 5.30pm; admission: €2.50
Art exhibits in the castle by appt.: tel. 01 87 49 44 00, admission €2

In the late 10th century the foundation stone for the castle of the Castiglione family in Bagnone (2km/1.2mi eastwards) was laid. In 1351 the fiefdom passed to Marchese Franceschino Malaspina, who converted the eastern wing and had the defensive tower built. From 1451 the castle was the main seat for Florentine domination of the Magra valley for about three hundred years.

Bagnone, Castiglione del Terziere

Pontremoli

Pontremoli, a pleasant town, is the centre of the Lunigiana and lies 13km/8mi to the north-west. The * **Museo delle Statue-Stele Lunigianesi** in Piagnaro castle (16th–19th centuries) holds a collection of all the stele found in the Lunigiani either as a copy or an original. The approximately 60 female and male sandstone figures were made in the 2nd and 1st millennium BC by the inhabitants of the valley to honour their gods and heroes.

❶ May 1 – Sep 30 Tue – Sun 9am – 12pm, 3pm – 6pm, Oct 1 – Apr 30 Tue – Sun 9am – 12.30pm, 2.30pm – 5.30pm; admission: €4; www.statuestele.org

Certaldo

✦ H 9

Province: Florence/Firenze (FI)
Altitude: 130m/426ft above sea level
Population: 16,400

About 40km/25mi south-west of ▶Florence, the town of Certaldo lies in hilly country between wheat fields and olive groves. The upper town, Certaldo Alto, also called »Castello«, where the poet Boccaccio (▶Famous People) lived at the end of his life, is small and charming.

* CERTALDO ALTO

Charming
upper town

Its position high up on the hill, its complete, mostly intact town wall and red brick houses give the upper part of Certaldo an impressively harmonious appearance but also an almost **fortress-like character**. It does not take much time to see it. Only a few paces from the cable car station is the inner courtyard of the hotel restaurant Il Castello. Try Certaldo's speciality, sweet onions (cipolle), here or at Osteria del Vicario near the Palazzo Pretorio.

Casa del
Boccaccio,
Museo del
Arte Sacra

Below Palazzo Pretorio is Casa del Boccaccio. The tower is accessible and offers a panoramic view of the area as far as San Gimignano. Boccaccio (▶ Famous people) is presumably buried in the former monastery church Chiesa dei Santi Jacopo e Filippo nearby. The gravestone is inscribed with four verses by Boccaccio In the former monastery is the **Museo del Arte Sacra**, a collection of altar panels, sculptures and liturgical items from the churches in and around Certaldo.

❶ **Casa del Boccaccio** Apr 1 – Oct 31 Wed – Mon 9.30am – 1.30pm, 2.30pm – 7pm, Nov 1. – Mar 31 until 4.30pm; admission €4.50; www. casaboccaccio.it; **Boccaccio's grave:** daily 9.30am – 7pm

Museo del Arte Sacra: see Casa del Boccaccio

In the massive medieval palace with its rich decoration of coats of arms on the façade lived the Counts Alberti, and later administrators from Florence; it dates from the late 12th century. From 1530 court judgments and new laws were proclaimed from the front loggia. Visitors enter the beautiful inner courtyard, which is also decorated with coats of arms, Renaissance frescoes and a small well. In the former offices, which are used for exhibitions today, there are several frescoes to admire, including a pietà (1484) that is attributed to Pier Francesco Fiorentino as well as a fresco *Doubting Thomas* (1490), thought to be a work of Benozzo Gozzoli. On the walls of the 13th-century St Thomas chapel fresco fragments depict the 24 Florentine podestà. In the old prison cells the prisoners' writing on the walls can still be read. There is a view of enchanting scenery from the tower.

*Palazzo Pretorio

❶ see Casa del Boccaccio

Palazzo Pretorio, once the law courts and seat of the Florentine rulers

AROUND CERTALDO

Located 10km/6mi north-west in the Elsa Valley (population 24,000) Castelfiorentino goes back to a Roman settlement and was known in the Middle Ages under the name of Castel Timignano and owned by the Counts Alberti di Vernio. In the 12th century the city was renamed Castelfiorentino (»Florentine castle«) and expanded as a bulwark against the Sienese. A visit to the ***BEGO (Museo Benozzo Gozzoli)**, which is dedicated to the artistic genius of the Valdelsa by **Benozzo Gozzoli** and his important frescoes, is worthwhile. The fresco cycle was created between 1484 and 1490 and comes from the oratory of the Madonna della Tosse nearby in the street to Castelnuovo. It shows the Madonna with saints, the burial and assumption of the Virgin with the sacred belt as a symbol of the virgin birth of Christ. The tabernacle which Gozzoli created in 1490 for the Capella della Visitazione (Tabernacolo della Visitazione) also has the four evangelists, scenes from the life of St Joachim, the archangels Michael and Raphael as well as scenes from the life of Mary.

Castelfiorentino

Certaldo

INFORMATION
Pro Loco Certaldo
Via Boccaccio 18 (Certaldo Alto)
Tel. 05 71 66 12 65
www.comune.certaldo.fi.it

EVENTS
»Mercantia« is the most important
event, a mixture of theatre and music
festival, and medieval market. The old
walls of Certaldo are a wonderful setting
for the annual spectacle (3rd week in
July; (www.mercantiacertaldo.it).

The Tignano Festival per l' Ambiente
(classical, poetry, theatre, cabaret) and
the Tignano Music Festival (rock) on the
castle piazza of Tignano (www.tignano.
it) near Barberino Val d' Elsa are also attractive.

WHERE TO EAT
Osteria Vicario €€€€
Certaldo Alto
Via Rivellino 3
Tel. 05 71 66 82 28
www.osteriadelvicario.it
Closed Sunday evening, Mon and in January. In a former monastery Sara Con-
forti and Andrea Mancini entice with or-
ange-fennel salad, filet of rabbit with
almonds and onions, linguine with artichokes or potato ravioli with a truffle fill-
ing. The small, covered terrace with a
wide view of the hilly landscape is especially charming. Equally pretty: the 4
guestrooms that used to be monks' cells
with Renaissance beds (double
€85 –100).

WHERE TO STAY
La Rocca Chianto €
Strada del Cerro 7
Tavarnelle Val di Pesa)
Tel. 05 58 05 01 06
www.laroccachianti.it
Claudia and Angelo Rizzone offer an old
farmhouse in the country with a beauti-
ful garden and simple rooms. Bicycles
are available.

CABLE CAR OR ON FOOT
The narrow street up to Certaldo Alto is
closed to all but local traffic. An alternative to the steep steps is a cable car (funicolare) that runs up every 15 minutes
between Piazza Boccaccio and Porta Alberti (April 15 – Oct. 15 daily 7.30am –
1am, Oct. 16. – April 14 daily 7.30am –
7.30pm; ticket: €1).

❶ BEGO: Via Testaferrata; June 1 – Sep 19 Sat – Tue 10am – 12pm, 4pm –
7pm, Thu 4pm – 7pm, Fri 10am – 12pm, Sep 20 – May 31 Mon and Fri 9am
– 1pm, Tue and Thu 4pm – 7pm, Sat, Sun 10am – 12pm, 4pm – 7pm;
admission: €3; www.museobenozzogozzoli.it

*Barberino
Val d'Elsa
15km/9mi east of Certaldo, the town of Barberino Val d' Elsa (population: 4,300) lies in the middle of broad vine-covered slopes on the
old road Via Regia and the pilgrimage route Via Francigena: it is not
visited nearly as often as the neighbouring towns in ►Chianti. Yet
Barberino Val d'Elsa is still a **pretty medieval town**. The fortress
walls served the Florentines in battles against Siena. The two city

gates, the impressive Porta Romana and the Porta Fiorentina, date from the 14th century, as does the pilgrims' hospice built by Cecco Barberino at the end of Via Francesco da Barberino. Palazzo Pretorio on the central Piazza Barberini is decorated with coats of arms, the oldest from the 15th century. Next to it is the parish church San Bartolomeo with fresco remnants from the 14th–15th centuries (Annunciation).

✶✶ Chianti

 G – I 10 – 12

Provinces: Florence/Firenze (FI), Siena (SI)

Everyone who has seen Florence or Siena, done the full programme of culture and longs for a rural scene should go to Chianti, which welcomes visitors with gently rolling hills, olive groves, forests and vineyards.

The Via Chiantigiana runs 70km/45mi through the **famous wine region**, past vineyards, farms and majestic castles and through pretty little towns and medieval villages.

FIRST STAGE: FROM FLORENCE TO CASTELLINA IN CHIANTI

The town, which is enchantingly sited amongst vineyards; its wine festival in September and weekly market on Saturdays attract many visitors. mayn believers visit the miraculous picture of the Virgin Mary in the sanctuary of Santa Maria. Legend has it that St Luke made it; it was hidden under cedar trees (in prunetis) and gave the town its name. Impruneta is known for its **pottery and terracotta art**. The roof tiles for Florence cathedral were fired in the terracotta ovens of Impruneta. The traditional craft is still very popular. Mario Mariani, Via di Cappello 29, makes terracotta pots in a process that has been historically documented. Family Masini fires the ovens of Master Vanni di Imprunet (known since 1681), Via dei Fornaci 57-59 (www.fornace-masini.it). One of the oldest terra-

*Impruneta

MARCO POLO TIP

! *Not just for insiders*   Insider Tip

The Romans called pure wine merum; it was so sweet and strong that it first had to be diluted with water to vinum. But Merum is also the name of a bimonthly journal that informs lovers of Italian wines independently and critically, so that he can find his/her way around the wine regions of Chianti. Information at www.merum.info

Chianti

INFORMATION

Gaiole in Chianti
Via G. Galilei 1 and Via Ricasoli 50
Tel. 05 77 74 94 11
www.terresiena.it
www.comune.gaiole.si.it

Greve in Chianti
Piazza Matteotti 9-11
Tel. 05 58 54 68 99
Via Giovanni da Verrazano 59
Tel. 05 58 54 62 87
www.chiantiechianti.it
www.comune.greve-in-chianti.fi.it

Castellina in Chianti
Piazza del Comune 1
Tel. 05 77 74 23 11
www.comune.castellina.si.it

WINE FESTIVALS
Of course every town in Chianti has a wine festival every year in September or October – the festival in Greve lasts a week (mid-September). 5 % discount on wine purchases, in restaurants, at wine tastings, seminars and tours are available in May/June with the »Classico è Card« (€10), available at the tourist offices in Greve and Castellina (www.classico-e.it)..

BICYCLE RENTAL
Along with excellent information brochures the tourist information in Castellina in Chianti (address above) also rents bicycles.

WHERE TO EAT
Monna Ginevra €€€ – €€€€
Gaiole in Chianti, Molinaccio
Tel. 05 77 74 62 12

www.lepozzedilecchi.it
Closed Wed. Francesca und Donato serve top class food made with local products, on the garden terrace in the summer.

Ristorante Relais Vignale €€€
Radda in Chianti, Via Pianigiani 9
Tel. 05 77 73 80 94
www.vignale.it
No closing day
(only open Apr. 1 – Oct. 31
Top class restaurant with beautiful balcony terrace and enoteca.

Osteria Mangiando Mangiando €€
Greve in Chianti
Piazza Matteotti 80
Tel. 05 58 54 63 72
www.mangiandomangiando.it
www.slowchianti.it
www.slowfoodsiena.it

Insider Tip

Closed Mondays and all of Jan. and Feb. Friendly family atmosphere. Mirna and Salvatore Toscano value Slow Food and serve Italian specialities, e.g. with Chianina beef. Tagliatelle con suga di cinta senese is also good.

Ristorante Locanda Borgo Antico €€
Lucolena – Greve in Chianti
Via Case Sparse 115
(Loc. Dimezzano)
Tel. 055 85 10 24
www.ilborgoantico.it
Closed Tue. Patrizia and Stefano run a stylish trattoria in an old farmhouse and serve Florentine cooking. The risotto with pears and grogonzola is especially good.

Albergaccio €€€
Castellina in Chianti
Via Fiorentina 63
Tel. 05 77 74 10 42
www.albergacciocast.com
Sonia Visman and Francesco Cacciatori
swear by creative local cuisine. Specialities: basil ravioli with pine nuts or almond biscuits with cherries in Chianti
wine.

Badia a Coltibuono €€€
Gaiole in Chianti
Loc. Badia a Coltibuono
(5km/3mi north of Gaiole)
Tel. 05 77 74 90 31
www.coltibuono.com
No closing day, closed Tue Nov. 8 – Mar.
4. Beautiful ambience: tables in the
vaulted rooms of the monastery or in
the summer outside under a rose pergola.

Oltre il Giardino €€
Panzano – Greve in Chianti
Piazza Bucciarelli 42
Tel. 05 58 28 28
Closed Mon
The homemade pasta and the selected
cheeses taste especially good. Seating
on the pleasant terrace in summer.

WHERE TO STAY
Relais Vignale €€€€
Radda in Chianti
Via Pianigiani 9
Tel. 05 77 73 83 00
www.vignale.it
37 rooms, 5 suites
One of the best addresses in Chianti – in
a historic building. The hotel is also the
seat of the wine consortium Chianti
Classico; gourmets should try the restaurant.

Podere Le Vigne €€
Radda in Chianti
Loc. Podere le Vigne (1km/0.5mi outside
of town)
Tel. 05 77 73 81 24
www.lodgingchianti.it
The old manor of an estate, transformed
into quiet accommodation with rustic
charm. With pool, bar and restaurant.

Belvedere di San Leonino €€€
Castellina in Chianti
Loc. San Leonino
Tel. 05 77 74 08 87
www.hotelsanleonino.
A hotel in Tuscan country-house style
with beautifully furnished rooms and a
well-tended garden with pool.

Residenzia del Sogno €€€
Castellina in Chianti
Loc. Pietrafitta 50
Tel. 05 77 74 13 94
www.residenziadelsogno.com
10 rooms, 3 apartments. Delightful accommodation in a house on the Chiantigiana that was carefully renovated. Furnished with period furniture.

Pensione Elio Pistolesi €
Via Roma 46
Radda in Chianti
Tel. 05 77 73 81 24
www.lodgingchianti.it
In the middle of Radda. Not always qui-
et, but centrally located and very cheap.

La Fonte del Cieco €€
Via Ricasoli 18
Gaiole in Chianti
Tel. 05 77 74 40 28
www.lafontedelcieco.com
Nice little accommodation in the centre
of Gaiole. Tasteful rooms.

cotta workshops belongs to Ugo Poggi, Via Imprunetana 16 (www.poggiugo.it).

*Castello Vicchio- maggio

Framed in cypresses, Castello Vicchiomaggio occupies a hill commanding a wonderful view just about 4km/2.5mi before Greve. Its oldest parts – tower and enclosure wall – date from the 13th century. It is said that Leonardo da Vinci once stayed in the carefully restored villa, which today holds a vineyard with hotel and restaurant – the castle is at least mentioned in one of his writings (www.vicchiomaggio.it).

*Castello di Verrazzano

In the nearby Castello di Verrazzano the production of Chianti has a tradition back to the 12th century. The most famous offspring of the Verrazzano family was Giovanni (1485 – 1528), who in 1524 was the first European to see the peninsula of Manhattan. The New York bridge between Brooklyn and Staten Island is named after him. The castle wine cellars of Verrazzano are open to the public.
Wine sales along the SS 222: Mon – Sat 10am – 1pm, 2pm – 7pm, Sun 10am – 1pm, 3pm – 7pm; admission: €14; www.verrazzano.com.

Surrounded by vineyards and high walls: Montefioralle is a picture book village in Chianti

On the SS 222 about 1.5km/1mi before Greve there is a detour east-wards. A steep road leads up between vineyards and olive groves to the medieval castle of Uzzano, where Tuscan cuisine in the restaurant is an opportunity for indulgence. The Capponi family had the castle converted to a villa in the mid-16th century. In 1641 the estate was passed on the Counts Masetti.

Castello di Uzzano

Park: Mon – Fri 8am – 12pm, 2pm – 6pm, in the summer until 7pm

The estate with a Renaissance villa received an award in 2011 for beautiful architecture, parks and gardens in the area of wine tourism. The photogenic grounds have even been used as a film setting. Whether or not Leonardo da Vinci's model for the *Mona Lisa* was really born here in 1479, as is often claimed, is not documented.

Castello Vignamaggio

Tours of the garden and wine cellar: daily 10.30am, 3.30pm on appt.; admission: €10; www.vignamaggio.com

> **MARCO POLO TIP**
> *Country luxury* **Insider Tip**
>
> A stay in this villa has its price: double room €150 – 200, suites €230 – 450; apartments (luxurious agriturismo in restored farm houses nearby): €200 – 275 (2-4 people). Information: tel. 05 58 54 66 53, www.vignamaggio.com

The small town of ***Greve** is the wine centre of Chianti. It has a beautiful triangular Piazza Matteotti with a statue of **Giovanni Verrazzano**, whose home is not far away (see above). Comfortable trattorias in houses with flower-decorated loggias and cafés line the square, which is transformed into an outdoor enoteca during the one-week wine festival (Rassegna del Chianti Classico) in mid-September. **Museo d' Arte Sacra di San Francesco** exhibits paintings, sculptures and sacred art from, including works by Baccio da Montelupo. A little shopping tip: excellent sausage can be bought at Macelleria Falorni on the sqaure in Greve. Of course there is wild boar salami, a Tuscan speciality, but also fennel salami, ham and many other delicacies (www.falorni.it).

Museo d' Arte Sacra di San Francesco: Via San Francesco 4; Apr 1 – Oct 31 Tue, Thu, Fri 4pm – 7pm, Sat, Sun 10am – 1pm, 4pm – 7pm; Nov 1 – Mar 31 Tue – Thu 3pm – 6pm, Sat, Sun 10am – 1pm, 3pm – 6pm; admission: €5; www.chiantimusei.it

An excursion absolutely to be recommended (2km/1.2mi above Greve, extreme inclines but a wonderful panoramic view) is to the castle village of Montefioralle, where excellent olive oil is produced. Park in the parking lot behind the village since only residents may drive into Montefioralle. The amateur painters in the steep streets decorated with flowers show that Montefioralle is no longer an insider's tip.

*Montefioralle

Wines With a Tradition

The word Chianti has a long history. At first it was an Etruscan family name; in the Middle Ages it was a military alliance of the feudal lords of Radda, Gaiole and Castellina. Then it became the name of the region and later of its wines. Finally it became the generic name for a popular type of Tuscan wine.

The original Chianti territory included, according to Cosimo III's Bando decree of 1716, only the lands of Radda, Gaiole and Castellina. In 1932 parts of Greve, San Casciano and Tavernelle in the north and Castelnuovo Berardenga in the south were added. In 1967 the introduction of the DOC appellation brought legal recognition of a wine region which had meanwhile spread to cover almost all of Tuscany. The year 1841 was decisive; on his vast estate of Brolio Castle, Bettino Ricasoli then realized his vision of a modern Chianti with a mixture of Sangiovese, white Malvasia and Canaiolo grapes. Due to the great demand, high-yield Trebbiano was added to the Chianti mixture, the yield per acre was increased without consideration for quality and Chianti grapes were planted in unsuitable areas. All of this led to a large drop in Chianti consumption in the 1970s. In the following decade, however, broad-based improvements in quality made Chianti Classico one of the most sophisticated Italian wines and restored its international reputation.

The Black Rooster

As early as the 14th century the famous »fiasco« bottles in braided straw were produced near San Gimignano. They became the trademark of Chianti in the whole world. Today the original bottle is increasingly being replaced by the Bordeaux bottle, but the sparkling fresh, fruity Chianti of the old days still exists. The naked pink cherub on the bottleneck is the promise of an uncomplicated, pleasant drink. Today even the simplest **Annata Chianti** wines are robust and contain tannins, so that it is advisable to store them for two or three years. The **Riserva Chianti** wines have even more body, mostly with a good dose of tannin and marked by wood when young. They are intended for longer storage. A black rooster on the bottleneck is the sign of Chianti Classico, produced by members of the Gallo Nero consortium.

Chianti Classico

Chianti (including all sub-zones) may be grown on about 23,000 ha/57,000 acres of the total 32,000 ha/79,000 acres of the Tuscan DOC regions. Of the 90 million litres of Chianti produced, about half are ordinary Chianti without any additional appellation. Another 25 million litres are Chianti Classico, and the rest is from other sub-regions. Neither the Rufina region east of Florence in the Sieve valley nor Montalbano west of Florence, nor the hills of Arezzo, Pisa or Siena have much in common with the actual Chianti region apart from the type of grape (Sangiovese). Nevertheless the wine politicians decided in an unhappy moment that these regions would be called Chianti, while the original regions would be elevated to **Chianti Classico**. Apart from a few Chianti Rufina and excellent Chianti Colli Fiorentini vintages, the best Chianti still comes from the Classico region.

Prime Locations

Chianti Classico is actually less of a wine than a forest region. Only one tenth of the 70,000 ha/173,000 acres **between Florence and Siena** are vineyards. The best locations for Chianti Classico are between 250m and 450m (800–1,500ft) above sea level in stony, unfertile alberese or galestro soil and on slopes facing south-east, south or south-west. Good conditions can be found in the north, above all near Greve, and in the south around Castelnuovo Berardenga. The classic sites, where soil, microclimate, elevation and sunshine are ideal, and the Sangiovese vine can give its best, can be found in the sunny basin of Conca d'Oro near the village of Panzano, on the hills around Gaiole and further south in Monti, near Radda and around Castellina. Very high locations produce rustic, strong, sometimes joyless wines, while lower, mostly more fertile and warmer locations produce a full-bodied, powerful but unrounded Chianti. The new **production regulations**, which define the parameters of quality for Chianti Classico production, provide for the following varieties:

Sangiovese (75–100 %), Canaiolo (up to 10 %), Malvasia and Trebbiano (up to 10%), other varieties (up to 15%). Riserva can be pressed only from red grapes. The prescribed period for maturing is one year for Annata, two years for Riserva.

The black rooster on the bottle neck is the trademark of the Gallo Nero consortium

*Badia a Passignano
A narrow road leads further to Badia a Passignano (6km/3.5mi), which looks like a fortress with its towers and battlements. The Gothic monastery can be seen from afar in the shade of tall cypress trees. San Giovanni Gualberto founded it in 1049 The wonderful *Last Supper* in the refectory was painted by Domenico Ghirlandaio in 1476. The abbey has again been occupied by Vallombrosian monks since the 1980s. It can bev viewed only on Sunday afternoons in a guided tour (www.badia-a-passignano.com).

Panzano in Chianti
The main attraction in the sleepy town of Panzano is the market on Sundays and the wine festival in September. The Romanesque church Pieve di San Leolino is worth a look. It holds a 13th-century triptych by the Master of Panzano.

*Castellina in Chianti
Around Castellina the landscape gets mountainous and forested. The first view of the town is disappointing. Nevertheless, in the main street of the medieval town centre, Via Ferruccio, there are several proud palazzi and many small gourmet and wine shops. The lookout platform of the small **castle** provides a wonderful view of the Chianti landscape. The **archaeological museum** in the castle displays finds from the Etruscan necropoli of Chianti. There is a confined feeling by contrast in **Via delle Volte** on the east side of the town wall, which has been completely covered by other buildings. But almost every visitor strolls through the old street, as it is filled with chic galleries and shops with original souvenirs. The burial mound from the 7th century BC at the northern exit from the town, formerly the border between Florence and Siena, bears witness to the fact that it was already settled in the Etruscan period.
Archaeological museum: Apr 1 – Oct 31 Thu – Tue 10am – 6.30pm, Nov 1 – Mar 31 only Sun 11am – 6pm; admission: €5

SECOND STAGE: FROM CASTELLINA TO SIENA

*Radda in Chianti
In the sunny valleys of the Monti del Chianti the best **DOCG wines** of the region ripen. Before the year 1000 Radda belonged to the Counts Guidi, in 1203 it passed to the Florentine republic, and from 1415 it was the capital of the Chianti Liga. The medieval town sits on the crown of a hill. Park along the old city wall, which is also an observation platform (parking limited to one hour). On Via Roma in the centre stands the Palazzo del Podestà (15th century), which today houses the tourist information office. The palace clock has marked the hours since the Middle Ages. The **Museum of Sacred Art** in the monastery S. Maria in Prato exhibits a Madonna with child by Bernardo Daddi and a terracotta statue of St Antonius in Padua.
Museum: Thu – Mon 10am – 1pm, Fri – Sun also 4pm – 7pm

The charm of Chianti vinyards

Volpaia, one of the prettiest villages in southern Chianti, 5km/3mi north of Radda, has less than 50 residents. The castle was already mentioned in 1172. Its owner, Giovanella Stianti-Mascheroni, is the daughter of a publisher and produces select top-quality wines like Coltassala, which is produced almost exclusively from Sangiovese-Grosso grapes. Every year in September the castle is transformed into an art gallery with exhibitions on the subject of wine and art.

*Volpaia

The neighbouring town (13km/8mi from Volpaia) in the valley is famous for its excellent vineyards, most of which also sell directly (vendita diretta). Gaiole itself has no special charms. The Romanesque parish church Santa Maria e Spaltenna west of the town was built in the first half of the 12th century. The former monastery attached to it is now a luxury hotel.

Gaiole in Chianti

About 5km/3mi to the north (signposted) is the Abbey of Coltibuono, which was consecrated in 1049. It was taken over in 1402 by Benedictine monks from Vallombrosa, who renovated the cloister and refectory. Today it is possible to visit the Romanesque church and eat afterwards with a beautiful view of the Arno valley.

*Badia a Coltibuono

Tours: Apr – Oct daily every hour 2pm – 5pm, May – Oct also Tue, Wed, Fri 11am; admission: €5; www.coltibuono.com

Chianti Sculpture Park

South of Gaiole the small detour to the Chianti Sculpture Park near **Pievasciata** is worthwhile; it is a village where lots of contemporary art can be seen. What makes the park attractive is the symbiosis between landscape and modern sculptures by contemporary artists. Worth seeing are the labyrinth and the amphitheatre made of Carrara marble and black granite from Zimbabwe, where the audience includes Hitchcock, Fellini or Charlie Chaplin. There is a good cultural programme in the summer with **operas** and **jazz concerts**.

Hours: Apr 1 – Oct 31 daily 10am until sunset; admission €7.50; www.chiantisculpturepark.it

Castello di Trebbio

On the eastern route of the Chiantigiana (484) is called the **Strada dei Castelli dei Chianti**, (Chianti castle route) Meleto appears about 4km/2.5mi south of Gaiole. Round towers (11th cent.) crown the **castle**, which the Firidolfi family developed in the 13th century into the strongest fortification of the Chianti Liga. It defied all sieges until 1498.

Strada dei Castelli del Chianti: www.castelli-del-chianti.com
Castle: tour/wine tasting: €10; www.castellomeleto.it

*Castello di Brolio

8km/5mi south-east,the imposing Castello di Brolio looms on a mountain ridge 530m/1,739ft high. Its history is connected closely with the Ricasoli family, which ruled the region from the 13th century. This stronghold not far from the border between Florence and Siena was again and again the site of fierce battles. After repeated destruction it was thoroughly renovated in the 16th century. Bettino Ricasoli (1809–1890), who developed the classical concept of the full-bodied Chianti in 1841 through his blending of grapes, had the castle converted around 1860 in neo-Gothic style. The **Ricasoli art collection** with works from the 14th–19th century is worth seeing as are the wine cellar and gardens.

❶ Ricasoli art collection: Mar – Nov Tue – Sun 10.30am – 12.30pm, 2.30pm – 5.30pm; evening tours Tue, Sat 6pm
Gardens: Tue – Sun 10.30am – 12.30pm, 2.30pm – 5.30pm; admission: gardens €5, museum with gardens €8
Castle and wine cellar: Mar – Nov daily 3pm, Mon, Fri also at 5pm, Mon, Wed, Fri and Sun also 10.30am
Enoteca: Apr – Oct Mon – Fri 9am – 7.30pm, Sat, Sun 11am – 7pm
Castle, cantine and vineyards: Tue, Thu 10.30am; www.ricasoli.it

Fonterutoli, Quercegrossa

Between the wine village of Fonterutoli, first mentioned in 998 and with a pretty piazzetta, and Quercegrossa the charms of the landscape along the Chiantigiana become more concentrated again: past the forested hills, vineyards and olive groves, dark rows of cypress trees, rural farms and estates. Finally the rust-red houses of ▶Siena slowly appear.

Chiusi

L 14

Province: Siena (SI)
Altitude: 375m/1,230ft above sea level
Population: 8,900

This is the right place for those who are interested in the art and culture of the Etruscans: in Chiusi, a pretty town on a high plateau of tuff stone almost 20km/12mi south-east of ▶Montepulciano, there is an excellent Etruscan museum.

In the 6th century BC the settlement – then called Chamars – became an important Etruscan city and a member of the twelve-city federation. Chiusi flourished under King Porsenna, who defied Rome in 520 BC, after the rising republic on the Tiber chased Porsenna's ally Tarquinius Superbus out of the city. The legendary labyrinthine grave of Porsenna, which was mentioned by Pliny, was discovered in 1840 under a 15m/50ft-high tumulus. Under the name of Clusium the city joined the expanding Roman empire in 296 BC. In the Middle Ages Orvieto, Siena and Florence alternated as rulers before Chiusi was added to the Grand Duchy of Tuscany in 1556.

WHAT TO SEE IN CHIUSI

The centre of the small town is the cathedral square. The Roman forum once occupied this site. The history of the cathedral goes back to the 6th century; the bell tower was built in the 12th century. In its present form the cathedral dates from the 13th century and bears the marks from less-than-successful restorations between 1887 and 1895, when the imitation mosaics inside were also made. The 18 ancient columns inside the church presumably come from Roman buildings in the area.

* Cathedral square, Duomo San Secondiano

The Museo della Cattedrale has 22 precious choir books decorated with miniatures (15th cent.) from the Abbey Monte Oliveto Maggiore. From the museum go into the bishop's garden and the **Labirinto di Porsenna**, an tunnel or canal system from Etruscan times with a cistern (1st cent. BC), which was used as a water supply and escape route until the 1st cent. AD.

Museo della Cattedrale

Tickets for the early Christian **catacombs** Santa Mustiola and Santa Caterina d'Alessandria can also be bought at the ticket office. Santa Mustiola, which was named after the patron saint of Chiusi who was buried here in AD 274 after being martyred, is about 1km/0.5mi from the Centro Storico towards Lago di Chiusi. The catacombs of St. Catherine of Alexandria are located 2km/1.2mi away in Chiusi Scalo.

❶ **Museo della Cattedrale:** Sun all year 9.45am – 12.45pm, 4pm – 6.30pm; June 1 – Oct 15, Dec 24 – June 6 daily 9.45am – 12.45pm, 4pm – 6.30pm, Oct 16 – Dec 23, Apr 1 – May 31 daily mornings, Jan 7 – Mar 31 Tue, Thu, Sat mornings; admission: €2

Labirinto di Porsenna: Tours during opening hours Museo della Cattedrale: 10.10am, 10.50am, 11.30am, 12.10pm, 4.10pm, 4.50pm, 5.30pm and 6.10pm; admission: €3

Catacombs: Tours during opening hours Museo della Cattedrale: 11am and 4.30pm (winter 5.30pm); admission: €5

Museo Civio della Città Sotteranea

The museum is dedicated to three locations in the **underground city**. Access and tickets (Via Il Cimina 2) are to the right of Palazzo delle Logge (Piazza XX Settembre), the first station (»Il Labirinto«):

In the former typographical workshop Gentilini the history of the excavations, geology and the functioning of the Etruscan hydraulic system are explained. Station 2 (»Attività produttive«) in the storerooms and basements of Palazzo Bonci Casuccini is concerned with the relationship between humans and nature in the valley of the ancient Clanis River, which gave Chiusi its name. Station 3 (»Epigrafia«) lies under the palazzi on der Via Petrarca and Via Serafino Petrozzi. 300 Etruscan urns are on display here.

Tours: Maý – Oct Tue – Sun 10.15am, 11.30am, 12.45pm, 3.15pm, 4.30pm, 5.45pm; Nov – Mar Thu – Sun 10.10am, 11.10am, 12.10pm, Sat, Sun also at 3.10pm, 4.10pm, 5.10pm; admission: €3.

*Museo Nazionale Etrusco

The long-established Archaeological National Museum (Via Porsenna) with a neo-classicist temple façade from 1870 shows Etruscan, Greek and Roman finds. On display are burial urns – including an urn from the 2nd century BC, whose coloured relief depicts the battle of the sons of Oedipus, Eteocles and Polynices – sarcophagi, frescoes removed from graves and photographs of wall paintings in closed graves as well as masks of bronze or clay. The most interesting items include so-called canopic urns of the Villanova culture, terracotta urns in the form of a portrait of the deceased, and Cippi, gravestones decorated with reliefs.

❶ daily 9am–8pm admission €4

*Etruscan graves

Around Chiusi **Tomba della Pellegrina** and **Tomba del Leone** still have wall paintings, which are protected by limiting the number of visitors. The cross-shaped Tomba della Pellegrina (»Grave of the (woman) Pilgrim«; 3rd cent. BC) is a corridor grave. The **Tomba della Scimmia**, the »monkey grave« from the 5th century, in Poggio

Chiusi

INFORMATION
Pro Loco Chiusi
Via Porsenna
Tel. 05 78 22 76 67
www.prolocochiusi.it

EVENTS
Palio delle Torri and medieval festival (last week in June) right after that a festival in honour of the patron saint San Mustiola on July 2, when the urn is opened.

WHERE TO EAT
La Pace €€€
Via del Teatro 5
Celle sul Rigo (between Radicofani and San Casciano dei Bagni)
Tel. 05 78 537 16
www.lapace-albergo.it
Closed Tue. A picture-book rural restaurant: outwardly unassuming – hidden in a street of the tiny hill-top village – and furnished in a rather spartan manner, but with wonderful local cuisine. There is no menu, but you can confidently try the daily menu in all its variations. There are few foreign guests here, instead local families and residents.

La Solita Zuppa €
Via Porsena 21
Tel. 057 82 10 06
www.lasolitazuppa.it
Closed Tue. Soups are the speciality of the house. The restaurant is housed in 18th-century vaults. Good reasonable menus for lunch and dinner.

WHERE TO STAY
La Fattoria €€
Via Lago di Chiusi
Tel. 05 78 214 07
www.lafattoria.it
Renovated farm with 8 comfortable rooms near Lago di Chiusi. Camping is also possible. Mountain bike rental and horses for riding available.

Sette Querce €€€
Viale Manciati 2
San Casciano dei Bagni
Tel. 05 78 581 74
www.settequerce.it
Anyone who loves the brilliant fabrics of Tricia Guild is just right in this design hotel. The suites may be small, but they are decorated with great taste. With balcony or terrace.

Frateria di Padre Eligio €€€€
Convento di San Francesco
Via San Francesco 2
Cetona
Tel. 05 78 23 82 61
www.lafrateria.it
A unique mixture of luxury hotel and monastery hospice with 7 rooms. It was started many years ago by Padre Eligio in the oldest Franciscan monastery of Tuscany (1212) as »Project Mondo x«, where the cleric enabled young drug addicts to be resocialized. A famous restaurant is attached.

Renzo (toward Lago di Chiusi) has an almost completely painted burial chamber with scenes of a burial, musicians, athletic competitions and the drawing of a monkey. To the east of town **Tomba del Colle** (»Hill Grave«; early 5th cent. BC) is not accessible. The wall paintings of a dinner and a chariot race with an elegant pair of horses, have been photographed for documentation by the Archaeological National Museum.

❶ Visits to the burial sites on appt. only in the Archaeolog. National Museum (tel. 0 57 82 01 77): Mar– Oct Tue, Thu, Sat 11am and 4pm, Nov – Mar Tue, Thu, Sat 11am and 2.30pm; admission: €2

* FROM CHIUSI TO RADICOFANI

Sarteano   10km/6mi west of Chiusi lies the town of Sarteano. The hot springs of the so-called Bagno Santo were already known in antiquity. Today they feed water at a temperature of 24°C/75°F into three pools in the »Parco delle Piscine«. Finds from the Etruscan necropolis are on display in the **Archaeological Museum**. The **Tomba della Quadriga Infernale**, which was discovered in 2003 in the Pianacce Necropolis, is one of the most important Etruscan finds of the 20th century. The corridor-style travertine tomb with a 20m/66ft-long corridor has outstanding iconographic pictures. The quadriga is pulled by two lions and two griffons and steered by a demon. One wall shows two men at a banquet table, another one is decorated by a three-headed snake. The fortress-like castle with a beautiful park goes back to 1038. The neo-classical church of San Martino has an annunciation of Mary (1552), a masterpiece by the Sienese painter Domenico Beccafumi.

Archaeological Museum: Via Roma 24; Apr 1 – Nov 2, Dec 23 – June 6 Tue – Sun, Nov 3 – Dec 22 and Jan 7 – Mar 31 only Sat, Sun 10.30am – 12.30pm, 4pm – 7pm; admission: €4; www.ctnet.it/museo/sarteano
Tomba della Quadriga Infernale: Tours Sat 11am and 6pm, winter only 11am; admission: €5; www.archeologiaviva.tv

Cetona   6km/3.5mi south on winding roads lead to Cetona (population 3,000). The rocca, the town's highest point, is privately owned today and not open to the public. From the expansive Piazza Garibaldi a steep ascent on Via Roma leads up to the historic centre. 200m/220yd along on the left stands the imposing Palazzo Minutelli from the 17th century, which now houses the city hall and the interesting **Museum of Monte Cetona**. The various phases of human settlement from its beginnings to the end of the Bronze Age are vividly documented. Almost all finds come from the Belvedere area nearby, where the main settlements were located. The **Archaeological Natural Park** (Parco Archeologico Naturalistico di Belverde) protects the travertine caves.

❶ **Museum of Monte Cetona** Sun 9.30am – 12.30pm, Tue – Sat June – Sep 9am – 1pm, 5pm – 7pm, Oct – May 9.30am – 12.30pm; admission: €3
Archaeological Natural Park: July 1 – Sep 30 Tue – Sun 10am – 7pm, Apr – June, Oct Sun 10am – 1pm, 3pm – 5pm; admission: €6; www.ctnet.it/museo/cetona

San Casciano 14 km to the southeast has been known for its hot springs since antiquity – there are supposed to be more than 40 springs here. **Centro Termale Fonteverde** offer wellness. The most important healing spring is Bagno della Ficoncella; Grand Duke Ferdinand I honoured its miraculous waters by building it a portico at the entrance. The former spa house (17th cent.) was converted into the **Fonteverde Natural Spa Resort €€€€** (www.fonteverdespa.com), considered to be one of the world's best spa resorts.

About 17km/11mi south-west of Sarteano lies Radicofani. Long before reaching the unspectacular town, the tower of its rocca is visible – a good point of orientation in the stark but fascinatingly beautiful hilly landscape of southern Tuscany. Within the walls of the castle, which was destroyed in the 18th cent., there is now an archaeological museum, **Museo del Cassero**. The Romanesque village church S. Pietro has terracotta figures by Andrea della Robbia. Below Radicofani on the old Roman road Via Cassia stands Palazzo La Villa, built in the 16th century as a customs and postal station, later a hotel where many famous people stayed including Charles Dickens.

*Radicofani

Museo del Cassero: Nov 1 – Mar 31 Sat, Sun 10am – 5pm, Apr 1 – June 30, Sep 1 – Oct 31. daily 10am – 7pm, July 1 – Aug 31. daily 10am – 12am; admission: €3

MARCO POLO TIP

Fattoria La Palazzina **Insider Tip**

The beautiful and absolutely quiet panoramic location, the lovingly decorated old-fashioned rooms and the fabulous pool location are only three of the many reasons to visit this 18th cent. villa. The breakfast buffet with homemade tarts, cakes and salads leaves every hotel breakfast in the dust. There are also 5 apartments, 3 suites and a holiday cottage (Radicofani, Le Vigne, ca. 4km/2.5mi from Radicofani toward Celle sul Rigo, www.fattorialapalazzina.com).

★ Colle di Val d'Elsa

✦ I 9

Province: Siena (SI)
Altitude: 140–250m/459–820ft above sea level
Population: 21,500

This prosperous town is known above all as the centre of the Italian glass industry, which has mainly settled in the modern lower town Colle Basso and accounts for 95% of Italy's and 15% of the world's total glass production. The historic old part of the city, Colle Alto, is surprisingly pretty.

Colle di Val d'Elsa

INFORMATION
Pro Loco Colle di Val d' Elsa
Via Francesco Campana 43
Tel. 05 77 92 27 91
www.comune.colle-di-val-d-elsa.si.it

EVENTS
Late September glass festival »Silicio«
(www.festivalsilicio.it) with spectacular
crystal installations by modern artists. In
2010 the largest crystal goblet in the
world was on display and was entered
into the Guinness Book of Records.

WHERE TO STAY
Podere il Caggiolino €
Loc. Picchena
Castel San Gimignano
Tel. 05 77 95 31 90
www.caggiolino.net
This house in quiet surroundings in the
middle of the country is a very good alternative to the hotels in Colle di Val
d'Elsa or San Gimignano. There are 5
comfortable rooms and the day starts
with a generous breakfast buffet.

WHERE TO EAT
Arnolfo €€€€
Via XX Settembre 52
Colle di Val d' Elsa
Tel. 05 77 92 05 49
www.arnolfo.com
Closed Tue and Wed, as well as all Jan.,
Feb. and early Aug.
Gaetano und Giovanni Trovato run a
top-class restaurant (2 Michelin stars) in
an old palazzo in the old city. Accom-
modations available in the palazzo.

Da Simone €€€
Piazza Bartolomeo Scala 11
Colle di Val d' Elsa
Tel. 05 77 92 67 01
www.ristorantedasimone.it
Closed Mon. as well as 2 weeks in Jan.
and Nov.
Cinzia and Simone offer creative cooking and a good selection of wines. In the
summer the tables are set on the small
veranda in front of the door.

---

*Collo Alto Colle Alto consists of two lively centres: **Borgo**, which begins right
behind the massive round towers of the Renaissance fortress Porta
Nuova, and **Castello**, which is connected to Borgo by a bridge. A lift
runs up to Castello from Colle Basso (Via Garibaldi). In Borgo several Renaissance palaces catch the eye – for example Palazzo Renieri
(Palazzo Comunale) or the elegant Palazzo Campana. With its brick
houses and narrow, vaulted streets, the Castello quarter still has a
medieval feel, with shops for crystal objects in the narrow Via del
Castello. Piazza del Duomo with the cathedral from 1619 is the centre of Castello. Giuliano da Maiano created the cathedral pulpit in the
late 15th century. The archaeological museum **Museo R. Bianchi
Bandinelli** in Palazzo Pretorio shows finds from the Monteriggioni
necropolis. The **Museo Civico e Diocesano** in the Palazzo dei Priori shows sacred art and exhibits on the town's history.
What was once the glass and crystal factory Boschi near the church

Colle di Val d' Elsa, a charming little town

of San Agostino now houses the **Museo del Cristallo**, dedicated to preindustrial glass production (15th – 17th cent.) and the development of the glass industry in Colle from 1820 to 1963. Unique pieces by prominent glass designers (Ettore Sottsass Jr., Angelo Mangiarotti) and the one-of-a-kind »crystal forest« are high points of the exhibit.

Museo R. Bianchi Bandinelli: Piazza Duomo 42; May 1 – Sep 30 Tue – Sun 10.30 am – 12.30pm, 4.30pm – 7.30pm, Oct 1 – Apr 30 Tue – Fri 3.30pm – 5.30pm, Sat, Sun 10am – 12pm, 3.30pm – 6.30pm; admission: €3

Museo Civico e Diocesano: Via del Castello 31; May 1 – Oct 31 Tue – Sun 11am – 12.30pm, 4pm – 7.30pm, Nov 1 – Apr 30 Tue – Sun 10am – 12pm, 3.30pm –6.30pm; admission: €3

Museo del Cristallo: Via dei Fossi 8a, Easter until Oct 31 Tue – Sun 10am –12pm, 4pm – 7.30pm; Nov 1 until Easter Tue – Fri 3pm – 7pm, Sat, Sun 10am – 12pm, 3pm – 7pm; admission: €3; www.cristallo.org

** Cortona

— ✶ K 14

Province: Arezzo (AR)
Altitude: 500–651m/1,640–2,136ft above sea level
Population: 23,100

The home town of the famous Renaissance painter Luca Signorelli is certainly one of the prettiest towns in Tuscany – not least because of its location with fine views on the steep slope of Monte San Egidio on the edge of Val di Chiana.

Cortona

INFORMATION
Uffizio Informazioni
Turistiche Cortona
Piazza Signorelli 9
(Palazzo Casali)
Tel. 05 75 63 72 23
www.comunedicortona/turismo

EVENTS
Tuscan Sun Festival with world famous
stars like Martha Argerich, Sharon Stone
or Jeremy Irons (July/August; www.tus-
can-sunfestival.com).
The Giostra del' Archidado (hist. cross-
bow competition; last week in May) was
first held in 1397.
The Sagra della Bistecca festival (14/15
August) celebrates the famous Chianina
cattle; vegetarians prefer the Sagra del
Fungo Porcino (porcino mushrooms) on
20/21 August.

WHERE TO EAT
❶ *Osteria del*
Teatro €€
Via Maffei 2
Tel. 05 75 63 05 56
www.osteria-del-teatro.it
Closed Wed and all of Nov..
Comfortable osteria, very popular
among Tuscans as well. Try the cheese
with fresh truffles or gnocchi with egg-
plants and mozzarella made from buffalo milk.

❷ *Trattoria La Grotta* €
Piazza Baldelli 3
Tel. 05 75 63 02 71
www.trattorialagrotta.it
Closed Tuesdays.
In the summer the most beautiful place
in this trattoria is outside on the tiny Pi-
azza Baldelli. The homemade past dishes

are very tasty – followed by a semifreddo all'amaretto.

❸ *La Bucaccia* €
Via Ghibellina 17
Tel. 05 75 60 60 39
www.labucaccia.it
Closed for 2 weeks in late Jan.
Agostina recommends her own chestnut
ravioli »Sant' Egidio« and especially the
traditional Cortona dishes. Guests dine
in the vaulted 12th cent. Palazzo Cattani
(with a fireplace).

WHERE TO STAY
❶ *Relais eRelais & Chateau*
Il Falconiere €€€€
Loc. San Martino 370
(by Cortona)
Tel. 05 75 61 26 79
www.ilfalconiere.it
Anyone with a sense for nostalgia will
love this tastefully decorated old country
house with 22 rooms. The two rooms in
the former chapel San Girolamo are particularly nice. There is a spa and the
gourmet restaurant »Il Falconiere«.

❷ *San Michele*
€€ – €€€€
Via Guelfa 15
Tel. 05 75 60 43 48
www.hotelsanmichele.net
Dignified hotel within the walls of Palaz-
zo Baldelli. In the centre of Cortona.

❸ *Athens* €
Via Antonio 12
Tel. 05 75 63 05 08
Reasonably priced hotel in a good loca-
tion in the old city. The 22 rooms are
simple, but spacious.

The difference in elevation between the entrance to the town at Sant' Agostino or on Piazza Garibaldi and the Medici fortress at the highest point of the town is no less than 150m/492ft. An escalator (scala mobile) runs to Piazza Garibaldi from the parking lot Pacheggio Spirito Santo.

Cortona probably developed out of an Umbrian settlement. In the 8th century BC the Etruscans conquered the hill and added »Curtuns« to their twelve-city federation. In the late 4th century BC the city made a treaty with Rome; in 130 BC it received Roman citizenship and later became a Roman colony. Cortona flourished as an independent community in the 12th and 13th centuries. In 1325 it became a bishop's seat. In 1409 King Ladilaus of Naples conquered the city and sold it to Florence in 1411. Cortona is situated on the old pilgrimage route Via Teutonica. | History

WHAT TO SEE IN CORTONA

Approaching Cortona on the SS 71 from the valley, the Renaissance church Madonna del Calccinaio can be seen on the slope below the town. The church was built because a miracle-working Madonna image was found here. Near the church are a few **Etruscan graves** as well as Hellenistic burial sites. The best known is the **Tanella di Pitagora** (2nd cent. BC), which has erroneously been associated with Pythagoras and which was damaged by French soldiers in 1808. | Outside the town

A well-preserved wall encloses the old town, which is built on a slope. A possible point to start touring Cortona is the Porta Sant'Agostino (large parking lot). The way up on Via Guelfa to the centre, Piazza della Repubblica, is steep. The Palazzo Comunale, which dominates the west side of the piazza, was recorded in 1241, enlarged in the 16th century and restored not very skilfully in 1896. The clock tower and the outdoor stair date from the 16th century. The painting on the ceiling beams in the large council chamber also dates from this period. The east side of the square is taken up by the Palazzo del Popolo (14th–16th centuries). | *Piazza della Repubblica

The death doors (Porte del Morto), narrow, high doors right next to the main entrances of a medieval house, are a regional curiosity. They were used only to transport the dead out of the house. A fine example of a death door can be seen in Palazzo Cinaglia in Via Roma, not far from the Palazzo Comunale. | Porte del Morto

The narrow street next to the steps of the Palazzo Comunale leads to Piazza Signorelli, which is bordered by Palazzo Fierli, the Teatro Si- | Palazzo Casali

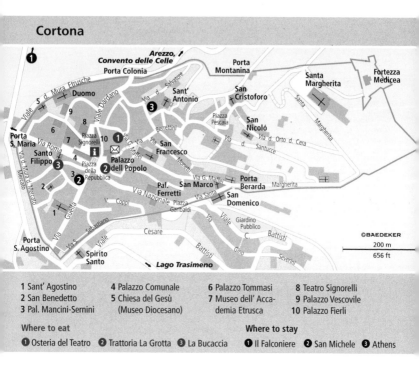

Cortona

1 Sant' Agostino
2 San Benedetto
3 Pal. Mancini-Sernini
4 Palazzo Comunale
5 Chiesa del Gesù
(Museo Diocesano)
6 Palazzo Tommasi
7 Museo dell' Accademia Etrusca
8 Teatro Signorelli
9 Palazzo Vescovile
10 Palazzo Fierli

Where to eat
❶ Osteria del Teatro ❷ Trattoria La Grotta ❸ La Bucaccia

Where to stay
❶ Il Falconiere ❷ San Michele ❸ Athens

gnorelli and Palazzo Casali. The last-named was built in the 13th century by the Casali family, which lived there until 1409. The façade (reconstructed in 1608) and the walls of the inner courtyard are decorated with **coats of arms** of the Florentine town governors and the stone coats of arms with the Golden Fleece of Francesco dei Medici, who was governor in 1570. At the beginning of the 16th century the painter Luca Signorelli had his workshop in the palace. Since the mid-18th century the Etruscan academy has had its seat here.

*Museo dell' Accademia Etrusca
The Etruscan museum in Palazzo Casali is worth a visit, as some of its pieces are very rare. The highlights include the large Etruscan **wheel lamp** (5th cent. BC) with 16 decorated wick openings and the head of Medusa on the bottom, surrounded by an ocean wreath that dolphins jump over and 16 winged harpies. The artistic skill of the Etruscans can be admired in the **bronze statuettes**, including Zeus hurling a thunderbolt and a winged goddess (both 7th–6th cent. BC). The burial urns for ashes made of alabaster and terracotta (6th–5th century BC) date from the Hellenistic period. Egyptian and Roman finds as well as works by Gino Severini complete the collection.

Two routes lead to the most important places in the **Archaeological Park**. The spectacular **Circuito Extraurbano** outside of town to the Etruscan graves like the Tomba di Mezzavia (3rd/2nd cent. BC) and the two ***Tumuli graves of Sodo** (6th cent. BC) on Rio Loreto (parking/tickets at Tumulus 1). Finds are exhibited there in the Centro Restauri. Continue on to Tannela Angori, **Tannela di Pitagora**, which Vasari visited in 1566, the Tumulus of Camucia (200m/660ft circumference), the mosaics of ancient Roman villas in Ossaia (about 50 BC to AD 80) as well as the palaeontological museum »Don Sante Felici« in Farneta, which exhibits fossils from the Pleistocene era. A walking path with seven stops connects the sights in Farneta (1 hr. 40 min.).

❶ MAEC: Piazza Signorelli 9; Apr – Oct daily 10am – 7pm, Nov – Mar Tue – Sun 10am – 5pm, open evenings in June; admission: €8; www.cortonamaec.org

Tumuli graves: Tumulus 1: Apr – Oct Tue, Fri and Sun 9.30am – 12.30pm; admission: €2; Tumulus 2: Tue – Sun 9.30am – 12.30pm; free admission

The Renaissance cathedral was built over a Romanesque church and in its present form it is mainly the work of Giuliano da Sangallo (1445–1516). The Baroque high altar (1664) is by the Cortonese Francesco Mazzuoli. Some of the paintings in the choir are attributed to pupils of Luca Signorelli.   **Duomo Santa Maria**

The church was built between 1498 and 1505 directly opposite the cathedral. A second storey was added in 1543, when it was changed to plans by Giorgio Vasari. The upper church nave with its side rooms is used as the ****Museo Diocesano** today. The most important work is the colourful *Annunciation* **by Fra Angelico**. The painting, which was executed in 1433/1434 for San Domenico, has naturalistic elements and foreshadows the Renaissance in its feeling for form. Fra Angelico also created the triptych with scenes from the life of St Dominic on the predella. In the *Visitation* with views of Lake Trasimeno and the town of Castiglione del Lago the artist was obviously inspired by the surroundings of Cortona as Lago Trasimeno lies 15km/9mi away in Umbria. Pietro Lorenzetti's Madonna with Child and Four Angels and a Madonna attributed to the school of Duccio di Buoninsegna, as well as Luca Signorelli's and Sassetta's painted altar panels are further highlights of the museum. The so-called Vagnucci reliquary (1457) of gilded bronze, silver and gems is also worthy of note. Giorgio Vasari painted frescoes on the vaulted ceiling in the lower church nave. The twelve biblical figures there are by Christoforo Gerardi (16th century), also called Doceno.   **Chiesa del Gesù**

❶ Apr 1 – Sep 30 daily 10am – 7pm, Oct 1 – 31 Tue – Sun 10am – 7pm, Nov 1 – Mar 31 Tue – Sun 10am – 5pm; admission: €5

San Francesco The building of the church of San Francesco, east above Piazza della Repubblica, started in 1245. That makes it the second-oldest Franciscan church after Assisi. The exterior of the church is without decoration; the interior was remodelled in early Baroque style in 1526. The most important treasure of San Francesco was brought back from Constantinople by Brother Elijah in the 13th century: a relic of the cross, which was framed in the 16th century with a Byzantine ivory tablet. The founder of the church, Fra Elia da Cortona, is buried in the choir. Luca Signorelli is also supposed to have been buried here in 1523.

*Via Naziona-le, Piazza Garibaldi, San Domenico Via Nazionale with many shops, bars and cafés begins at Piazza della Repubblica. Piazza Garibaldi, a popular meeting point for young people, is at the end of the main street. The church of San Domenico is located outside the town walls to the south. It was once part of a Dominican monastery, where the painter **Fra Angelico** (around 1400–1455) lived for a while. It was built in the early 15th century in the plain style of the mendicant orders; it has a beautiful triptych by

Piazza della Repubblica in Cortona

Lorenzo Gherini (15th century), which shows the *Coronation of the Virgin*. On the wall of the presbytery there is an *Assumption of the Virgin* by Bartolomeo della Gatta (15th century); the lunette is decorated by a *Madonna with Saints* by Fra Angelico. A good place to take a break after this sightseeing programme is the adjoining Giardino Pubblico.

The small, simple 15th-century church between Piazza Repubblica and the Medici fortress is worth a look – because of the processional standard that was painted on both sides by Luca Signorelli and now serves as an altar painting.

San Nicolò

Via Santa Margherita leads east up the hill to the pilgrimage church of Santa Margherita, a Byzantine-style building that was dedicated in 1897. Even though St Margaret of Cortona (1247-1297), whose mortal remains rest here in a tomb (1362) inside a silver reliquary (1646), had an unhappy marriage, the church is very popular for weddings today. There is a beautiful view from the front of the church over the ▶Val di Chiana.

Santuario di Santa Margherita

The interior of the fortress, which was built in 1556 and which is also called Fortezza del Girifalco, is used for art exhibits and the medieval event »Medioevo in Fortezza«.
❶ Apr 1 – June 30 10am – 6pm, Jul 1 – Oct 10 11am – 1.30pm, 2.30pm – 7pm; admission: €3

Fortezza Medicea

The Franciscan convent just about 4km/2.5mi north-east on the flank of Monte Sant'Egidio is a **collection of monk's cells**, of which the first were established 1211–1221 by Francis of Assisi. The small church from 1573 and a few cells, including that of St Francis, are open to the public. Group accommodations available (www.lecelle. it.).

*Convento delle Celle

** Elba / Isola d'Elba

✷ M/N 3 – 5

Province: Livorno
Area: 223.5 sq km/86 sq mi
Population: 31,600

Elba is the largest and best-known island in the Tuscan archipelago. With numerous yacht harbours, wonderful beaches for swimming, a varied interior and a good infrastructure for tourism, it is not surprising that the island is a popular Italian holiday venue.

Elba

FERRY CONNECTIONS
Toremar
www.toremar.it

Mobylines
www.mobylines.it

Piombino Habrour
Tel. 05 65 22 92 10
www.porto-piombino.li.it

AIR CONNECTIONS
There are no direct flights to Elba from the UK, but the island can be reached by air via Pisa, Florence or Milan.

Aeroporto Marina di Campo
Marina di Campo
Tel. 05 65 97 60 11
www.elbaisland-airport.it

INFORMATION
Agenzia per il Turismo dell' Archipelago Toscano
Portoferraio, Via Carducci 150
Tel. 05 65 91 46 71
www.isoleditoscana.it

WHERE TO EAT
Osteria dei Quattro Gatti €€ – €€€
Porto Azzurro
Piazza Mercato 4
Tel. 05 65 952 40
Only evenings. Osteria ithe historic part of Porto Azzurro. Serves good fish

Lo Zodiaco €
Procchio (Marciana)
Via del Mare 21
Tel. 05 65 90 76 30
Closed Mon and from Oct. 15 to Easter. Popular restaurant close to the sea. What Osio Mazzei serves includes spa-

ghetti frutti di mare and gamberoni in vodka curry sauce

Emanuele all' Enfola €€
Località Capo Enfola
(6km/4mi west of Portoferraio)
Tel. 05 65 93 90 03
Closed Mon. For seafood-lovers!
Food is served outdoors under an old fig tree with a view of the sea.

WHERE TO STAY
Hermitage €€€€
Portoferraio – Biodola, Via Biodola
Tel. 05 65 97 40, www.hotelhermitage.it
Luxury hotel (130 rooms) in the most exclusive bay of the island. The holiday bungalows nestle harmoniously in the landscape of this large complex between beach and cliffs right on the sea. Activities: wellness, golf, sailing, diving, surfing school and much more.

Belmare €€€
Porto Azzurro
Banchina IV Novembre 21
Tel. 05 65 950 12
www.elba-hotelmare.it
A little holiday hotel on the beach promenade of Porto Azzuro. Some of the rooms have a wonderful view of the sea. Sailing, mountain-bike, trekking and kayak tours.

Country Hotel & Residence Da Pilade €€€
Capoliveri, Loc. Mola
Tel. 05 65 96 86 35
www.hoteldapilade.it
Open all year, family-run apartment hotel with 24 rooms and apartments. Generous breakfast buffet.

Most holiday-makers use the ferry between Piombino and Portofer- **Arrival**
raio to get to Elba. In the high season reservations are absolutely recommended. The car ferries of Toremar and Moby Lines both run
between 5.30am and 10.30pm during the high season; the crossing
takes about an hour. There are also connections from Piombino to
Cavo (40 minutes) and Rio Marina (45 minutes) on Elba. From Piombino hydrofoils (aliscafo) cross to Portoferraio (30 minutes) and
Cavo (15 minutes). Take a ferry fom Piombino or Rio Marina to get
to Pianosa, the smaller neighboring island.

The island, which is rich in mineral resources, was already occupied **History**
in the Bronze Age. The Etruscans established their dominance in Italy by exploiting the ore deposits, and the Romans also worked the
mines for centuries after founding several colonies on Elba around
246 BC. In the Middle Ages Elba was raided by Saracen pirates many
times, and in the 11th century the Republic of Pisa took control. The
Medici (1546–1559) were followed until 1799 by the Spanish Habsburgs and finally France. In May 1814 the island became the home
of the exiled **Napoleon**, who had full sovereignty – he stayed until 26
February 1815. Pig iron was produced on Elba well into the 20th century; the last plant closed only in 1982.

The name Piombino comes from the Italian word »piombo« for lead. **Ferry port**
In the nearby Populonia (▶Livorno) Elban ore was already smelted **Piombino**
in ancient times. *** Museo Archeologico del Territorio di Populo-**
nia, Piazza della Cittadella 8, has more than 3,000 artefacts, including
a silver amphora and a fish mosaic from the 1st cent. BC. Restoring
the fortress has improved that harbour as well. **Museo del Castello**
e della Cittá di Piombino is dedicated to the 800 year history of the
castle and its relationship to the sea and the interior.
Museo Archeologico del Territorio di Populonia: June, Sep Tue – Sun
10am – 1pm, 3pm – 7pm, July/Aug Tue – Sun 10am – 1pm, 4pm – 8pm,
Apr/May Tue – Fri 9am – 1pm, Sat, Sun 10am – 1pm, 3pm – 7pm, otherwise
only on weekends; admission: €6; www.parchivaldicornia.it
Museo del Castello e della Cittá di Piombino: June, Sep Tue – Sun
10am – 1pm, 3pm – 7pm, July/Aug Tue – Sun 10am – 1pm, 4pm – 8pm,
Mar – May, Oct only on weekends; admission: €4

The Tuscan Archipelago includes seven main islands (»Park of the
Seven Stars«): Elba, the islands of Montecristo, Pianosa, ▶ Giglio, Giannutri, Capraia and Gorgona as well as uninhabited islets and rocks
in the sea. All of the islands can be visited. The **Tuscan Island Archi-**
pelago National Park, which was established in 1996, includes more
than 70,000ha/175,000ac, of which two thirds are under water. The
park administration is committed to soft exploration of the island
world and organizes hiking festivals (www.tuscanywalkingfestival.it),

among other things. Lega Ambiente Arcipelago Toscano offers ecological trekking tours and excursions.

Park visitor centres: Casa del Parco »Fortezza Pisana«, Marciana, Casa del
Parco »Franco Franchini«, Rio nell' Elba, (both Apr 21 – Oct 31); »Info Park
Are@«, Portoferraio, hydrofoil landing
Lega Ambiente Arcipelago Toscano: Salita Napoleone, Portoferraio,
http://www.virtualelba.it/elba-utility/legambiente/en/

✷ PORTOFERRAIO AND SURROUNDINGS

Capital of the archipelago
On a rocky spit of land with a natural harbour along the north coast
lies the pretty town of Portoferraio (population 12,300). The ferries
land at Ponte Massimo. The old town on a **rocky spur** jutting into the
sea was once cut off from the island by a water channel which was
only filled up in 1919. As a reminder of the drawbridge between the
old town and the main island the area around the broad Viale Man-
zoni is called »Ponticell« (little bridge). From 1548 Cosimo I de Medici fortified the town, creating a masterpiece of Renaissance military
architecture.

Begin a tour of the town at the old fishing harbour Darsena, today a
yacht harbour. This is a very busy place in the summer. The gate at
the harbour basin, Porta a Mare or Porta Medicea, was built as part
of the Medici fortifications. Cross the long Piazza Cavour to get to
Piazza della Repubblica with the cathedral (begun in 1549).

✷Chiesa della Misericordia, Pinacoteca Foresiana
In the small church Chiesa della Misericordia (Via Garibaldi) a mass
is read for Napoleon every year on 5 May. It has a picture of the Madonna which is attributed to Tino da Camaino (1285–1337). the
church museum displays a bronze copy of Napoleon's death mask
and a plaster cast of his hand from the island of St Helena.

The former Franciscan monastery opposite the church houses the
Pinacoteca Foresiana, which exhibits paintings and furniture of the
Foresi family as well as a **library** with more than 40,000 volumes
from five centuries.

Church museum: daily 9.30am – 12pm, 3pm – 5pm; admission: €1
Pinacoteca Foresiana: Wed, Thu 9am – 12pm; admission: €3
Library: Mon, Wed, Fri 9am – 12pm, Tue, Thu 3pm – 6pm;
free admission

Forte Falcone, Forte Stella
East of Piazza Napoleone, above the lighthouse built in 1788, stands
the star-shaped **Forte Stella**, where Napoleon's guard was quar-
tered. West of the piazza the »falcon fortress« (Forte Falcone) rises
up. In Forte Inglese, which was built around 1700 under Grand
Duke Cosimo III, there is now an artists' meeting point. The bastions, **Fortezze Medicee**, with the gardens (entrance Via Guarazzi),

Dream beach: Cavoli Beach east of Campo nell' Elba

which were built by Grand Duke Cosimo I around 1555, are worth seeing.

Forte Stella: daily 10am – 1pm, 3pm – 6pm; admission: €1.50
Fortezze Medicee: Apr 3 – June 14, Sep 16 – Oct 31 daily 10am – 1pm, 3.30pm – 7pm, June 15 – Sep 15 daily 8am – 8pm; admission: €3

Napoleon has the simple Villa dei Mulini remodelled in 1814 as his town residence. In the bedroom is one of the few pieces of original furniture: **Napoleon's baronial bed**; other furnishings were supplied by Palazzo Pitti. His personal library comprised about 2,000 volumes. The upper floor was the apartment of his sister Pauline Borghese. The shady garden high above the rocky coast has a wonderful view of Forte Stella and the mainland coast.

*Villa dei Mulini

❶ Mon – Sat 9am – 7pm, Sun 9am – 1pm, July 3 – Sep 15 Thu – Sat until 11.30pm, admission €7.

The museum at Darsena harbour shows finds from prehistoric and ancient times, which come in part from sunken wrecks off the coast.

*Museo Archeologico

❶ Museo Civico Archeologico: Apr 3 – June 14, Sep 15 – Oct 31 daily except Thu 10am – 1pm, 3.30pm – 7pm; June 15 – Sep 14 daily 9am – 2.25pm, 6pm – 12am; admission: €3

Teatro dei Vigilanti	In the secularized Chiesa del Carmine the horseshoe-shaped Teatro dei Vigilanti (Piazza Gramsci) was built in 1814 under Napoleon. The inauguration on Jan. 1, 1815 was repeated after Napoleon's defeat at Waterloo in May 1815. **Teatro dei Vigilanti:** Mon – Sat 9am – 1pm; admission: €3
*Villa Romana delle Grotte	In 1960 about 6km/3.5mi west of Portoferraio in Le Grotte the ruins of a **Roman villa** (1st cent. AD) were excavated, which had a heated swimming pool and was surrounded by a water channel through which hot water circulated.
*Villa Demidoff, Villa San Martino	About 6km/3.5mi south-west of Portoferraio on the slopes of Monte San Martino stands the neo-classical manor house of the Russian Duke Anatolio Demidoff. To the left of Demidoff's palace a path leads up to the emperor's summer residence, which is outwardly and inwardly modest compared to the villa. On the second floor eight rooms are open to visitors. Only the **dining room in Egyptian style** is ostentatious. Its decorations glorify Napoleonic victories. 10,000m²/ 100,000sq ft **open air museum Italo Bolano** in the Valle di San Martino is worth the detour; it has 24 works by the Elban artist and the Art Center has rotating exhibits. **Villa Demidoff:** Mon – Sat 9am – 7pm, Sun 9am – 1pm, admission: €7 **Museum Italo Bolano:** Mon – Sat 10am – 1pm, 4pm – 7pm; free admission
Therme San Giovanni	The thermal baths of San Giovanni in Portoferraio Bay offer anti-stress and anti-smog treatments, peelings with sea algae gel, anti-cellulite or weight reduction treatments. They also offer a »Limo«, a healing iron-rich fango mud treatment. This fango relieves symptoms of arthritis, rheumatism, acne or psoriasis. ❶ Apr 20 – Oct 31; www.termelbane.com

✻ TOUR OF THE ISLAND OF ELBA

*Procchio, Marciana Marina	18km/11mi to the west of Portoferraio lies the pretty harbour town of Marciana Marina. The road passes the inviting cove of Procchio with one of the most beautiful beaches for swimming on the island. The so-called Saracen tower, which was built in the time of Pisan rule, rises over the town. In the coastal waters off Patresi there is an underwater park with nine statues, all of which refer to Greek mythology.
*Marciana (Alta)	8km/5mi inland lies Marciana, the centre of Elba's wine production. The charming village has narrow streets and the remains of a Pisan fortress, which was extended by the Appiani family around 1450.

Below the fortress the **Archaeological Museum** (Via del Pretorio 66) displays Etruscan and Roman excavation finds. The exhibit in the National Park house at the fortress is also worthwhile. A paved path passes twelve chapels on its way up (40 minutes to walk) to the oldest pilgrimage church on Elba, Madonna del Monte, with a picture of the Virgin Mary (15th century). In 1995 frescoes were discovered, which have been ascribed to Sodoma.

Archaeological Museum: May 29 – Sep 10 Wed – Mon 10am – 12.30pm, 3.30pm –7pm, Tue 9am – 1pm, 2.30pm – 6.30pm; admission: €2.

The highest point on the island of Elba is the 1,018m/3,340ft-high Monte Capanne, which can also be reached by cable car. An undersea flow of magma created this stone panettone. From the granite peak there is a wonderful panorama of the entire archipelago on clear days. ***Monte Capanne**

❶ Cable car Marciana – Monte Capanne: Apr – Oct daily 10am – 1pm, 2.20pm – 5pm, last trip down at 5.30pm; July – Sep last trip down at 6pm

Continue via Poggio, Sant'Ilario in Campo and San Piero in Campo down to Cavoli, a resort with a beach of fine-grained sand. From Cavoli boats go to the nearby Grotta Azzurra. Two kilometres (1.3mi) further on lies Seccheto, with a beach with coarser sand, but as a result it is much quieter than the cove of Cavoli. Some consider the beach of Fetovaia in a wonderful cove to be the most beautiful because of its white sand. ***Beaches of Cavoli, Seccheto and Fetovaia**

The main attraction of the southern coast is the popular seaside resort **** Marina di Campo** (population 4,200) with the **largest sandy beach on Elba**. Water-sport lovers find sailing, surfing and diving schools; nighthawks enjoy the bars and restaurants of the former fishing village. Medici Tower is a 12th-century Pisan fortification. About 2km/1.3mi outside Marina di Campo towards Lacona in the Località La Foce, the **aquarium of Elba** with its many varieties of fish is worth a visit.

> **!** MARCO⊕POLO TIP
>
> *Natural bathtubs* **Insider Tip**
>
> A path leads down to the sea between Fetovaia and Seccheto. In the course of time natural seawater pools formed there in the granite – today a wonderful place for swimming.

L'Aquario dell'Elba: Mar 15 – May 15 and Sep 16 – Nov 4, 9am – 7.30pm, June 1 – Sep 15 9am – 11pm; admission €7; www.acquarioelba.com

The Gulf of Lacona and Golfo Stella further east also have beautiful beaches. Lacona belongs to the commune of Capoliveri on the southeastern peninsula Calamita. The picturesque village, once a mining town and today one of the most popular holiday addresses on Elba, possesses romantic streets and old houses, of which many have been ****Capoliveri**

Marciana charms with its old houses and narrow streets

carefully restored in the last years. The mine park reflects the village history of mining.

*Porto Azzurro

The second-largest harbour on Elba is in the charming village of Porto Azzurro (population 3,550) on the east coast, which Spain fortified in the 17th century. Fort Longone, the star-shaped fortress built by King Philip II of Spain, which has served as a prison since 1858, rises impressively above the »azure-blue harbour«. In the Spanish Baroque pilgrimage church of Madonna del Monserrato (built 1606) there is an altar panel with a black *Madonna with Child* (18th cent.). Day trips by boat to the nearby islands leave from the harbour.

Rio Marina

The next stop on the north-east coast of the island, Rio Marina, is the former shipping port for ore. The rust-red façades of the buildings along the main street lined by plane trees shows the high content of iron oxide in the nearby mines. The mineral museum in Palazzo del Burò is the centre for the Elba mining park.

❶ daily 9.30am – 12.30pm, 4.30pm – 6.30pm; admission €2.50
www.parcominelba.it

La Chiusa

Wine production on Elba is on a small scale but excellent in quality. The best comes from the estate La Chiusa. Its »Elba Rosso« is pressed from Sangiovese grapes, »Elba Bianco« from Procanico grapes. The owner, Signora Bertozzi Corradi, a cartoon film producer also sells dessert wines, grappa and olive oil.

❶ Località Magazzini 93; Apr – Sep Mon – Sat 8am – 12.30pm, 4pm – 8.30pm, otherwise only Mon – Sat 8am – 12pm; www.tenutalachiusa.it/introduction.php

Before arriving back in Portoferraio, the **medieval mountain castle** Volterraio, which crowns a 394m/1,293ft-high mountaintop, can be seen from a distance. This former place of refuge was built by the Pisan Gherardu Rau around 1284. In the 17th century the outer bulwark was improved. Enemy ships could be seen quickly from up here. The car can be parked near an abandoned sheep barn. From here a difficult path (about 40 min., hiking shoes a must) leads to the castle on the summit. The wonderful view rewards the effort!

**Volterraio

ISOLA PIANOSA AND ISOLA DI MONTECRISTO

Only 8 sea miles separate Elba from the former prison island of Pianosa. Only 280 people live on the flat, 10 sq km/3.8 sq mi island today. Ten years ago there were about twice as many. The Romans called it Planasia. In the Middle Ages the island was ruled by Pisa, later Genoa and the Appiani family, before North African pirates carried the inhabitants off into slavery in the mid-16th century. From 1835 until 1997 Pianosa was a prison colony. Meanwhile the island can be viewed as part of an organized tour; hiking, mountain biking or snorkelling is also possible. A National Park house was also opened, and there are simple accommodations run by a cooperative (www.hotelpianosa.it).
i www.islepark.it; boats from Rio Marina to Pianosa: www.toreMarit

Isola Pianosa

The granite island Montecristo, which has a size of almost 11 sq km/4 sq mi and the 645m/2,116ft Monte Fortezza as its highest point, lies 32 sea miles south of Elba. In 1996 the island was made part of the **Parco Nazionale dell'Arcipelago Toscano**. The island owes its name to St Maximilian, who took refuge here around 450 and renamed it from Mons Jovis to Mons Christi. At the end of the 19th century members of high society met in the Villa Reale for exclusive hunting parties; after that the Prince of Naples and later king of Italy, Vittorio Emmanuele, took over the lease of the Cala Maestra. Date palms, eucalyptus trees and magnolias grow in the botanical garden behind the villa. The legend of a treasure buried by Camaldolese monks on Montecristo gave the idea for one of the most successful adventure novels of world literature: Alexandre Dumas' bestseller published in 1846, *The Count of Monte Christo*.
❶ The island is only accessible as part of a guided one-day tour (max. 15 people); Jan 1 – Apr 30 & Aug 31 – Oct 31 with a visit to the island museum and the Cala Maestra; registration for tour 30 days in advance, tel. 0 56 64 06 11.

*Isola di Montecristo

✳ Fiesole

—————————————————————————— ✳ G 10

Province: Florence/Firenze (FI)
Altitude: 295m/968ft above sea level
Population: 14,350

**When the summer gets hot and humid in Florence, the Floren-
tines like to get away to Fiesole, where the wealthy have built
their baronial villas. The pretty town is only 8km/5mi away,
nestled between two hills above the city on the Arno and easily accessible with public transportation.**

WHAT TO SEE IN FIESOLE

**Piazza Mino
da Fiesole**
The centre of this likeable town is the broad Piazza Mino da Fiesole,
named after the sculptor Mino da Fiesole (around 1430–1484). The
monument on the piazza is named »Incontro di Teano« (1906) and
shows two bronze equestrian figures that represent King Vittorio
Emanuele II and Garibaldi. The north-west side of Piazza Mino da
Fiesole is occupied by the seminario (1697) and the 11th-century
bishop's palace (Palazzo Vescovile). On the south-west side of the
square are the 14th-century Palazzo Pretorio – its portico and loggia
were added in the 15th century – and the adjacent medieval oratory
Santa Maria Primerana with a portico dating from the 16th century.

***Duomo San
Romolo**
On the north side of the square is the cathedral, which was begun in
1024, expanded in the 13th and 14th centuries and remodelled in the
19th century. The bell tower, completed in 1213, stands 42m/138ft
high and is fortified with battlements. The church contains several
notable works of art. The terracotta statue of its patron saint San Romolo is by Giovanni della Robbia.

**Museo
Bandini**
Adjacent to the cathedral in the north is the Museo Bandini, devoted
to works of sacred art collected in the 18th century by Canon Angi-
olo Maria Bandini, scientist and librarian of the Biblioteca Medicea
Laurenziana in Florence.
❶ Apr 1 – Sep 30 Wed – Mon 10am – 5pm, Mar/Oct Wed – Mon 10am –
6pm, Nov 1 – Feb 28 Thu – Mon 10am – 4pm; admission €12

***Zona
Archeologica**
Behind the cathedral to the north-east is the excavation site, Zona
Archeologica, dominated by a **Roman theatre** that was rediscovered
in the early 19th century. It was constructed in the imperial period
(1st century BC) and enlarged under emperors Claudius and Septi-
mius Severus. The semicircle has a diameter of 34m/37yd and seats

Fiesole

INFORMATION
Via Portigiani 3-5
Tel. 05 55 98 720
www.comune.fiesole.fi.it

WHERE TO EAT
La Panacea del Bartolini €€
Località Olmo – Via Bosconi 58/a
Tel. 05 55 48 972
www.ristorantelapanacea.com
Closed Mon. Tuscan home cooking and
fish specialities in a family atmosphere.

Pizzeria Oliva €
Piazza Mino da Fiesole 2
Tel. 05 55 99 484
Closed Thu in winter. Apart from pizza
they also serve pasta at acceptable pric-
es.

Caffè al Numero 5 €€
Piazza Mino da Fiesole 5
Tel. 05 53 95 92 50
www.caffealnumero5.com
This café in an unbeatable location has
existed since 1906. 10am – 12pm
Breakfast and cocktails, afterwards restaurant and winebar with passable prices, but also crostoni, pizza, snacks and
panini caldi.

WHERE TO STAY
Pensione Bencistà €€€€
Via Benedetto da Maiano 4
Tel. 05 55 91 63
www.bencista.com
Pleasantly located country inn with 42
rooms and suites in the middle of olive
groves. Some of the rooms have views
of Florence!

Villa San Michele €€€€
Via Doccia 4, Tel. 05 55 67 82 00
www.villasanmichele.com
Villa San Michele with 46 rooms and suites and every imaginable comfort is one
of the top hotels in the Europe.

Le Canelle €€
Via Gramsci 52-56
Tel. 05 55 97 83 36
www.lecannelle.com
Charming inn with only 5 rooms near
the central piazza.

Villa Le Capanne €
Via Partenese 2
Tel. 05 55 90 63
www.villalecapanne.it
Quiet accommodation in an old tower
that was converted into a villa 3km/2mi
north of Fiesole.

about 3,000 spectators. In the summer months the theatre is used for
classical theatre and pop music concerts.
❶ see Museo Bandini

Not far from the theatre are the ruins of Roman baths, which were   **Roman baths**
also built during the imperial period and expanded under Emperor
Hadrian. Even though the arches, which were carried by massive columns, were always visible, the site was recognized as a bath and excavated only at the end of the 19th century. In the eastern part the
water was heated by means of furnaces and hypocausts; the three

central rooms were for cold baths (frigidarium), lukewarm baths (tepidarium) and warm baths (caldarium); the larger pools in the western part served as swimming pools and reservoirs. In the north-west corner are the remains of a Roman and an Etruscan temple (1st and 3rd century BC respectively). Towards the north the site is bordered by a section of the massive Etruscan city wall from the 3rd century BC.

Museo Archeologico

Fiesole was founded by the Etruscans in the 7th/6th century BC; the Roman settlement named Faesulae followed in the 1st century BC. The small archaeological museum to the south and above the Roman theatre exhibits finds from the Etruscan and Roman periods, including remains of a marble frieze for the stage decoration of the Roman theatre, a grave stele (470–460 BC; with funeral banquet, dance and animal battle), a copy of the head of Emperor Claudius (41–54) and a Dionysius statue, a Roman copy of a Greek original.

❶ see Museo Bandini

Museo Primo Conti

North-west of the excavation site is the foundation and a small museum for the Tuscan painter Primo Conti (1900 – 1988). Conti first painted in Futurist and Cubist styles but after World War II he developed his own style with wild colours. In addition to works by Conti, documents on Italian Futurism are also exhibited.

❶ Via Dupré 18; Mon – Fri 9am – 1pm; admission €3

*Sant'-Alessandro, observation platform

Between the bishop's palace and the seminar building a path leads up to two small churches and an observation platform, from which there is a good view of Florence. In the small park a monument honours the soldiers who fell in World War I; another one honours three carabinieri who were killed by the SS in 1944.

San Francesco, Giardini Pubblici

Diagonally opposite is the monastery church of San Francesco, established by Augustinian monks in 1330. In 1407 it passed to the Franciscan order, was later remodelled and in 1905 renovated extensively. The main altar is particularly worthy of note: The *Annunciation* is by Raffaellino del Garbo, the *Adoration of the Magi* by Cosimo Rosselli. The mission museum and the idyllic cloisters are also worth seeing. From the monastery plaza a path leads through the municipal park and back to the centre of town.

❶ Fall/winter Tue – Fri 9.30am – 12pm, 3pm – 5pm, Sat 10.30am – 12pm, 3pm – 5pm; spring/summer Tue – Fri until 7pm; admission: donation

Villa Medici

Via Vecchia Fiesolana, which runs south-west down from Fiesole, leads to Villa Medici, which Michelozzo built in 1458–1461 for Cosimo the Elder. The Pazzi conspirators at first planned to murder the brothers Lorenzo and Giuliano de Medici in 1478, before they decided that the Duomo Santa Maria del Fiore in Florence would be a better site.

❶ Via Beato Angelico 2; Mon – Fri 9am – 1pm (only groups; appointment tel. 05 55 91 64); admission: €6; www.villamedicifiesole.it

From Fiesole the ATAF bus 47 runs to the monument park of Villa Peyron. The villa was built on Etruscan ruins by Ugo Giovannozzi. The last owner, Paolo Peyron, bequeathed it in 1998 to the Fondazione Parchi Monumentali Bardini e Peyron. The are grand views of Florence and Castel di Poggio from here.

Giardino e Museo di Villa Peyron

❶ Via Vincigliata 2; Park/Garten/Villa: Apr 20 – Jul 27 and Sep 5 – Oct 5 Mon and Wed 10am – 4pm; admission: €10; www.bardinipeyron.it

A good 1km/0.5mi to the south-west of Fiesole and right on the Florence city limits lies a group of houses called San Domenico di Fiesole. The church of San Domenico here was built between 1406 and 1435 with funds from Barnaba degli Agli, a citizen of Fiesole, and extended in the 17th century. On the altar in the first chapel on the left notice the beautiful **triptych**. It was created around 1430 by **Fra Angelico**, who also painted the Crucifixion and an image of the Virgin in the chapter house of the monastery. The son of a wealthy farmer from the Mugello Valley, he entered the Dominican monastery at the age of twenty. His reputation as an outstanding painter spread

***San Domenico di Fiesole**

Take the bus! Insider Tip

MARCO ⊕ POLO TIP

To enjoy the view of Florence from the panoramic road to Fiesole at leisure, take bus no. 7, which commutes between Florence and Fiesole every 15 minutes (departure from the main railway station, cathedral square and Piazza San Marco).

quickly and when the Dominican monastery of San Marco in Florence was remodelled in 1436, Fra Angelico received the commission to paint the cells with themes from the passion of Christ. Fra Angelico's realism apparently had quite an effect: it is said that his fellow monks fainted at the sight of his crucifixion scene because of the blood depicted.

North-west of San Domenico lies Badia Fiesolana at 123m/403ft elevation; the church façade still has Romanesque elements.. The cathedral church of Fiesole stood here until 1028, on the supposed site of the martyrdom of St Romulus, when it was replaced by the duomo. After Camaldolese monks had rebuilt the church with a monastery (badia = abbey), it was handed over to the Benedictine order. In the Renaissance the monastery and church were remodelled. In 1778 the church and monastery were dissolved. Since 1976 Badia has housed the international institute Università Europea, a renowned centre for doctoral and post-doctoral research in the social sciences.

Badia Fiesolana

** Florence / Firenze

⟡ G 10

Capital of Regione Toscana:
Altitude: 50m/164ft above sea level
Province: Florence/Firenze (FI)
Population: 374,000

The combination of dolce vita and cultural pleasures is probably nowhere more charming than in Florence. The city on the Arno is the cradle of the Renaissance. Brunelleschi, Michelangelo, Donatello, Leonardo da Vinci, Boccaccio, Dante, Petrarch, Galileo and the mighty Medici were active here; it was the cradle of written form of the Italian language and the centre of Italian literature.

Since the Middle Ages the Florentines have known how to keep and multiply their wealth as craftsmen, able businessmen and competent administrators. Florentine banks controlled Europe's money market at times, and its bankers influenced European politics decisively. The city became rich through weaving and dying, tailoring and trading in silk; the clothing industry is still an important source of income.

The Etruscan and Roman settlement on the Arno had little importance. Not until the early 13th century did the city begin to flourish through the fortunes of war and industrious trading, and became the most respected city in central Italy. The guilds gradually grew stronger and took control of the government in 1282. From 1434 **the Medici, a wealthy merchant family,** controlled local politics. The most important members of the family, Cosimo (1434 – 1464) and Lorenzo (1469 – 1492), led the republic to its greatest prosperity and made it a centre of the arts and sciences. In 1494 the Medici were driven out. The short-lived **theocracy under the penitential preacher Girolamo Savonarola** ended in 1498 with his execution and led to a new republic. In 1512 the Medici were brought back by Spanish troops, but driven out again in 1527. In 1530 finally, after the city was taken by Charles V, Alessandro de Medici was installed as Duke of Florence. After his murder in 1537, Cosimo I ruled as Grand Duke of Tuscany from 1569. When the Medici line died out in 1737, Tuscany passed to the house of Habsburg-Lorraine, which ruled until 1860 except for the Napoleonic period. When Tuscany joined the unified Kingdom of Italy, Florence flourished again as the **temporary**

City of the Medici

Piazza del Duomo with the cathedral, the 82m/265ft-high campanile and the baptistery are some of the highlights in Florence

capital of the monarchy (1865 – 1870). Despite war damage in 1944 and the catastrophic Arno flood in 1966, Florence remains one of the most beautiful cities in Italy.

GRANDE MUSEO DEL DUOMO
www.ilgrandemuseodelduomo.it

The newly established Grande Museo del Duomo includes the Battistero (baptistery), the Duomo Santa Maria, the Brunelleschi cathedral dome, the Santa Reparata Crypt in the cathedral, the Campanile and the Museo dell'Opera del Duomo. There is a **single ticket for all monuments at € 15**, valid for 24 hours.

** BATTISTERO (BAPTISMAL CHAPEL SAN GIOVANNI)
❶ Mon – Wed, Fri 8.15am – 10.15 am and 11.15am – 6.30 pm; Thu, Sat, Sun 8.30am – 6.30pm

The oldest building on the cathedral square **Piazza del Duomo** is the baptistery (1059 – 1128). Its octagonal form derives from early Christian baptisteries. The three storeys of the well-proportioned building

are differentiated by the varying designs of their marble covering in square and rounded forms. The baptistery owes its fame to the three monumental bronze doors. Between 1330 and 1336 Andrea Pisano created the oldest, southern bronze doors with 28 scenes in relief from the life of John the Baptist framed in Gothic quatrefoils. Pisano's figures, some of which are modelled in high relief or dressed in robes with many folds, move calmly but their gestures are full of suspense. A competition for the north door in 1401 was won by **Lorenzo Ghiberti** against six rivals (including Filippo Brunelleschi and Jacopo della Quercia from Siena). Ghiberti's decorative illusionist style convinced the judges. Between 1403 and 1424 he and his assistants made the double bronze

The reliefs (copies) on the Porta del Paradiso

Highlights Florence

▶ **Piazza del Duomo**
Cathedral, baptistery and campanile: a unique ensemble, since 1982 on the Unesco list of world heritage and a milestone of Florentine architecture!
▶page 232

▶ **Piazza della Signoria**
This majestic square is the heart of Florence. Where once political assemblies were held ice cream and cappuccino are now enjoyed in sidewalk cafés.
▶page 247

▶ **Uffizi Gallery**
What the Louvre is to Paris, the Uffizi Gallery is to Florence. One day is not nearly enough for this world-class art collection.
▶page 251

▶ **Ponte Vecchio**
Florence's most famous and oldest bridge
▶page 256

▶ **Galleria dell' Accademia**
Do you want to see Michelangelo's original David? Here he is!
▶page 272

▶ **Santa Maria Novella and Santa Croce**
Anyone who associates mendicant order churches with spartan furnishings will know better after seeing the rich works of art in these two churches.
▶page 265, 276

▶ **Palazzo Pitti and Giardino di Boboli**
Several museums under one roof, and the largest and most beautiful park in the city
▶page 257, 260

▶ **Museo Nazionale del Bargello**
This museum is a must for those interested in Renaissance sculpture and historic craftsmanship.
▶page 274

doors with 28 quatrefoil fields depicting 20 scenes from the New Testament as well as the four evangelists and four fathers of the Latin church. Since Ghiberti's style was received well, he also obtained the commission for the eastern doors, which Michelangelo later called **Porta del Paradiso** because of their beauty. It took Ghiberti almost 30 more years (1425 – 1452) to complete them. The doors mounted on the baptistery are copies; the originals are in the cathedral museum.

The inside walls are also clad with thin marble panels in geometric **Interior** patterns. The two-storey interior with its powerful granite columns and pilasters receives little light from outside; an eight-sided, double-skinned dome construction gives it added height. The vaults are decorated with wonderful 13th-century mosaics. From the middle of the dome, six concentric rings show first plant ornamentation, then the heavenly host, followed by the story of the creation, the legend of Joseph, scenes from the life of Christ and the life story of John the Baptist. It is also worth noting the tomb (1425 – 1427) of the antipope John XXIII, by both Donatello and Michelozzo, and the marble floor.

★★ DUOMO SANTA MARIA DEL FIORE

❶ **Cathedral:** Mon – Wed, Fri 10am – 5pm, Thu 10am – 4.30pm, Sat 10am – 4.45pm Sun 1.30 – 4.45pm
Dome: Mon – Fri 8.30am – 6.20pm, Sat 8.30am – 5.00pm; Sun 1.00pm – 4.00pm
Santa Reparata: opening times like cathedral, but closed Sun

With its area of 8,300 sq m/9,930 sq yd, Santa Maria del Fiore is the third-largest church in Italy after St Peter's in Rome and the cathedral of Milan. It holds about 25,000 people. Even though it was begun during the Gothic period in 1294, the cathedral does not have such typical Gothic elements as flying buttresses, tracery and distinct architectural sculptures. Like the baptistery, the cathedral is richly panelled in marble of various colours. The side doorways are also late medieval, while the richly decorated main façade was carried out only in 1875 – 1886, to plans by Augusto Conti in the neo-Gothic style. The first cathedral architect was **Arnolfo di Cambio**. After his death the guild of wool weavers took charge of the cathedral office of works in 1330 and made Giotto its supervisor in 1334. However, Giotto essentially worked only on the campanile. The plans for the nave were changed repeatedly until 1368, when a small trial church was built to scale and heavy fines imposed for any deviation from this model. Thus, the nave, the walls for the choir and the drum for the dome were completed by the early 15th century.

Interior   The interior of the cathedral has the form of a pillared basilica. The broad nave seems cool, hall-like, monumental. Hardly anything recalls the filigree, ascending forms of Gothic architecture in France and other countries. The inside of the façade with three round windows designed by Ghiberti is decorated by a mosaic of the coronation of the Virgin (around 1300) and the wall tomb of Bishop Antonio d'Orso by Tino di Camaino. The clock face of the painted 24-hour clock (1443) with heads of four prophets or evangelists is by Paolo Uccello. At the beginning of the right-hand aisle a bust commemorates Filippo Brunelleschi, the architect of the cathedral dome, whose grave is in the crypt. Only a few steps further is the tondo-shaped monument (1490) to Giotto, painter, sculptor and architect of the campanile. The adjacent marble statue (around 1409) depicts Daniel and is considered to be an **early work of Donatello**. To the right above the side entrance is a bust set up in 1521 for the philosopher Marsilio Ficino (1433 until 1499), head of the Platonic academy founded by Cosimo de Medici in 1459.

Leaving the aisle for the crossing, look up at the dome fresco of the *Last Judgement* (1572 – 1579) by Giorgio Vasari and Frederico Zuccari. The main altar in the crossing and the marble balustrade are mainly the work of Baccio Bandinelli (around 1555). The middle chapel of the choir houses the bronze shrine (1432 – 1442) of St Zenobius, Bishop of Florence and patron of the city, by Ghiberti, while the angel bearing a candelabra on the altar was made around 1450 by Luca della Robbia.

In the left transept is the **Old Sacristy** with a bronze door (1446 – 1467) by Michelozzo and Luca della Robbia portraying the church patron Mary and the evangelists and church fathers. In the lunette is a white and blue faience *Resurrection of Christ* (1442 – 1445) by Luca della Robbia. In 1478 as a consequence of the so-called Pazzi conspiracy an assassination attempt was carried out on Lorenzo and Giuliano de Medici. Giuliano was murdered while his brother Lorenzo was able to flee into the sacristy.

In the left aisle at the fourth pillar a painted panel (1465) by Domenico di Michelino commemorates Dante Alighieri, who is portrayed with his main work, the *Divine Comedy*, with the silhouette of Florence in the background. Two **equestrian portraits** on the aisle wall

Piazza del Duomo

1 Porta del Paradiso	A Portale Maggiore	F Santa Reparata
2 North portal (entrance)	B Porta dei Cornacchini	(crypt)
3 South portal	C Porta della Mandorla	G Old Sacristy
4 Main altar	D Porta del Campanile	H New Sacristy
	E Porta dei Canonici	

Brunelleschi's Legacy

The dome of Florence's cathedral is the first structure of this kind with a double-skinned construction and the legacy of Filippo Brunelleschi.
He was the first to use herringbone (a spinapesce) brickwork on an octagonal layout where the bricks were wedged together at increasing angles the higher the construction went.

▶ **Facts and figures on the cathedral dome**

Constructor/engineer	Filippo Brunelleschi
Commission date	1420
Closure of the dome	1436
Frescoes (Vasari, Zuccari)	4000 sq m/43,060 sq ft
Diameter	42m/137ft
Height of vault	84m/275ft
Höhe einschl. Laterne	114m/374ft
Weight	37,000 t

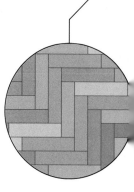

▶ **Building materials:**
Marble, stone, natural stone, tuff stone, brick, oak wood, chestnut wood, glass (windows), stone chains, iron chains

▶ **Famous domed structures in comparison**

Dome of the Rock (AD 690)
Jerusalem (Israel)
Diameter of dome: 20m/66ft

Hagia Sophia (AD 537)
Istanbul (Turkey)
31m/102ft

Saint Paul's Cathedral (17
London (England)
34m/112ft

Structure of the dome

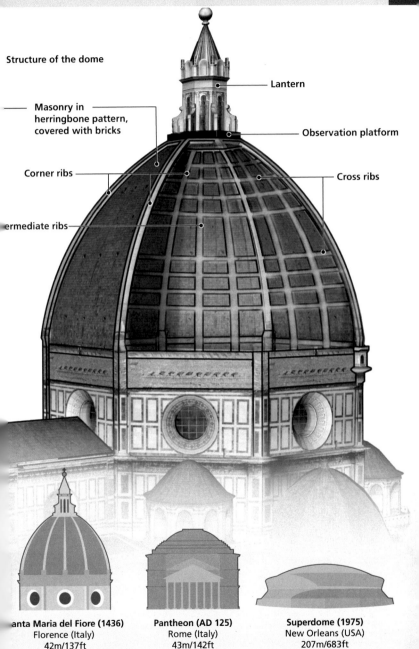

Lantern

Masonry in
herringbone pattern,
covered with bricks

Observation platform

Corner ribs

Cross ribs

Intermediate ribs

Santa Maria del Fiore (1436)
Florence (Italy)
42m/137ft

Pantheon (AD 125)
Rome (Italy)
43m/142ft

Superdome (1975)
New Orleans (USA)
207m/683ft

View from the campanile, which has overshadowed the cathedral for a long time

are especially impressive. Giovanni Acuto, an English mercenary leader whose real name was John Hawkwood and who first fought in the wars against France in the service of Edward III, was recruited by the Florentines in 1377 to fight against the pope. In 1394 the city government decided to erect a monument for him, which was only carried out in 1436 when Paolo Uccello painted the portrait using newly discovered perspective techniques. The equestrian portrait of Niccolò da Tolentino, the victor of the battle of San Romano (1432), which was painted twenty years later by Andrea del Castagno, is striking for its illusionistic manner. Under Santa Maria del Fiore remains of the previous cathedral church Santa Reparata have been exposed and show early Christian mosaics and Romanesque structures.

✳ CAMPANILE
❶ daily 8.15am – 6.50pm

The 82m/270ft-high bell tower was built between 1334 and 1384 to plans by Giotto di Bondone. Apart from the marble relief carvings, the lower walls are decorated with **reliefs by Andrea Pisano** including the seven planets, the seven virtues, the seven liberal arts and the seven sacraments. In the niches above are statues of the prophets, sibyls and patriarchs, some of which were done by Donatello in the years 1420 – 1435. 414 steps lead to the top of the tower; there is no lift.

** MUSEO DELL'OPERA DEL DUOMO
❶ daily 9am – 7pm

The Museo dell`Opera del Duomo was re-opened with great pomp and ceremony after years of renovation in October 2015. It now exhibits 750 great works of art and cultural history in 28 rooms. It is one of the leading collections of sculpture in the world.

On the ground floor in the **Salone del Paradiso** (room 6), the cathedral's unfinished first façade, which was dismantled in 1587, has been reconstructed. Many of the statues that were previously only exhibited as individual pieces have been restored to their original positions in the façade. Opposite the façade, as also in reality on the cathedral square, are the original and restored relief panels of the **famous Gates of Paradise of the Baptistery** by Lorenzo Ghiberti. In room 8 there is a late work by Donatello, *St Magdalene*; room 9 contains one of the most famous statues of Western art: the **Pietà by Michelangelo**, which stood in the cathedral choir from 1722 until 1891. At the age of 23 Michelangelo created the Pietà of St Peter's in Rome, a consummate work in the traditional style of a Vesperbild (a votive picture). At the age of 80 he created another Pietà, which by thematically connecting the man of sorrows, the deposition from the cross and the lamentation of Mary set itself apart considerably from his first work. Michelangelo left the group incomplete and even broke it to pieces; at the same time he was so fascinated by it that he wanted to be buried at its feet.

> **?** **Don't miss**
>
> MARCO ⊕ POLO INSIGHT
>
> - the original wooden model of the dome lantern by Brunelleschi
> - the Pietà by Michelangelo
> - the reconstructed first façade, with the niche figures by Donatello
> - the reliefs from the Gates of Paradise by Ghiberti

On the first floor in room 14 the reliefs of the Campanile are exhibited. The adjacent Galleria della Cupola (room 15) is dedicated to Brunelleschi and the cathedral dome. Exhibits include the builder's death mask and the **original wood model of the lantern** of the cathedral dome. In Sala delle Cantorie (room 23) there are two marble cantor chancels – the one on the left was made by Lucca della Robbia, the one on the right by Donatello – that were in use in the cathedral as organ rails until they were removed in 1688. In room 25 there are missals and precious reliquaries as well as other gold and silver objects from the cathedral treasury.

Florence

Where to eat

1 Cibrèo
2 Winter Garden
3 Il Latini
4 Sostanza
5 Zà Zà
6 Trattoria Mario
7 Pizzeria Antica Porta
8 Trattoria Alfredo
9 Ruth's

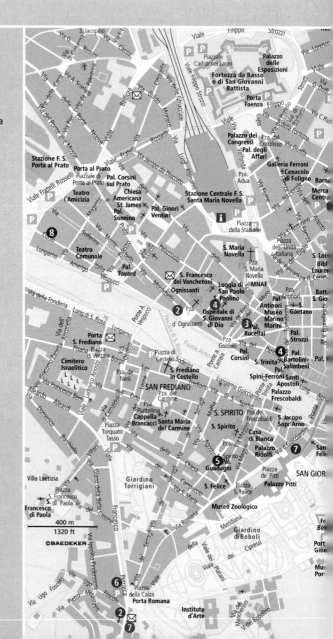

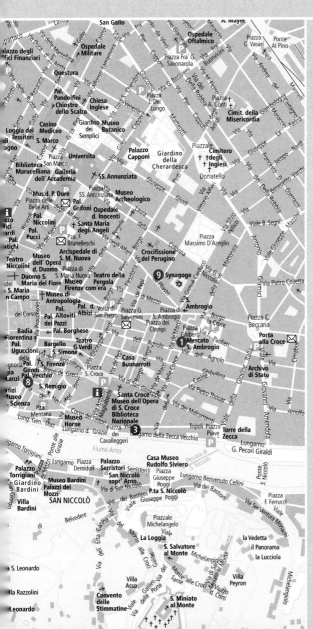

Where to stay

1. Brunelleschi
2. Villa Mangiacane
3. Plaza Hotel Lucchesi
4. Beacci Tornabuoni
5. Palazzo Guadagni
6. La Terrazza su Boboli
7. La Scaletta
8. Crocini

Florence

INFORMATION
Uffizio Informazioni Turistiche
Via Cavour 1/R
Tel. 0 55 29 08 32
www.firenzeturismo.it
Mon – Sat 8.30am – 6.30pm, closed
Sun

Aeroporto »Amerigo Vespucci«
Firenze-Peretola
Via del Termine 1 (arrivals area)
daily. 8.30am – 8.30pm

Santa Maria Novella (Hbf.)
Mon – Sat 8.30am – 7pm, Sun 8.30am
– 2pm

Borgo Santa Croce 29/R
Mar. 1 until 1st week of Nov. Mon – Sat
9am – 7pm, Sun 9am – 2pm;
2nd week of Nov. until Feb. 28 Mon –
Sat 9am – 5pm, Sun 9am – 2pm

CITY TAX
The municipality of Florence levies an
»Imposta« or »Tassa di soggiorno«, a
city tax that tourists pay on their overnight stays. It is not included in the hotel
price and is assessed according to the
quality standard: For a one- to five-star
hotel €1 – €5 per person for a maximum
of 10 consecutive nights is charged.
Children up to 10 years are exempt.

FIRENZE CARD
The Firenze Card (valid 72 hrs, €50) is
valid for one adult and one minor under
the age of 18 years (EU citizen). With
the card 33 museums and monuments
can be viewed free of charge; public
transportation is also free (ATAF busses,
trams). They are sold in tourist information offices and the bookshops of museums (including the Uffizi Gallery, Palazzo
Vecchio, Palazzo Pitti, Museo Stefano
Bardini).
Online sales/info: www.firenzecard.it

DRIVING INTO THE CITY
Centre and Oltrarno are traffic-free
(Zona a traffico limitato – ZTL). Driving
to hotels in the ZTL is allowed, but the
hotel must be informed beforehand of
the licence plate number and arrival
time. Most hotels have information on
parking availability. There are video cameras all over the ZTL and all cars are recorded. The fines for illegal parking are
very high. More information and a map
of the ZTL zone is available at www.co-
mune.fi.it.

It is best to park in one of the surrounding zones of the ZCS (Zona a controllo
sosta) in a guarded parking lot or a parking place that is marked in blue and
which must be paid for; use public transport (ATAF, tram) to get to your destination. Parking lots that offer daily rates include »Oltrarno« (Porta Romana),
»Beccaria« or »Fortezza Fiera« (Fortezza
da Basso) as well as the recommendable
parking garage »Parterre« (Piazza Libertà, ATAF Bus 1 runs from here into the
centre); www.firenzeparcheggi.it.
Parking is also available at one of the
stops of the tram T 1, which runs from
Scandicci to the main railway station.
Schedule: www.gestramvia.it/orari.html.

CITY BUSES
Tickets at the ATAF office at the railway
station, in bars, at kiosks and in tobacco
shops. One way costs €1.20, airport bus

Almost like being in the stadium: the Calcio in costume, the historic football game in Florence always attracts enthusiastic fans.

(Volainbus) costs €5 (return €8). Schedule at www.ataf.net.

EVENTS

At Scioppio del Carro on Easter Sunday, when a rocket in the form of a dove is ignited at the cathedral altar. It then »flies« on a rope through the church to the square and there sets off an oxcart full of fireworks.

»Calcio in Costume«: On a sanded square (Piazza Santa Croce) two teams in historical costumes and with pretty rough manners fight to get a ball into a net. The final game generally takes place on 24 June during the Festa di San Giovanni.

All events of the current month are in the city magazine *Firenze Spettacolo* (www.firenzespettacolo.it).

SHOPPING

Florence is a mecca for fashion, leather goods, fabrics, gourmet foods and jewellery, but prices can be exorbitant. The main shopping streets are Via Calzaiuoli between the cathedral and Piazza della Signoria. The heart of the fashion world beats on Via Tornabuoni and in the adjoining streets, where all big names from Armani to Dolce & Gabbana can be found. The best place for shoes is Borgo San Lorenzo or Via Cerretani, for jewellery the Ponte Vecchio, for antiques Borgo Ognissanti, Via Maggio and Via Fossi. To see a lively market, go to the Mercato San Lorenzo in Via dell' Ariento or the Mercato Centrale.

WHERE TO EAT

❶ *Cibreo* €€€€

Via Andrea Verocchio 8 R
Tel. 055 234 11 00
www.edizioniteatrodelsalecibreofirenze.it
Closed Sun and Mon. Gourmet restaurant of Fabio Picchi near the Sant'Ambrogio market.

❷ *Winter Garden* €€€€

Piazza Ognissanti 1
Tel. 0 55 27 15 37 70

www.stregis.com/Florence
In the fabulous Art deco hall of the St. Regis luxury hotel this restaurant offers very good Florentine cooking.

❹ *Sostanza* €€
Via del Porcellana 25
Tel. 055 21 26 91, Closed Tue
Traditional Florentine restaurant where Chagall and Steinbeck once ate; recommendation: homemade tortellini.

❺ *Zà Zà* €€
Piazza del Mercato Centrale 26/R
Tel. 055 21 54 11
www.trattoriazaza.it
Daily 12pm – 3pm, 7pm – 1am. Popular restaurant with creative Florentine cuisine. Local people come here above all; reservations and tasting the Pollo alla Cacciatora or Ribollita must!

❼ *Pizzeria Antica Porta* €
Via Senese 23/R
Tel. 055 22 05 27
www.antica-porta.it
Closed Mon.
Traditional and excellent pizzas with buffalo mozzarella. The Calzone with truffle creme is worth it.

❻ *Trattoria Mario* €   Insider Tip
Via Rosina 2/R
Tel. 055 21 85 50
www.trattoriamario.com
Mon – Sat only 12pm – 3.30pm, closed Aug.
The tiny trattoria near the Mercato Centrale is a typical family restaurant and very popular – where else would you wait on the sidewalk when the restaurant is full until the patrone invites you to come in? Son Romero even cooked on TV.

❸ *Il Latini* €€€
Via dei Palchetti 6/R
Tel. 055 21 09 16
www.illatini.com
Closed Mon.
Hams hang from the ceiling, and plates are weighed down by the famous bistecca fiorentina, an inch-thick cut from the loin, seasoned only with a splash of olive oil.

❽ *Trattoria Alfredo* €
Via dei Leoni 14/R
Tel. 0 55 29 49 12
Mon – Fri, Sun 12pm – 3pm, 6.45pm – 10.30pm, closed Sat.
Alfredo Lettieri and his five companions offer a different menu every day in the shadows of the Uffizi: unpretentious, strictly seasonal and at civil prices. Fish is always served on Fridays.

❾ *Ruth's* €
Via Farini 2
Tel. 05 52 48 08 88
www.kosheruth.com
Closed Fri evenings, Sat noon and on Jewish holidays.
Friesh vegetarian, kosher cooking, also fish, in the community hall to the right of the synagogue. Take-away available.

WHERE TO STAY
❷ *Villa Mangiacane* €€€€
Via Faltignano 4
San Casciano
Tel. 055 829 01 23
www.villamangiacane.it
Luxuriously restored Renaissance villa (26 rooms) on the crown of a hill surrounded by olive groves and vineyards 12km/7mi south of Florence. Unforgettable view of the city on the Arno from the wonderful loggia; with a spa.

Luxurious Villa Mangiacane

❶ *Brunelleschi* €€€€
Piazza Sant'Elisabetta 3
Tel. 055 273 70
www.hotelbrunelleschi.it
A Byzantine tower in the heart of Florence. A small private museum tells the history of the house and the man it was named after. Rooftop terrace with a wonderful panorama.

❸ *Plaza Hotel Lucchesi* €€€€
Lungarno della Zecca Vecchia 38
Tel. 05 52 62 36
www.plazalucchesi.it
Traditional hotel on the Arno that has been in existence since 1860. 10 suites and 87 rooms with WIFI, some with a balcony and view of Santa Croce, cathedral and Palazzo Vecchio.

❹ *Beacci Tornabuoni* €€€
Via de Tornabuoni 3
Tel. 055 21 26 45
www.tornabuonihotels.com
Centrally located, well-kept bed & breakfast in the famous shopping street. Breakfast on the roof terrace.

❺ *Palazzo Guadagni* €€ – €€€
Piazza Santo Spirito 9
50125 Firenze (Oltrarno)
Tel. 05 52 65 83 76
www.palazzoguadagni.com
In 2009 this Renaissance palace with 14 rooms in the heart of Oltrarno with ceiling frescos, fireplaces and loggia was restored perfectly. Guests stay in a gold, silver or green room and enjoy elevated 3-star comfort. In the Roof Garden Bar have a cocktail prepared and enjoy the grand view of the city.

❻ *La Terrazza su Boboli* €€ – €€€
Viale Petrarca 122
50125 Firenze (Oltrarno)
Tel. 05 52 33 73 94
www.laterrazzasuboboli.com
Elegant, quiet B&B with a view of the Boboli Gardens. There are six beautiful rooms with parquet floors, some with a balcony. The delicious breakfast is served in the lounge on cooler days, on the terrace on summer mornings. Free parking.

❼ *La Scaletta* € – €€
Via d. Guicciardini 13
Tel. 0 55 28 30 28
www.hotellascaletta.it
Hotel in a beautiful historic building with 11 simple, stylish rooms. View of the city from the pretty roof terrace.

❽ *Crocini* €
Corso Italia 28
Tel. 0 55 21 29 05
www.hotelcrocini.com
Inexpensive hotel near the Teatro Comunale with a pretty garden. 20 simply furnished, quiet rooms and a breakfast room facing the inner courtyard garden.

It is worth going upstairs to the second floor in order to see the cathedral dome from an unusual perspective from the **Belvedere della Cupola**.

FROM PIAZZA DEL DUOMO TO PIAZZA DELLA SIGNORIA

Several routes lead from the cathedral square to Piazza della Signoria: the elegant Via Calzaiuoli or the narrow streets that run parallel, such as Via dei Cerchi, where tiny shops and excellent gourmet food shops are tempting places to look and buy.

*Orsan-michele This palace-like building (1337 – 1350) on Via dell'Arte della Lana was once both the city's grain warehouse and an oratory. The outer arcades of the lower storey, where a market used to be held, were added in Gothic tracery decades after the building was built. At the end of the 14th century the guilds took on responsibility for decorating the building and hired renowned sculptors to do the work. Thus most of the figures (in part replaced by copies) in the 14 outer niches date from the early 15th century, including important examples of Renaissance sculpture.

Figures in niches: In Via Calzaiuoli, beginning on the left: the first figure is a bronze statue (1414) of John the Baptist by Lorenzo Ghiberti, made in a transitional style between Gothic and Renaissance for the guild of cloth traders. The bronze group *Christ and Doubting Thomas* (1465 – 1483) by Andrea del Verrocchio is a work of the high Renaissance for the niche of the court of commercial law. The next two niches contain the evangelist Luke (1597 – 1603) by Giambologna for the guild of the judges and notaries and the apostle Peter (around 1420) by associates of Donatello for the butchers. For the next two niches Nanni di Banco created St Philip (1410 – 1412), a robed figure for the tanners' guild that still appears flat despite its contraposto, and four crowned saints (1414 – 1417) for the guild of stonemasons and carpenters, representing a group of four early Christian sculptors who were martyred under Diocletian (with a relief around the pedestal). Donatello carved St George (around 1416) as a holy knight for the niche of the armour makers (the original is in the Bargello; this is a bronze copy). Even though the figure stands in a niche, the path of development to free-standing sculpture is already apparent. The bronze figure of the evangelist Matthew (1424) by Lorenzo Ghiberti for the money-changers' guild shows more confidence in the physical form than that of St John. Instead of facing forward as in the traditional representation, it now faces slightly to one side. In the next

> **MARCO POLO TIP**   **Insider Tip**
>
> *Book ahead instead of waiting*
>
> Endless queues especially at the Uffizi, the Galleria dell' Accademia and Palazzo Pitti can be avoided by ordering tickets ahead of time (at least 3 days, tel. 0 55 29 48 83). This official service (€4) is also available online (www.firenzemusei.it, www.uffizi.firenze.it). Some hotels also order tickets for guests. Watch out for unauthorized ticket sales on the Internet!

niches are St Stephen (1427 – 1428) by Ghiberti for the traders in woollen cloth and the tall, slender St Eligius (around 1420) by Nanni di Banco for the blacksmiths' guild. The evangelist, Mark (1411 – 1415), was made by Donatello for the guild of linen drapers. In the next niches are St James (after 1422) by Niccolò di Pietro Lamberti for the furriers and fur traders, the Madonna della Rosa (1399), attributed to Giovanni di Piero Tedesco, for the doctors and pharmacists, and the evangelist John (1515) by Baccio da Montelupo for the guild of silk weavers and goldsmiths.

Inside Orsanmichele, a two-aisled Gothic hall, there is a marble tabernacle (1359) by Andrea Orcagna with scenes from the life of the Virgin and a panel painting of the Virgin (1347) by Bernardo Daddi to replace a miraculous votive image that was destroyed by fire. There is a sculpture museum on the first floor (Museo delle Sculture). Classical concerts are held in Orsanmichele.

Church: daily 10am – 5pm
Museum: Mon 10am – 5pm; free admission

** PIAZZA DELLA SIGNORIA

Piazza della Signoria has been the political centre of the city since the 14th century. Today visitors from all over the world populate the cafés around the broad square. The showpiece of the piazza is the **fountain of Neptune**, which the Florentines mockingly call »biancone« (big white one). It was intended for the wedding of Francesco de Medici, the son of Cosimo I, and Princess Johanna of Austria in 1565, but was only completed in 1578 by Bartolomeo Ammanati. A granite plaque in the ground near the fountain of Neptune commemorates the execution and burning of Savonarola and his fellow monks Buonvicini and Maruffi in 1498. The equestrian figure (1594) by Giambologna depicts Grand Duke Cosimo I de Medici.

** *Heart of the City*

The impressive square where public assemblies were held in the past is dominated by the massive tower of the Palazzo Vecchio. With other important sights like the Loggia dei Lanzi and especially the Uffizi Gallery it is the tourist heart of Florence.

❶ Palazzo Vecchio

Building of the massive and fortified Palazzo Vecchio, once the seat of the government of the city-republic of Florence, the Signoria, began around 1300. The palace is a symbol of the political and cultural glory of the city.

❷ Loggia dei Lanzi

The open triple yoked hall, the landsknecht hall, displays famous statues like *Perseus with the Head of Medusa* by Benvenuto Cellini. Under the right-hand arcade is the marble group *Rape of the Sabine Women* by Giambologna.

❸ David

In front of the Palazzo Vecchio stands a copy of the David by Michelangelo, one of the most famous sculptures in the world. Anyone who wants to see

the original has to go to the ▶Galleria dell' Accademia.

❹ Fontana del Nettuno

The Fountain of Neptune was made for the wedding of Francesco de' Medici with Princess Johanna of Austria in 1565 by Ammanati. Maybe the building went too quickly because the results were not satisfactory. The Florentines mocked: »Ammanato, che bel marmo hai rovinato!« (»Ammanato, what a beautiful block of marble you have ruined!«).

❺ Palazzo degli Uffizi

The Galleria degli Uffizi is housed in the palazzo on the Piazza della Signoria, one of the most famous art galleries in the world with countless masterpieces, especially of Italian painting.

The Fontana del Nettuno was created as a wedding present

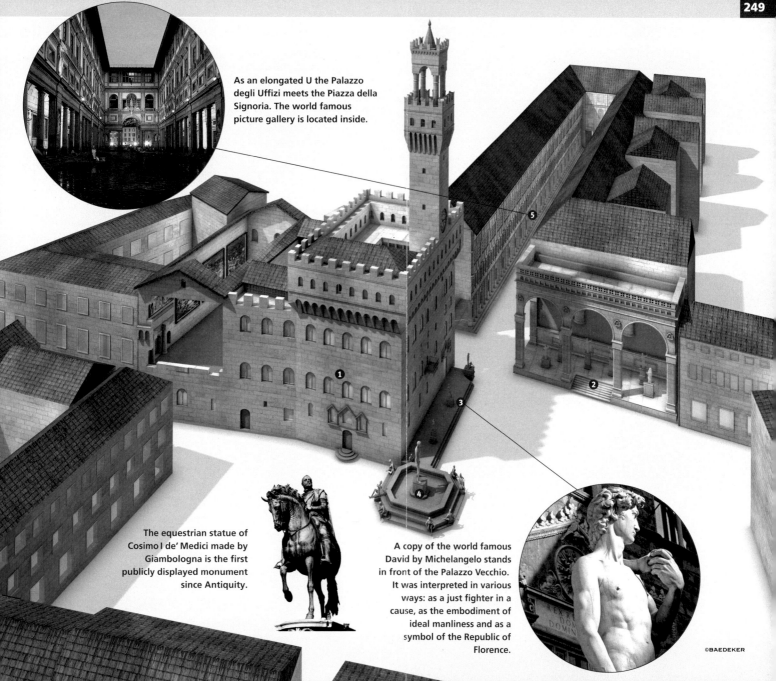

As an elongated U the Palazzo degli Uffizi meets the Piazza della Signoria. The world famous picture gallery is located inside.

The equestrian statue of Cosimo I de' Medici made by Giambologna is the first publicly displayed monument since Antiquity.

A copy of the world famous David by Michelangelo stands in front of the Palazzo Vecchio. It was interpreted in various ways: as a just fighter in a cause, as the embodiment of ideal manliness and as a symbol of the Republic of Florence.

©BAEDEKER

✶✶ PALAZZO VECCHIO

❶ Palazzo Vecchio: Mon – Sat 9am – 5pm, Sun 9.30am – 12.30pm;
admission €6, www.museicivicifiorentini.it/palazzovecchio
Museo dei Ragazzi Palazzo Vecchio: Mon – Sat 9.30am – 5pm, Sun
9.30am – 12.30pm; admission: €6, family €14/€16 (4/5 people); www.
palazzovecchio-museoragazzi.it.

The Palazzo Vecchio on the south-west corner of Piazza della Signoria still radiates the self-confidence of the city state of Florence.
From the beginning of the 14th century and as long as the city was
ruled as a republic by a nine-man college, the Signoria, it was the
seat of communal government. The Signoria consisted of eight
priori (principals) and the gonfaloniere della giustizia (banner
bearer of justice). They were chosen by the citizens, who were organized into guilds, in a complicated process of election, drawing
lots and rotation. In 1540 Cosimo I de Medici took over the palace.
When the Medici moved into the newly built Palazzo Pitti, Palazzo
Vecchio became less important and was called from then on the
»old palace«. In order to get from Palazzo Vecchio to Palazzo Pitti
more easily and without being seen Cosimo I had a connecting
walkway built between the two palaces across the Arno, the Vasari
corridor (Corridoio Vasariano) designed by Vasari. The Palazzo
became city hall and seat of the communal government again in
1872.
The children's museum in the palace, Museo dei Ragazzi Palazzo
Vecchio, allows children to playfully explore the Renaissance in
»secret passages« (Percorsi segreti).

Building history and façade The exterior of Palazzo Vecchio with its slender towers is much like
a medieval fortress. Decades of running battles between the city's
leading families ended in the late 13th century. The building of the
communal palace between 1299 and 1314 was the expression of the
newly won communal independence and the government's need for
security. Numerous statues were erected in front of the palace, **symbols of the commune's desire for liberty**, including the lion
bearing the city coat of arms (copy after Donatello, around 1420),
the bronze group *Judith and Holofernes* (copy after Donatello,
around 1460), *David* (copy after Michelangelo, around 1504, original in the Galleria dell' Accademia) and the *Hercules and Cacus*
marble group (1533) by Bandinelli. The medieval inner courtyard
where a fountain with figures of a putto and dolphin (copy after
Verrocchio, around 1475) splashes, was remodelled by Michelozzo
in 1453 in the early Renaissance style. On the upper parts of the wall
are 18 large city panoramas from the Habsburg empire, which were
painted for the wedding of Francesco de Medici and Johanna of
Austria (1565).

Palazzo Vecchio is truly a treasure chamber. Worth seeing is the **Chamber of the Five Hundred** (Sala dei Cinquecento), a work of Cronaca (1495). The ceiling has 39 fields with allegorical depictions of the history of Florence and the Medici, while the long side walls are decorated with giant battle scenes by Vasari. The famous marble statue *Victory* by Michelangelo is on the southern end wall. The small but sumptuous * **study of Grand Duke Francesco** (Studiolo di Francesco I) was designed by Giorgio Vasari 1570 – 1575 and decorated by important painters and sculptors of his time. It is a gem of Florentine Mannerism. The **Room of the Lilies** (Sala dei Gigli) on the third floor with frescoes by Ghirlandaio and his studio (1482 – 1484) holds the expressive bronze group Judith and Holofernes (around 1460) by Donatello. The private rooms of Eleonora of Toledo, wife of Cosimo I, who died in 1562, are decorated with ceiling frescoes in the Mannerist style. The **private chapel of Eleonora** is notable for the paintings of the story of Moses (between 1540 and 1545) by Agnolo Bronzino.

Palace rooms

This open Gothic columned structure was named Loggia dei Lanzi (1374 – 1381) after the mercenary foot soldiers who served there from the 16th century as guards of the Medici rulers. Before that the loggia was used for official ceremonies: ambassadors and princes were received here, the priori and gonfalonieri were installed in office here. Above the arches outside in niches are allegories of the virtues (1383 – 1391). On a tour of the hall clockwise, the first work is the bronze statue *Perseus with the Head of Medusa* (1545 – 1554), a masterpiece by Benvenuto Cellini commissioned by Duke Cosimo I. In a gesture of triumph the ancient hero holds up the severed head of the Medusa, a monster that Perseus killed with the help of the gods. Under the arcade on the far right Giambologna's *Rape of the Sabine Women* (1579 – 1582) is another example of Mannerism.

**Loggia dei Lanzi

** GALLERIA DEGLI UFFIZI

Uffizi: Tue – Sun 8.15am – 6.50pm, last Tue/month 7pm – 11pm; admission €11, »Martedì in Arte« (last Tue/month) free admission
Vasari Corridor: tours in Italian, limited number of participants, registration required (tel. 0 55 29 48 83); times on the website or at tourist information; admission: €15; www.polomuseale.firenze.it/musei/uffizi.it

Between Palazzo Vecchio and Loggia dei Lanzi lies the entrance to one of the richest museum collections in the world, the Uffizi Gallery, built originally between 1560 and 1580 for the administrative offices (uffizi) of the duchy. A corridor connected it with Palazzo Vecchio and Loggia dei Lanzi. The world-famous collection of the Uffizi with masterpieces of European painting and ancient sculp-

Entrance Loggiato degli Uffizi

Galleria degli Uffizi

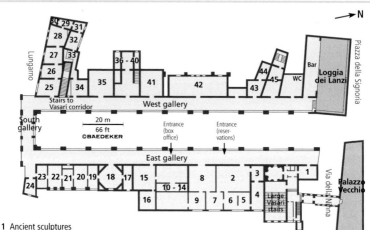

1 Ancient sculptures
2 Tuscan painters of the 13th century, including Cimabue, Giotto
3 Sienese painters of the 14th century
4 Florentine painters of the 14th century
5-6 Gothic painting
7 Tuscan painters (Early Renaissance)
8 Filippo Lippi
9 Botticelli, Pollaiolo
10-14 Botticelli, van der Goes
15 Perugino, da Vinci a. o.

16 Maps
17 Hermaphrodite room
18 Tribune: Greek sculptures Paintings by Vasari, Bronzino, Pontormo
19 Perugino, Signorelli
20 Dürer, Cranach
21 Bellini, Giorgione, Carpaccio a. o.
22 Holbein, David, Altdorfer, Memling

22 Correggio, Mantegna
23 Miniatures of the 15th – 18th century
24 Michelangelo
25 Fra Bartolomeo
26 Sarto, Raffael
27 Pontormo, Rosso Fiorentino
28 Tizian
29 Parmigianino, Dossi
30 Artists of the 16th century from the Emilia
31 Veronese

32 Tintoretto, Bassano
33 Vasari, Bronzino
34 Lotto, Moroni
35 Barocci and the Tus Counterreformatior
36-40 Archaeological roo
41 Rubens, van Dyck
42 Niobe room
43 Caravaggio
44 Dutch painting of the 17th century
45 Works of the 18th century

tures developed from a private gallery of the Medici, which was left to the city of Florence by the last Medici heiress. Room 1 holds **archaeological exhibits** from ancient Rome. The tour begins on the first floor in room 2 with Tuscan painting of the period around 1300. From here the paintings are arranged chronologically up to room 16 and then according to schools, regions and countries until 1700. The Vasari Corridor, which connects Palazzo Vecchio with Palazzo Pitti, can only be viewed in a tour; these are not offered on a regular basis. It holds an impressive collection of portraits of Italian and foreign artists (Leonardo, Raphael, Michelangelo, Rembrandt, Ensor etc.).

In room 2 three large-scale Madonna panels stand out: *Santa Trinita Madonna* (around 1275) by Cimabue, *Maestà* (1285) by Duccio and *Maestà* (around 1310) by Giotto. They show the transition from Byzantine painting depicting the Virgin as an incorporeal queen of heaven to a portrait of a woman based on observation. In room 3 is Simone Martini's *Annunciation* (around 1333), a painting of great delicacy and elegance; in rooms 5 – 6 the international Gothic style is represented by works including the extravagantly composed *Adoration of the Magi* (1423) by Gentile da Fabriano. The early Renaissance works in room 7 are important for the first use of central perspective including *Madonna and Child with Saint Anne* (around 1420) by Masaccio, *The Battle of San Romano* (around 1456) by Paolo Uccello, *Enthroned Madonna with Saints* (around 1445) by Domenico Veneziano, which is flooded with natural sunlight, and the **Portrait of the Duke and Duchess of Urbino** (around 1465), in stark profiles in the style of ancient medallions, by Piero della Francesca. In room 8 Filippo Lippi's maidenlike *Madonna and Child with Two Angels* (around 1465) radiates cheer and grace. The small figures by the brothers Antonio and Piero Pollaiuolo in room 9 are expressions of intensive anatomical studies.

Rooms 2 to 9 Tuscan art: 13th century to early Renaissance

? Don't miss
MARCO POLO INSIGHT

- Room 2: Madonna panels by Cimabue, Giotto and Duccio.
- Room 7: portraits of the Duke and Duchess of Urbino by Piero della Francesca
- Room 10: *Birth of Venus* by Botticelli
- Room 15: *Annunciation* by Leonardo da Vinci
- Room 25: *Holy Family* by Michelangelo
- Room 26: *Madonna of the Goldfinch* by Raphael

At the age of about thirty (around 1475), Sandro Botticelli painted the altarpiece *Adoration of the Magi*, in which he inserted numerous portraits of contemporaries. **Birth of Venus** and **Primavera** followed, works commissioned by Lorenzo di Pierfrancesco de Medici, a cousin of Lorenzo il Magnifico. *Birth of Venus* probably dates from 1482 – 1483. In it Botticelli combined ancient and Christian ideas. Thus he painted a female nude modelled on an ancient statue of Venus, the goddess of love, and indirectly referred to the model of a Christian baptismal painting. The same room contains the famous **Portinari Altar**, a commissioned work which was painted a short time before the *Birth of Venus* for Tommaso Portinari, the head of the Medici bank in Bruges, by Hugo van der Goes. The naturalism and realism of the altar are impressive, but all in all painting north of the Alps remained strongly influenced by mysticism and religion.

Rooms 10 to 14 Botticelli

Leonardo da Vinci was a pupil of Andrea del Verrocchio, with whom he painted the **Baptism of Christ in the Jordan** (around 1470). His

Rooms 15, 16 Verrocchio, Leonardo

Annunciation (around 1470 – 1475) in an extremely wide format stands out for its atmospheric treatment of landscape and the emotion expressed in the figures. In the *Adoration of the Magi* (begun 1481) Leonardo subtly captured the developing mood of crisis of his time. His *Madonna and Child* are surrounded by people who react to the birth of the Son of God with a mixture of amazement and horror.

Room 20 German Renaissance painting German Renaissance painting in room 20 is represented by masterpieces by Lucas Cranach: portraits of Martin Luther and his wife Katharina von Bora, a self-portrait, an impressive portrait of Melanchthon and Adam and Eve in slightly erotic poses. Albrecht Dürer's works include *Madonna and Child* (1526), *The Artist's Father* (1490) and *Adoration of the Magi* (1504), painted shortly before his second trip to Italy.

Room 21 Venetian Renaissance painting Venetian Renaissance painting, which is characterized by soft colour tones and balanced light as well as harmonious landscape and quiet portrayals of figures, is represented by *Christian Allegory* (around 1485) by **Giovanni Bellini** and two scenes (*Judgement of Solomon, Moses Undergoes Trial by Fire*) and a portrait of a Maltese knight by Giorgione.

Rooms 25 and 26 Michelangelo, Raphael Michelangelo's *Holy Family* (1503 – 1504) in round format is without any religious pathos. The picture, which was painted for the wedding of Agnolo Doni with Maddalena Strozzi, shows Michelangelo's unmistakeably strong interest in sculpture, as the family appears to be carved out of a block of stone. Three important works by Raphael can be seen in room 26: a self-portrait (around 1506) which shows him at the age of twenty-three, his charming *Madonna of the Goldfinch*, an effective triangular composition, and the portrait *Pope Leo X with two Cardinals*.

Room 27 Rosso Fiorentino Rosso Fiorentino was one of the early Mannerists. His preference for composing bodies with plane surfaces and cool colours can be seen in the painting *Moses Defends Jethro's Daughters* (1523), which refers to the Old Testament story in which Moses drove the shepherds away from the well and allowed the herds of the seven daughters of Jethro to drink.

Room 28 Titian Titian's paintings *Venus of Urbino* (1538), the adjacent *Ludovico Beccadelli* (1552), *Venus and Cupid* (1560), Eleonora Gonzaga della Rovere, *Francesco Maria, Duke of Urbino* and *La Flora*, one of his most beautiful portraits of a woman, are shown here. *Venus of Urbino*, painted for the Duke of Urbino, stands out especially because of its colour composition. The red tones tie together the separate parts of the picture in their spatial perspective and diagonal positions.

Stand amazed – enjoying art in the Uffizi

In room 31 works by Paolo Veronese can be seen. In room 32 *Leda and the Swan*, *Venetian Admiral* and portraits by Tintoretto as well as *The Concert* and *Two Dogs* by Jacopo Bassano are worthy of note. Corridor 33 has small works by such Mannerist painters as Alessandro Allori and Giorgio Vasari. The highlights of room 34 are portraits by Giovanni Battista Moroni and the *Holy Family with St Jerome and St Anne* (1534) by Lorenzo Lotto.

Rooms 31 – 34

Dutch art of the »golden« 17th century is also represented in the Uffizi, including works by Peter Paul Rubens: portraits of Emperor Charles V and the artist's first wife Isabella Brant. In a room decorated in the classical style in 1779 – 1780 (no. 42) stands the Niobe Group, a Roman copy of Greek originals which is the most valuable ancient sculpture in Florence apart from the Medici Venus.

Rooms 41 – 44

In the last room the exhibition returns to Italian painting. In the 18th century the Venetians took the lead again – especially with the famous **city views by Canaletto** and Guardi, some of which are exhibited here.

Room 45

*Museo di Storia della Scienza (Museo Galileo) Behind the Uffizi Gallery just before the river Arno, the museum of the history of science in Palazzo Castellani is well worth seeing. Certainly less overcrowded than the Uffizi, but with a very interesting collection of scientific precision instruments from the time of the Medici and Habsburg-Lorraine rulers. A fascinating room holds **Galileo Galilei's original instruments**, including the telescope with which he discovered the moons of Jupiter.

❶ Wed – Mon 9.30am – 6pm, Tue only until 1pm; admission €8

Ponte Vecchio It is probably that there was a bridge here already in the **Etruscan period. The Roman Via Cassia crossed the Arno here on a wooden bridge. From the 13th century the city government allowed shops and apartments to be built here. Since the increasing noise and odours bothered the grand duke on his way to Palazzo Pitti, a law was passed in 1593 that allowed only the **goldsmiths** to open shops on the bridge. Since 1900 a bust of the most famous Florentine goldsmith, Benvenuto Cellini, has adorned the middle of the bridge. On the east side the Vasari Corridor runs across the Old Bridge above the small houses.

Ponte Vecchio with small shops and the Vasari Corridor

PALAZZO PITTI AND
THE SOUTH BANK OF THE ARNO

On the broad Piazza dei Pitti, which is like a palace forecourt, stands the monumental Pitti Palace. The Pitti were a **respected Florentine merchant family** who competed with the Medici in pride and ambition. Under Luca Pitti a large city palace was built on the left bank of the Arno a short distance outside the city. The architect Luca Fancelli was in charge of the first construction work (1457 – 1466), possibly following a design by Brunelleschi. Eleonora of Toledo, Cosimo I's wife, acquired the palazzo in 1549 and had it completely renovated and enlarged between 1558 und 1570. The decorations in the rooms formed the basis of the famous Galleria Palatina. Ancient and contemporary statues were added. Today several museums are housed in the palace.

**Palazzo Pitti

From the inner courtyard take the stairs on the right to the Galleria Palatina, the art gallery on the second floor. The pictures are not organized chronologically but on decorative criteria in order to display the state rooms and their valuable furnishings according to the tastes of the Medici rulers. From the stairs the tour passes through the vestibule, the Sala degli Staffieri, the Galleria delle Statue and the Galleria delle Nicchie to the Sala di Venere, where the first paintings are to be seen.
❶ Tue – Sun 8.15am – 6.50pm; admission: €8.50

Galleria Palatina

Sala di Venere: The *Italic Venus* (1810) by Antonio Canova stands in the middle of the room. It was commissioned by Napoleon. Four paintings show the development of the Venetian painter Titian: *The Concert*, *Portrait of a Lady*, portraits of Pope Julius II and Pietro Aretino. *Venus, Amor and Vulcan* comes from Tintoretto's early period. The important works in the adjacent Venus room include the *Return of the Hunters* (by Susterman), *The Return of the Farmers from Work* and *Odysseus with the Phaeacians* (by Rubens) as well as the *Seascape at Sunset* by Salvatore Rosa.

Painting gallery

Sala di Apollo: Of the works of the 16th and 17th centuries in the Apollo room, the following deserve special mention: *Mary Magdalene* (around 1531) and *Portrait of Ippolito Riminaldi* (around 1540 – 1545), both by Titian. The double portrait of King Charles I of England and his wife Henrietta of France (after 1623) is by van Dyck. Around 1520 Rosso Fiorentino painted the monumental *Sacra Conversazione*, also called *Pala Dei*, for the chapel of the Dei family in Santo Spirito.

Sala di Marte: The ceiling paintings in the Mars room are by Pietro da Cortona and show war in allegorical scenes. Rubens' large-scale work **The Consequences of War** corresponds to the theme. It shows

Palazzo Pitti

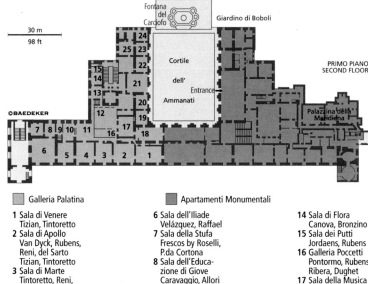

30 m
98 ft

Fontana del Cardofo

Giardino di Boboli

Cortile

dell'
Entrance
Ammanati

PRIMO PIANO
SECOND FLOOR

Palazzina della Meridiana

©BAEDEKER

Galleria Palatina

Apartamenti Monumentali

1 Sala di Venere
  Tizian, Tintoretto
2 Sala di Apollo
  Van Dyck, Rubens,
  Reni, del Sarto
  Tizian, Tintoretto
3 Sala di Marte
  Tintoretto, Reni,
  Tizian, Rubens,
  Murillo, Veronese
4 Sala di Giove
  Raffael, Bordone,
  Rubens, del Sarto,
  Perugino, Guercino
5 Sala di Saturno
  Raffael, Perugino,
  Ghirlandaio

6 Sala dell'Iliade
  Velázquez, Raffael
7 Sala della Stufa
  Frescos by Roselli,
  P.da Cortona
8 Sala dell'Educa-
  zione di Giove
  Caravaggio, Allori
9 Bagno di Napoleone
10 Sala di Ulisse
  Raffael, Reni, Lippi
11 Sala di Prometeo
  Signorelli, Lippi,
  Botticelli, Reni
12 Corridoio d. Colonne
13 Sala della Giustizia
  Veronese, Tizian

14 Sala di Flora
  Canova, Bronzino
15 Sala dei Putti
  Jordaens, Rubens
16 Galleria Poccetti
  Pontormo, Rubens,
  Ribera, Dughet
17 Sala della Musica
18 Sala Castagnoli
19 Sala delle Allegorie
20 Sala delle Belle Arti
21 Salone d'Ercole
22 Sala dell'Aurora
23 Sala di Berenice
24 Sala di Psiche
25 Sala della Fama

how Venus tries in vain to keep Mars from going to war. Rubens created the work in 1638 under the impression of the Thirty Years' War.
Sala di Giove: The Jupiter room is also decorated with ceiling paintings by Pietro da Cortona. They make reference to the fact that this
was the throne room of the grand dukes. The most important works
of art here include *The Three Ages of Mankind* (around 1510 – 1520),
which is attributed to **Giorgione**, *Madonna with the Little Swallow* by
Guercino, *John the Baptist* (around 1520) by Andrea del Sarto and
The Entombment of Christ (around 1511 – 1512) by Fra Bartolomeo.
La Velata (around 1516), also called *La Fornarina*, is one of Raphael's
most beautiful portraits of a woman.
Sala di Saturno: Pictures by Raphael and his contemporaries Perugino, Fra Bartolomeo and Andrea del Sarto hang in the Saturn room.

Sala dell' Iliade: The Iliad room was redecorated between 1819 and 1825. Luigi Sabatelli did the ceiling painting on the subject of Olympus and the lunettes with scenes from Homer's Iliad. Two large-scale pictures by Andrea del Sarto (1526, 1530), both of which depict the assumption of the Virgin into heaven, hang opposite each other. Philip IV of Spain by Velázquez, Raphael's *Pregnant Woman* and the *Portrait of Count Waldemar Christian* by Sustermans are further works to detain art lovers in this room.

Sala della Stufa: The small »stove room« was first decorated in 1627 by the Florentine artist Matteo Rosselli. The paintings for this room are by Pietro Cortona (1637 and 1640 – 1641). The subjects are the four eras: gold, silver, copper and bronze.

Sala di Ulisse: The ceiling of the Ulysses room is decorated with the return of the heroes of Troy, a reference to the return of Ferdinand III of Lorraine to Florence (1815). The showpiece, however, is Raphael's *Madonna dell'Impannata* (around 1512).

Sala di Prometeo: Almost all of the tondi (round pictures) that belong to the Galleria Palatina can be seen in the Prometheus room. Like the other paintings in this room they are works of the 15th and 16th century. Works by Filippo Lippi, Sandro Botticelli as well as Pontormo's *Martyrdom of the Ten Thousand* (1529 – 1530) are exhibited. The adjacent columned corridor is mainly dedicated to Flemish and Dutch landscape painters of the 17th century.

Sala della Giustizia: The hall of justice displays Venetian painting of the 16th century, including Titian's *Portrait of Tommaso Mosti*, Tintoretto's *Venus, Vulcan and Cupid* as well as Veronese's *Baptism of Christ* (1576).

Sala Castagnoli The room is named after the artist Giuseppe Castagnoli, who did the ceiling painting after 1815. Two colossal marble statues from the Villa Medici in Rome adorn the walls. The table of the muses in the centre of the room was made in the Florentine workshop for stone intarsia work.

Quartiere del Volterrano: The series of rooms that begins with the Sala delle Allegorie was the winter apartment of the grand duchess in the Medici period. Only the decorations from the first room come from the time of Medici rule; the other rooms were renovated after 1815.

Appartamenti ex Reali: The former rooms of the kings of Italy, where Vittorio Emanuele II, Umberto I, Queen Margherita and Vittorio Emanuele III lived, are furnished with valuable furniture, paintings, statues and tapestries.

Galleria d'Arte Moderna The gallery of modern art on the second floor of Palazzo Pitti gives a good overview of Italian and Tuscan painting in the 19th and 20th centuries; the works of the »Macchiaioli« are especially interesting.

Representatives of this Tuscan school (including Giovanni Faltori, Silvestro Lega, Telemaco Signorini) got their name from their anti-academic handling of the brush. The exhibition concludes with a collection of works by classic modern Italian masters such as Severini, Giorgio de Chirico and Morandi that is equally worth seeing.

i Tue – Sun 8.15am – 7.50pm, admission €8.50

Museo degli Argenti   On the ground floor and mezzanine of Palazzo Pitti the silver collection is housed in the rooms where the Medici lived during the summer months. Silver and gold jewellery, gemstones, ivory work belonging to the Medici are displayed here; also jewellery by contemporary designers of the 20th cent., including Bulgari, Pino Castagna, Franco Grilli, Mari Ishikawa and Cartier, as well as Jewellery by Tuscan (Bino Bini, Armando Piccini) and Venetian artists (Mario Pinton, Alberto Zorzi).

i daily 8.15am – 6.50pm, Apr/May, Sep /Oct until 6.30pm, Mar until 5.30pm, Jan/Feb, Nov/Dec until 4.30pm; closed 1st and 4th Mon/month; admission: €7

Galleria del Costume   The costume gallery in the adjacent Palazzina della Meridiana shows men's and women's clothing from 1700 until 1920.

❶ see Museo degli Argenti

*Giardino di Boboli   On the slope behind Palazzo Pitti the Boboli Garden is a **wonderful park** for taking long walks. After Duke Cosimo I bought Palazzo Pitti in 1549, the adjacent land, which had in part belonged to the Boboli or Bobolini family was also bought. Niccolò Pericoli began to redesign the park in 1550, Bernardo Buontalenti continued the work, and Alfonso Parigi the Younger completed it by 1658. The park's attractions include the Fontana del Bacco (after 1560) – a fountain with the figure of Cosimo I's court dwarf riding on a turtle – and the Grotta del Buontalenti (1583 – 1588) with figures of shepherds and sheep carved from stalactites and plaster reliefs of Michelangelo's *Prisoners*. There is also an **amphitheatre for court festivals** with Egyptian obelisks and Roman granite basins, as well as a fountain of Neptune (1565), a colossal statue *Abbondanza* (1636), the terrace garden Giardino del Cavaliere with a monkey fountain and, in the 18th-century Palazzina del Cavaliere, the porcelain museum with Italian, French and German ware.

❶ see Museo degli Argenti

> **! Coffee break**   *Insider Tip*
>
> MARCO POLO TIP
>
> Coffee has been served in the Boboli Garden Rococo pavilion that was built for Leopold II since 1775. Unfortunately the building is now closed. But an espresso, cappuccino or a glass of wine can still be enjoyed in the nice cafeteria in the inner courtyard of Palazzo Pitti!

View from the southern banks of the Arno towards the city

Odd and even a bit creepy, but above all of excellent quality are the 18th cent. wax figures – exact copies of nature – in the museum to the right of Palazzo Pitti.

Museo Zoologico La Specola

❶ Via Romana 17; winter Tue – Sun 9.30am – 4.30pm, summer 10.30am – 5.30pm; admission: €6

In Villa Bardini, Costa San Giorgio 2, east of Giardino di Boboli the life work of the artist Pietro Annigoni are exhibited in the **Museo Pietro Annigoni**; **Museo Fondazione Roberto Capucci** on the subject of silk is also in this villa. **BardiniContemporanea** offers special exhibitions on contemporary art. Ristorante Bardini with a beautiful terrace are a good place to spend the evening.

Entrances to **Giardino Bardini** are on Costa San Giorgio 2 and Via dei Bardi 1r. The hortensia, azalea and camellia gardens are especially impressive. The view of Florence from the terrace of the belvedere rivals that of Piazzale Michelangelo.

Villa Bardini, Giardino Bardini

Museo Pietro Annigoni and Museo Fondazione Roberto Capucci:
Tue –Sun 10am – 6pm; admission: €6; www.museoannigoni.it
BardiniContemporanea: daily 8.15am – 6.30pm; www.moba.fi.it
Giardino Bardini: Mar 8.15am – 5.30pm, Apr, /May, Sep /Oct 8.15am –daily until 6.30pm, June – Aug until 7.30pm, Nov – Feb until 4.30pm; admission: €9

Museo Stefano Bardini in Via dei Renai houses the collection of the famous art and antique dealer Bardini and includes sculptures, paint-

Museo Stefa-no Bardini

Abladen und Verbringen von Bildern aus den Uffizien
in den neuen Bergungsort S. Leonhard im Passeiertal

Photograph from the private collection of Rodolfo Siviero

ings, furniture, ceramics, carpets and weapons from antiquity, the Renaissance and the Baroque period.

❶ Via dei Renai 37; Fri – Mon 11am – 5pm; admission: €5; www.museicivicifiorentini.it/bardini

Casa Museo Rodolfo Siviero The little museum on the banks of the Arno shows the private collection of Rodolfo Siviero (1911 – 1983), which includes antiques and half a dozen paintings by Giorgio de Chirico (donations), works by Giacomo Manzù, Ardengo Soffici and Pietro Annigoni. The art historian and collector Siviero, who must have been a colourful figure and a kind of James Bond of the art scene, played a significant role after 1945 in researching art works that were taken out of the country or stolen by Nazi leaders. More than 100 art works from the Uffizi were taken to St Leonhard in South Tyrol at that time (including Botticelli, Perugino, Ghirlandaio) and to Taufers (sculptures). Siviero was commissioned with the research and reacquisition by the Italian government. The rescued works include Fra Angelico's *Annunciation*, among others.

❶ Lungarno Serristori 1; Sun, Mon 10am – 1pm; Sat June – Sep 10am – 2pm, 3pm – 7pm, Oct – May 10am – 6pm; free admission; www.museocasasiviero.it

* Piazzale Michelangelo From Piazza Giuseppe Poggi stairs and Viale Giuseppe Poggi lead up to Piazzale Michelangelo. The busy and touristy sqaure – with a copy of the famous *David* – offers a spectacular view of Florence.

Although the building is outwardly unassuming, the Renaissance church on Piazza Santo Spirito is a **masterpiece by Brunelleschi**. The work was begun by Brunelleschi in 1434 but only completed 35 years after the master's death in 1481. The austere composition and symmetry of the interior come as a surprise. The church is a basilica, in which columns separate the nave from the aisles and the dimensions of the square crossing serve as a basic unit of measurement for the rest of the plan. The determining building elements imitate Roman antiquity: the columns with Corinthian capitals, and the entablature resting on them. The rose window in the façade was designed by Perugino. The left aisle leads to a vestibule built by Cronaca (1494) and from there into the sacristy, an octagonal Renaissance structure on a central plan by Giuliano da Sangallo (1495 – 1496). The tabernacle altar (1709) by Caccini with stone inlays stands in the crossing. The impressive altarpiece Madonna with Child, Saints and Donors (1490) by Filippino Lippi is in the right transept.
**Santo Spirito

❶ Mon, Tue, Thu – Sat 10am – 12.30pm, 4pm – 5.30pm, Sun 4pm – 5.30pm. Andrea Orcagna's fresco of the Crucifixion and Last Supper in the refectory of the Augustinian monastery (Piazza Santo Spirito 24) can be seen on Sat 10.30am – 1.30pm; admission: €2.20

Piazza del Carmine is in a busy and traditional quarter of the city. The Carmelite church on the piazza was begun in 1268, but not finished until 1476. A fire in 1771 caused so much damage that the church had to be completely reconstructed. Inside, the **Baroque-style Cappella Corsini** by Pierfrancesco Silvani at the head of the left transept is impressive; its dome fresco was painted by Luca Giordano in 1682. The graves of Neri and Piero Corsini with three marble reliefs are in the chapel.
Santa Maria del Carmine

Access to the Cappella Brancacci is to the right of the Carmelite church via a cloister added in the early 17th century. Felice Brancacci, a rich Florentine merchant, had it decorated with frescoes by **Masaccio and Masolino** between 1424 and 1428. The painters used linear perspective for the first time and created one of the earliest nude paintings, of Adam and Eve. The unfinished frescoes on the lower part of the long wall were completed in 1483 – 1485 by Filippino Lippi. Since the latest restorations their enormous depth and subtle colouring can again be seen clearly.
*Cappella Brancacci

❶ Mon, Wed – Sat 10am – 5pm, Sun 1 – 5pm; admission €4

Return to the banks of the Arno and stroll along Lungarno Giucciardini to Palazzo Frescobaldi, a medieval family residence that was altered in the 17th century. The Ponte Santa Trinità (1567 – 1570), which was destroyed in in the Second World War but rebuilt to plans by Ammanati, is the connection to the city quarters on the north bank of the Arno.
Ponte Santa Trinità

WESTERN OLD CITY

Palazzo Spini-Feroni
At the northern end of Ponte Santa Trinità, in the Gothic Palazzo Spini-Feroni the ***shoe museum** displays about 10,000 creations by **Salvatore Ferragamo**. Greta Garbo, Audrey Hepburn and Marilyn Monroe all wore shoes by the designer. He opened his first shoe store in Hollywood at the age of 18.

❶ Piazza Santa Trinità 5 r; Sep – July Wed – Mon 10am – 6pm, Aug Mon – Sat 10am – 1pm, 2pm – 6pm; admission: €5; www.museoferragamo.it

*Santa Trinità
The Gothic church of the Holy Trinity (14th cent.) with an early Baroque façade (16th cent.) has a jewel of Renaissance art inside: the Sassetti chapel (second to the right of the altar) with a painting by Domenico Ghirlandaio. He produced the altarpiece *Adoration of the Christ Child* (1479 – 1485) and wall frescoes with scenes of the Legend of St Francis. A fresco cycle in the fourth chapel to the right on the long side (1420 – 1425) with scenes from the life of the Virgin Mary by Lorenzo Monaco is also worth seeing.

❶ Mon – Sat 8am – 12pm, 4pm – 6pm, Sun 4pm – 6pm

* Via de' Tornabuoni
Via de' Tornabuoni and nearby smaller streets are known for their many elegant fashion shops.

*Palazzo Davanzati
The simple façade of Palazzo Davanzati is divided at the bottom by three massive portals, closed off at the top by a loggia and decorated in the middle by a magnificent Davanzati coat of arms, the family who acquired ownership of the palace in 1578. Palazzo Davanzati houses Museo della Casa Fiorentina Antica, where furniture, drawings, sculptures, carpets, ceramics, fabric and household utensils from the Middle Ages, Renaissance and Baroque are displayed. A remarkable feature is the »parrot's hall« on the second floor, with wall paintings simulating tapestries adorned with the figures of parrots.

❶ Tue – Sun 8.15am – 1.50pm; tours 10am, 11am, 12pm; admission: €2

*Piazza della Repubblica
This is the place to sit and relax in a café. Literature fans should drink their cappuccino in the Giubbe Rosse (»Red Vests«), which the Futurists and writers of the 1920s frequented. Today it still has a larger selection of daily newspapers than any other café in the city. The piazza is located where the **Roman forum** once stood. Until 1888, when the stalls had to make way for a monumental triumphal arch (1895) and a row of administrative buildings, a market was here, which is dominated by Donatello's statue of Abbondanza (today a copy).

*Palazzo Strozzi
The palace was commissioned by Filippo di Matteo Strozzi, a member of the Strozzi family, which was banned from Florence for many

years as rivals of the Medici. The Renaissance palace, which was built 1489 – 1536 on plans by Giuliano da Sangallo with three free-standing façades is now an important cultural centre thanks to Fondazione Strozzi. The palace history is shown in the cortile. In the Piano Nobile internationally recognized exhibitions are held and in the lower floor CCC (Centro Culturale Contemporanea Strozzina) shows contemporary art. Spazio Agora Z was created by the architect Claudio Neri.
Piano Nobile: daily 9am – 8pm, Thu until 11pm
CCC: Tue – Sun 10am – 8pm, Thu until 11pm
Admission: €10, CCC Thu from 6pm €5, www.palazzostrozzi.org

Palazzo Rucellai in Via della Vigna Nuova was built by architect Bernardo Rossellino on plans by Leon Battista Alberti in 1446 – 1451. It is one of the most important Renaissance houses in Florence. It was commissioned by Giovanni di Paolo Rucellai, a rich merchant whose coat of arms, a wind-filled sail, can be seen on the frieze around the building. | *Palazzo Rucellai

Opposite is an arched hall that was built in 1460, also by Alberti, for representational purposes for the Rucellai. The loggia is glassed in today and used for exhibitions. | Loggia dei Rucellai

Behind the block of Palazzo Rucellai, the former church of San Pancrazio (14th – 15th century) was converted to a museum in 1988 for the Tuscan sculptor, painter and graphic artist Marino Marini (1901 – 1980). 176 sculptures, paintings, drawings and graphics by Marini are on display. They are from all his creative periods, beginning with the painting *The Virgins* of 1916. Horse and rider are one of the sculptor's central themes. Marini's also concentrated on Pomona, a voluminous goddess of fertility. | *Museo Marino Marini
❶ Wed – Sat, Mon 10am – 5pm, admission €4, www.museomarinomarini.it

The palace of the Antinori family (15th cent.) on Piazza Antinori has a pretty fountain courtyard that is worth looking at. In the famous but expensive enoteca wines along with choice Tuscan specialties can be tasted. | *Palazzo Antinori, Enoteca

** SANTA MARIA NOVELLA AND SURROUNDINGS

On the expansive Piazza Santa Maria Novella, where penitential processions took place in the Middle Ages the large Dominican church Santa Maria Novella was built on the site of an oratory in 1246 – 1300. The bell tower and sacristy date from the first half of the 14th century, and the façade was built 1458 – 1470 by **Leon Battista Alberti** for Giovanni Rucellai, whose sail emblem can be seen in the | ** Santa Maria Novella centre. Alberti used the building style of a baptistery, but added the innovation of an attic storey with a pediment, the mark of an ancient temple rather than a conventional Christian building.

❶ Mon – Thu 9am – 5.30pm, Fri 11am – 5.30pm, Sat 9am – 5pm, Sun 12pm – 5pm; admission: €3.50

Interior The columned basilica, which is almost 100m/110yd long, contains some **outstanding works of art**: a wonderful crucifix by Giotto, at the second column on the left a marble pulpit designed by Brunelleschi in 1445 and a mural of the Trinity (1425 – 1427) by Masaccio, for which he was the first since ancient times to use linear perspective. Nardo di Cione painted the frescoes in the elevated Cappella Strozzi around 1357 with subjects from Dante's *Divine Comedy*. The altarpiece *Redeemer and Saints* (1357) by Andrea Orcagna can also be seen here. On the right in the Cappella Gaddi the painting over the altar *Jesus Awakens the Daughter of Jairus* (1571 – 1572) by Bronzino catches the eye. In the next chapel Cappella Gondi is the **famous wooden crucifix by Brunelleschi** (1421 – 1425), the first depiction of Christ without a loincloth.

Main choir chapel and right transept: The main chapel of the choir was completely painted by Domenico Ghirlandaio in 1486 – 1490 with scenes from the lives of Mary and John the Baptist. It also has numerous portraits of famous contemporaries, scenes from cultured middle-class homes, panoramic landscapes and great banquets. To the right of the main choir chapel is the Cappella di Filippo Strozzi, with **frescoes by Filippino Lippi** (1497 – 1502) that have scenes from the lives of the apostle Philip and John. The tomb of Filippo Strozzi was made by Benedetto da Maiano 1491 – 1493. In Cappella Rucellai are the bronze tomb cover (around 1423) for a provincial of the Dominican order named Dati by Lorenzo Ghiberti and the marble statue *Madonna and Child* (around 1345) by Nino Pisano.

*Museo di Santa Maria Novella In the museum of Santa Maria Novella go first to the »green cloister«, which got its name from the green colour of the frescoes by Paolo Uccello. The story begins with the creation of the animals and the fall of man (around 1430); the dramatic depiction of the flood was painted 20 years later. Do not fail to see the **paintings in the Cappella degli Spagnoli** (Spanish Chapel), which was built after 1340 by Jacopo Talenti as the chapter house of the Dominican monastery and turned over to Eleonora of Toledo, the wife of Cosimo I, as a place of worship for her Spanish attendants. Andrea (di Bonaiuto) da Firenze created from 1365 a wonderful visual representation of the pro-

Scented world: Officina Profumo-Farmaceutica

gramme of Dominican theology, which shows the way to salvation for mankind.
❶ Mon, Thu, Sat 9am – 5pm, admission €2.70

An unusual attraction is the Officina Profumo-Farmaceutica di Santa Maria Novella. The pharmacy's products are sold all over the world, e. g. the popular potpourri. An attached museum shows historic pharmaceutical equipment, bowls and glasses.
❶ Via della Scala 16; 10.30am – 7pm; free admission; www.smnovella.com

Officina Profumo-Farmaceutica

The collection of the national museum of photography on Piazza Santa Maria Novella 14r is based on the unique archives, started in 1853, of the Alinari brothers. The museum in the so-called Palazzo »delle Leopoldine« has an inventory of 2.75 mil. negatives as well as 900,000 historical prints (prints, etchings, bromine prints, daguer-

* MNAF (Museo Nazionale Alinari della Fotografia)

rotypes, photographic plates). Seven exhibition sections show items from the inventory; there are also special exhibits by prominent photographers. Museo Tattile is integrated into the national museum and makes it possible for the visually impaired to explore photography.

❶ Thu – Tue 10am – 6.30pm, admission: €9, Mon €6; www.mnaf.it

** SAN LORENZO AND SURROUNDINGS

** San Lorenzo

North-west of the cathedral square stands the church of San Lorenzo. The market stands with clothing and souvenirs in front of the incomplete façade make a colourful picture. In the middle of it all stands the monument created by Baccio Bandinelli in 1540 for Giovanni delle Bande Nere (1360 – 1429), the father of Cosimo I and founding father of the Medici dynasty. The church is said to have been dedicated as early as 393 by St Ambrose, then outside the city walls. San Lorenzo was the parish church of the Medici, who commissioned Filippo Brunelleschi to give it its present appearance after 1419. The work was completed after his death by Antonio Manetti (1460). Michelangelo drew up plans for the façade, which were never used however.

❶ Mon – Sat 10am – 5.30pm, Mar – Oct also Sun 1.30pm – 5.30pm; admission €3.50 (including Museo del Tesoro)

Interior

The interior of San Lorenzo is a daring synthesis of early Christian basilica and elements of ancient architecture. Among the highlights is the altar painting in the second chapel in the right-hand aisle, the *Marriage of the Virgin* (1523) by Rosso Fiorentino, whose Mannerism is expressed in a complex composition and variations in colour. In the floor a round memorial tablet made of precious materials commemorates Cosimo de Medici the Elder (1389 – 1464), whose remains rest with those of the sculptor Donatello (around 1386 – 1466), whom he greatly admired, in the crypt below it. In the nave just before the crossing are two bronze pulpits by Donatello, expressive masterpieces which were completed after his death by his pupils. In the left-hand aisle Agnolo Bronzino's fresco *Martyrdom of St Lawrence* (1565 – 1569) is a **principal work of Mannerism** with extreme contortions of the figures and pale colours. In the first chapel in the eastern wall of the left transept is a striking altarpiece by Fra Filippo Lippi, the *Annunciation* (around 1440).

The entrance to the Old Sacristy is in the left transept. Its donor Giovanni di Averardo, known as Bicci de Medici (1360 – 1429) and clan father of the non-noble branch of the Medici, intended it to be a burial chapel but it was used as a sacristy. With its domed central plan, it is considered to be the first epoch-making work of Brunelleschi (1418 – 1428). Donatello produced the furnishings between 1437 und 1443. In the middle of the sacristy is the marble sarcophagus of Giovanni di Bicci de Medici and his wife Piccarda di Odoardo Bueri. In the wall of the transept is the double funerary monument (1472) for Cosimo's sons Giovanni and Piero by Andrea del Verrocchio. The cloister leads to the **Museo del Tesoro**. The reliquary bust of St Peter and Michelozzo's 1444 silver figure of Christ, which was part of a crucifix that was commissioned by Cosimo the Elder, are masterpieces.

Sagrestia Vecchia

A door in the left wall leads to the pleasant cloister, from which there are stairs to the Biblioteca Laurenziana. It was built in 1524 – 1571 to plans by Michelangelo in order to accommodate the valuable book collection of the Medici. The reading room benches and lecterns were designed by Michelangelo. Today codices, manuscripts and missals (6th – 16th cent.) are displayed here.

**Biblioteca Medicea Laurenziana

❶ Daily 9am – 1pm; admission €3, www.bml.firenze.sbn.it

The Medici chapels are annexed to San Lorenzo, but are a museum with a separate entrance (Piazza Madonna degli Aldobrandini). The entrance leads first to a crypt with tombs of the Medici family, then into the **monumental burial chapel of the famous Medici rulers** and finally into the New Sacristy. Construction of the gigantic mausoleum began in 1605, and the interior design with stone inlays was under construction until the 20th century.

** Museo delle Cappelle Medicee

❶ Mar 22 – Nov 1 Tue – Sat as well as every 1st, 3rd and 5th Sun and 2nd, 4th Mon of the Month 8.15am – 4.50pm; admission: €6

From the Medici chapel descend to the New Sacristy, which is actually a burial chapel. It was built and decorated by **Michelangelo** from 1520 until 1534 with interruptions, and was never completed. Lorenzo the Magnificent and his brother Giuliano, who fell victim to the Pazzi conspiracy in 1478, are buried at the entrance wall. To the right and left in wall niches are the graves of Giuliano, Duke of Nemour, a son of Lorenzo the Magnificent who gave Michelangelo the commission for the tombs, and Lorenzo, Duke of Urbino, a grandson of Lorenzo the Magnificent. Seated and dressed in the armour of a Roman commander, Giuliano de Medici turns his head sideways as he looks attentively at the Madonna and the two patron saints of the Medici, Cosmas and Damian. Under Giuliano the figures of night, with half moon and stars in its hair, and day lie on the slanted lid of the sar-

**Sagrestia Nuova

cophagus. Both sarcophagus figures were modelled on ancient statues. Opposite them another niche figure depicts Lorenzo de Medici, whose head rests pensively in his hand. On the sarcophagus lid below are the two allegorical figures of evening or dusk (left) and morning or dawn (right). The masculine figure of dusk stands for mental exhaustion, the lethargic mass of the body going to sleep, while the feminine figure shows awakening and the slowly developing power of the body and spirit. In this chapel Michelangelo aimed to create through a **combination of architecture, sculpture and painting** a philosophical work of art reflecting the path of life from matter (river gods, sarcophagus) via incarnation (day and night as life and death, statue of Giuliano) to eternal life (resurrection fresco).

*Palazzo Medici-Riccardi Between 1444 and 1464 Michelozzo created in the Palazzo Medici the **prototype of a Florentine city palace** for Cosimo the Elder, with a fortress-like front reminiscent of the Palazzo Vecchio. The non-noble branch of the Medici and the Medici rulers, whose coat of arms with five spheres (the »palle«) and a lily decorate the palace, lived here until Cosimo I moved to the Palazzo Vecchio in 1540. In 1659 the Riccardi family acquired it, enlarged it and lengthened the palace front. In 1818 it passed to the Grand Dukes of Tuscany. The arched entrance leads first into a square courtyard with twelve marble medallions over the rounded columned arch and a statue of Bacchus by Baccio Bandinelli. Behind it is a small garden courtyard.

From the main courtyard stairs lead to the Cappella dei Magi with the ***frescoes by Benozzo Gozzoli**, *The Procession of the Magi to Bethlehem* (1459/1460). Gozzoli portrayed the Milanese Duke Cosimo the Elder, Patriarch Josephus of Constantinople as the oldest king, followed by the Byzantine emperor John VII and Lorenzo de Medici as the youngest king.

❶ Entrance Via Cavour 3; daily except Wed 9am – 7pm; admittance every 7 min. (max. 12 visitors); admission: €7; www.palazzo-medici.it

AROUND PIAZZA SAN MARCO

*San Marco The church of San Marco, built from 1299 to 1310 by the Benedictine order of St Sylvester, was given to the Dominicans of ▶Fiesole together with the monastery in the year the cathedral was dedicated by Pope Eugene IV. Cosimo the Elder made a renovation of the church and construction of the monastery possible through a generous donation. The architect Michelozzo was commissioned to complete the work (1437 – 1452). Giambologna added the side altars and the chapel of St Antoninus as well as the Salviati chapel (1588). In 1678 Pier Francesco Silvani remodelled the church and in 1777 – 1780 the façade was altered.

Interior: The outstanding work in the aisle-less church is a crucifix from the school of Giotto. On the left is the burial chapel of St Antoninus, the archbishop and Dominican prior who was elevated to sainthood in 1526. It is **the major architectural work by Giambologna** (1578 – 1589), who also provided the decoration: six life-size niche statues and six bronze reliefs from the life of St Antoninus. On the way back to the entrance, three treasures are to be seen on the right: a Baroque marble door that leads to the sacristy, a Byzantine mosaic *Madonna at Prayer* (705 – 707) which came from Rome and Fra Bartolomeo della Porta's painting *Madonna and Child* (1509) with a canopy motif.

The monastery of San Marco (the entrance is to the right of the church) was built by Michelozzo in the Renaissance style; its decorations are an impressive example of late medieval piety. In the pilgrims' hospice are several panel paintings by Fra Angelico, including **the altar of the linen weavers** (1433) and further panels with scenes from the life of Jesus (1450), the *Deposition from the Cross* (1435) and the *Last Judgement* (1430). Directly opposite the entrance is *St Dominic at the Foot of the Cross*; diagonally opposite the entrance *Ecce Homo* can be seen in the lunette. Both works are frescoes by Fra Angelico. The works in the large refectory include Fra Bartolomeo's fresco *Last Judgement*. In the Sala dei Lavabo there is also a large and impressive panel by Fra Bartolomeo, the *Madonna with St Anne and Other Saints* (1510). In the chapter house the *Crucifixion* by Fra Angelico fills an entire wall; the small refectory holds a famous *Last Supper* (after 1480) by Ghirlandaio.

On the second floor are more than 40 **monks' cells** which Fra Angelico decorated with **frescoes** with the help of his students. Look out for the intimate depiction of the **Annunciation** opposite the stairs. The prior's apartment is a reminder of Girolamo Savonarola, prior of San Marco from 1491, who was executed as a heretic and schismatic in 1498. The large hall of the **library** with valuable manuscripts, missals and bibles was designed in an imposing and austere style by Michelozzo (1444).

**Museo di San Marco

❶ Mon – Fri 8.15am – 1.50pm, Sat, Sun 8.15am – 4.50pm, closed 2nd and 4th Mon of the month; admission: €4

**Galleria dell' Accademia

The east side of Piazza San Marco is bordered by the university building. Right next to it is the gallery of the academy of art, which emerged from the first academy of 1562 and was revived by Grand Duke Pietro Leopoldo I in 1784. The greatest treasures of the collection are outstanding sculptures by Michelangelo and paintings of the Middle Ages and Renaissance. In the Galleria del David are four incomplete figures of prisoners out of the total of six that Michelangelo created for the grave of Pope Julius II in Rome (1519 – 1536). After Michelangelo's death they were set up to decorate the grotto in the Giardino di Boboli and in 1909 were transferred to the academy. The figure of the apostle Matthew, which Michelangelo sculpted in 1505 – 1506, also remained incomplete. **Michelangelo's world famous David** was removed in 1873 from Piazza della Signoria, where it had suffered greatly from the rain and wind, and placed in the rotunda of the academy. At the age of 26 Michelangelo had taken over a giant block of marble that was considered to be misshapen and unusable because of its unfortunate proportions (more than 4m/13ft high, but with little depth) and in the years 1501 – 1504 created a figure of youthful power and beauty: David, a shepherd who according to the Bible won an apparently hopeless battle for the people of Israel against the giant Goliath. The Renaissance figure became a symbol of the Florentine desire for liberty. In the first of the three Florentine rooms is the so-called Adimari chest, an oblong clothes chest with a 15th-century wedding procession on the front. There are also works by Filippo Lippi, Fra Bartolomeo and Perugino here. The Byzantine rooms contain the oldest works of the academy's collection from the second half of the 13th century and the 14th century.

❶ Tue – Sun 8.15am – 6.50pm, July – Sep Tue until 10pm, Mar – Dec last Tue of the month until 11pm; admission: €11, May 31 – Nov 6 from 4pm €10; last Tue of the month evenings free admission; www.uffizi.firenze.it/musei/accademia

AROUND PIAZZA SANTISSIMA ANNUNZIATA

Via Cesare Battisti leads to the large and beautiful Piazza. On the north side is the church Santissima Annunziata, on the east side the orphanage and on the south side Palazzo Grifoni (16th century), the imposing seat of the regional administration today.

*Piazza Santissima Annunziata

The Church of the Annunciation, built around 1250 as an oratory of the Servite order, was thoroughly altered between 1444 and 1481 by Michelozzo. The centre door of the seven-arched portico gives access to the Chiostrino dei Voti, a forecourt named after the votive offerings displayed there, with an important cycle of early 16th-century frescoes which begins on the right wall with the *Assumption of the Virgin* (Rosso Fiorentino). It is followed by the *Visitation* (Pontormo), *Betrothal of the Virgin* (Franciabigio), *Birth of the Virgin* (Andrea del Sarto), the *Three Magi* (Andrea del Sarto), the *Nativity* (Alessio Baldovinetti) and scenes from the life of St Filippo Benizzi (Cosimo Rosselli, Andrea del Sarto). The aisle-less interior of the church is flanked by chapels; the choir has the shape of a rotunda. The first chapel on the left is the Cappella Feroni with the fresco *The Redeemer and St Julian* (1455) by Andrea del Castagno. *Holy Trinity* in the next chapel is by the same artist. The rotunda was begun by Michelozzo (1444) and finished by Leon Battista Alberti to a different design. The painting by Agnolo Bronzino *Resurrection* (1550) in the fourth chapel on the left and the Cappella della Madonna del Soccorso, a work of Giambologna (1594 – 1598), are also impressive. Giambologna designed the chapel with beautiful frescoes, statues and reliefs to be his own tomb. The dome of the choir rotunda is decorated by a fresco of the Coronation of the Virgin by Volterrano (1681 – 1683).

**Santissima Annunziata

❶ daily 7.30am – 12.30pm 4pm – 6.30pm, free admission

The foundling hospital, which was begun in 1419 by Filippo Brunelleschi, is the first modern secular building with a columned portico like an ancient temple instead of medieval pillars. The architecture is complemented by frescoes in the arcades and lunettes above the entrances as well as by ten coloured **terracotta medallions** in the outer corners of the arches with depictions of swaddled babies (around 1463), which Andrea della Robbia made. The commission for the new building came from the wealthy silk merchants' guild, which had the house built for abandoned new-born babies (innocenti). This institution is still the city's orphanage – until 1875 babies could be left here by their mothers in a revolving wooden cylinder on the left-hand wall of the portico.

*Spedale degli Innocenti

Museo degli Innocenti (MUDI) is dedicated to »Childhood in the Renaissance« and the relationship between the 600-year-old orphanage

* MUDI, Galleria dello Spedale

to Florence (»Gli Innocenti e la città«). Along with an historical archive the »Bottega dei Ragazzi« offers Italian and foreign children up to 11 years a playful approach to art. About 50 pictures, sculptures, miniatures and furniture from the 14th to the 18th century are displayed in the gallery, including works by Giovanni del Biondo, Rossellino, Benedetto da Maiano, and above all by Domenico Ghirlandaio and Andrea del Sarto as well as a terracotta *Madonna* by Luca della Robbia.

❶ daily 10am – 7pm; admission: €5; www.museomudifirenze.it

*Museo Archeologico Centrale dell'Etruria

Palazzo della Crocetta holds the most important archaeological museum of central Italy, which was founded in 1870. Items especially worthy of note include the coloured sarcophagus of Larthia Seianti (between 217 and 147 BC) from Martinella near Chiusi. In the garden are reconstructions of Etruscan graves and grave monuments. The Etruscan-Greek-Roman department comprises Etruscan urns and sarcophagi, including the painted marble sarcophagus of Ramtha Hucznai from Tarquinia, as well as Etruscan, Greek and Roman bronzes like Idolino, the Greek statue of a young Ephebos (5th century BC) or the Standing Orator (Aulus Metellus, 3rd century BC). Statues, busts, ceramics, reliefs, sarcophagi, mummies, pictures and utensils document the various Egyptian dynasties, including a well-preserved wooden wagon from the time of Ramses I. The collections of coins and jewellery as well as a vase collection with the famous Françoise Vase (6th cent. BC) are also remarkable.

❶ Via della Colonna; Tue – Fri 8.30am – 7pm, Sat, Sun 8.30am – 2pm; admission €4; www.firenzemusei.it/archeologico

** MUSEO NAZIONALE DEL BARGELLO

❶ daily 8.15am – 1.50pm; closed 1st, 3rd, 5th Sun and 2nd, 4th Mon of the month, exhibits until 5pm, last Tue/month 7pm – 11pm
Admission: €4, exhibits €7, last Tue/month evening free;
www.uffizi.firenze.it/musei/bargello

Building history

The monumental building on Via Proconsolo north-east of Piazza della Signoria was erected in 1250 by the citizens of Florence as a sign of their victory over the nobility. After 1261 the building was the seat of the podestà, from 1502 a court with prison and from 1574 the seat of the president of the police, who was called the »bargello«. Since 1859 it has housed one of the most important museums of sculpture in Italy.

❶ daily 8.30am – 1.50pm, closed Mon

First floor

The first room to the right of the entrance contains **major works by Michelangelo**, including the expressive early *Drunken Bacchus* (1496 / 1497). In its depiction of the Virgin as a seer, the round relief of the Madonna (1504 – 1505) for Bartolomeo Pitti is a precursor of his sibyls in the Sistine Chapel. Michelangelo's marble bust of Brutus (around 1540) alludes to the murder of the cruel Duke Alessandro de Medici by his cousin Lorenzino in 1537, but remained unfinished.

In the loggia of the second floor, the highlights are bronzes by Giam-   **Second floor**
bologna: the fountain figure of Mercury (1580), a virtuoso piece that appears to break the laws of structural engineering, as well as the classical coolness of *Allegory of Architecture*. Masterpieces by the great Renaissance sculptor Donatello are in the room named after him, in-

cluding the marble David (1410 – 1416), his earliest monumental statue, as well as a statue and relief of St George (1415 – 1417), which show his dramatic conception of figures. The marble lion *Marzocco* (1418 – 1420) is also a masterpiece, as is the softly modelled, youthful bronze figure of David (around 1435), **the first nude figure since antiquity**. It is also interesting to compare the styles of Ghiberti and Brunelleschi, whose **competing reliefs for the second door of the baptistery** *Sacrifice of Isaac* (1401 – 1402) have been preserved. Among the coloured ceramics *Enthroned Madonna* (around 1460) by Luca della Robbia is outstanding. Along

Studying sculptures in the Bargello

with these exhibits the following can also be seen on the second floor: frescoes of paradise and hell as well as legends of saints (around 1330 – 1340) in the chapel of the podestà, ivory works, majolica, enamel and goldsmith work as well as furniture and glass.

Andrea del Verrocchio, Leonardo da Vinci's teacher, made a finely   **Third floor**
modelled, naturalistic figure of a shepherd boy in his bronze David (before 1476). Further outstanding works are the highly realistic portrait bust of Pietro Melini by Benedetto da Maiano (1474), the marble bust of Matteo Palmieri (1468) by Antonio Rossellino and the ceramic bust of a Young Warrior (1479 – 1480) by Antonio Pollaiuolo with a Hercules and Hydra relief on the breastplate. Pollaiuolo modelled the bronze group of Hercules and Antaeus, also around 1480. Other rooms display the **Medici medallion collection**, a weapons collection, textiles, small bronze figures and works in glazed terracotta by Andrea della Robbia.

SANTA CROCE AND SURROUNDINGS

**Santa Croce
With its many **graves and monuments** as well as numerous **important paintings** – including impressive works by Giotto – the church is one of the finest in Italy. Its imposing dimensions (115m/125yd long and 38m/41yd wide) make it the largest Franciscan church. Building began in 1294, presumably under Arnolfo di Cambio. It was completed in 1385 except for the façade (19th cent.). As part of a guided tour visitors can watch Santa Croce's **conservators** at work in their workshops and the Cappella Maggiore.

❶ daily 9.30am – 5.30pm, Sun 1pm – 5.30pm; admission: €5; tours to the conservators: Mon – Fri 10am, 11am, 12pm, 2pm, 3pm, 4pm (appointment required: tel. 05 52 46 61 05); €13; www.santacroceopera.it

Flower market in the colonnades of the Piazza della Republica

The tour begins in the left aisle. Opposite the first pillar is the 18th-century monument to Galileo Galilei with allegories of geometry and astronomy. Near the fifth pillar the **tombplate of Lorenzo Ghiberti,** the creator of the paradise doors, is set in the floor. The chapel at the front of the left aisle holds the wooden crucifix (around 1421) by Donatello. Brunelleschi criticized it with the words that his friend had nailed a farmer to the cross, and then himself created a noble-looking crucified Christ for the church of Santa Maria Novella. On the right opposite is the Cappella Bardi di Vernio with frescoes (1340) on the life of St Sylvester by Maso di Banco. The painting in the adjacent Cappella Pulci *Martyrdom of the Archdeacons Lawrence and Stephen is* by Bernardo Daddi (around 1330). The large **main chapel of the choir** is decorated with wall frescoes (around 1380) on the Legend of the Holy Cross by Agnolo Daddi. The adjacent **Cappella Bardi** on the right, which has a fresco cycle (around 1320) with important stations from the legend of St Francis, has been attributed to Giotto. The revolutionary nature of his compositions is made clear in comparison to the altarpiece from around 1270 with small individual scenes and the large, flat-looking figure of St Francis.

Cappella Peruzzi has ****wall paintings by Giotto,** which can be called his main works: frescoes with scenes from the life of John the Evangelist and John the Baptist, made around 1320.

The Cappella Baroncelli is at the end of the transept. Taddeo Gaddi, a pupil of Giotto, painted the frescoes (1332 – 1337) of the prophets and the life of Mary, including the Annunciation to the Shepherds, a rare night scene in medieval painting. The frescoes in the adjacent Cappella Castellani were painted by Agnolo Gaddi and his pupils around 1383.

An elaborate door to a corridor (Corridoio della Sagrestia) designed by Michelozzo leads to the sacristy. It contains valuable cabinets from the Renaissance and a Crucifixion by Taddeo Gaddi. Behind the sacristy is the 14th-century Cappella Rinuccini with frescoes by Giovanni da Milano showing scenes from the lives of the Virgin and Mary Magdalene. At the end of the sacristy corridor is the novitiate chapel built by Michelozzo for Cosimo de Medici between 1434 and 1445. The corridor also leads to the leather school (Scuola del Cuoio), where handmade bags and leather articles are sold.

In the right-hand aisle is the funerary monument of the composer Gioacchino Rossini as well as the tomb of the Florentine scholar and chancellor of the republic, Leonardo Bruni, in which Bernardo Rossellino created the **prototype of the Florentine Renaissance tomb** around 1450. A few steps further is a graceful relief by Donatello of the Annunciation (1435). About in the middle of the aisle is the wall tomb (1787) with an allegory of diplomacy for the political philosopher Niccolò Machiavelli. At the next pillar is the Renaissance pulpit (around 1480) by Benedetto da Maiano. Vittorio Alfieri (†1803), a poet and forerunner of the Risorgimento, rests in a classical grave by Antonio Canova in the opposite wall. Next is the monumental cenotaph (1829) for Dante Alighieri, who died in Ravenna in 1321 and is buried there. Vasari designed the **tomb of Michelangelo** with personifications of sculpture, painting and architecture.

Monastery, cloisters, Santa Croce Museum
To the right of the church is the entrance to the monastery of Santa Croce. In the first cloister is the Cappella dei Pazzi built by Brunelleschi from 1430 and commissioned by Andrea de Pazzi. This early example of central-plan Renaissance architecture with terracotta reliefs by Andrea della Robbia served as family chapel and as chapter house for the Franciscan monks. A passageway leads from the first cloister to the large two-storey cloister built around 1452 by Bernardo Rossellino to plans by Brunelleschi. The museum is housed in the refectory and adjacent rooms. Its main works include the 120 sq m/1,300 sq ft Last Supper (1330 – 1340) by Taddeo Gaddi; a large crucifix (after 1270) by Cimabue, a masterpiece that was unfortunately severely damaged by the Arno flood in 1966; a bronze statue by Donatello, *St Louis* (1423); as well as *Stigmata*, a terracotta group by Andrea della Robbia.

*Casa Buonarroti
In Via Ghibellina no. 70, north of Santa Croce, which Michelangelo Buonarroti bought for his nephew Leonardo, is a place of memorial to the artist. It houses the powerful and dynamic *Battle of the Centaurs*, a marble relief which Michelangelo sculpted when he was 17 years old, and the flat marble relief which he created a little earlier, *Madonna with* Child (also called *Madonna della Scala* because of the steps). It is full of melancholy since Mary's eyes seem to look knowingly into the future at the death of Jesus. Further notable works here are a wooden crucifix (1494) for Santo Spirito, which shows Christ not as a man of sorrows but as a gentle youth, and a wooden model of the unfinished façade of the church of San Lorenzo.
❶ Wed – Mon 10am – 5pm; admission: €6.50; www.casabuonarroti.it

Sinagoga
The synagogue, which was built 1874 – 1882 as a copy of the Hagia Sophia in Istanbul with its green dome, is considered to be the most magnificent in Europe. Some of the architectural elements are Moorish style. Attached is the Museo Ebraico (»Jewish Museum«), whose displays include documents on the history of the Florentine Jews.
❶ Via Farini; Apr – Sep Sun – Thu 10am – 6pm, Oct – Mar Sun – Thu 10am – 3pm, Fri 10am – 2pm; admission €5;
http://moked.it/firenzebraica/itinerari/informazioni-turistiche

OUTSIDE THE OLD CITY

Via Monte alle Croci leads from Piazzale Michelangelo to the monastery San Miniato al Monte, which is built over the grave of St Minias, who was martyred in Florence in the year 250. It was founded by Cluniac monks around 1018 and building work began around 1050. The church was largely complete by the early 13th century. It was converted into a fortress in the 16th century, used as a hospital, paupers' and old people's home in the 17th century. The monastery was turned over to Olivet monks in 1924. To the left of the church lies **an atmospheric cemetery**, to the right the 14th-century summer palace of the bishops of Florence, part of the monastery since 1534. The two-storey façade is covered with thin marble panels. The mosaic (2nd half 13th cent.) on the upper floor depicts Christ between Mary

*San Miniato al Monte

Still there in the city on the Arno:
villas with generous gardens

and San Miniato. The gable is crowned by a gilded eagle with a bunch of wool in its talons. It is the figure from the coat of arms of the textile merchants' guild, which financed the construction and maintenance of San Miniato for a long time. The campanile collapsed in 1499 and was left incomplete.

Interior: The impressive interior takes up the late antique, early Christian form of the columned basilica: a long church consisting of a nave and two aisles, with an exposed roof structure and without a transept. The choir, which was traditionally built over a martyr's grave, originally gave the pilgrim entering the church a view of the hall crypt (11th cent.) and the remains of St Miniato. Michelozzo's barrel-vaulted **marble ciborium** with white and light-blue terracotta cassettes by Luca della Robbia in the nave was created in 1448 and commissioned by Piero de Medici. The back is an altarpiece by Agnolo Gaddi (around 1396) with scenes of the martyrdom of St Miniato.

Cappella del Cardinale di Portogallo: The funeral chapel of the Portuguese cardinal was commissioned by King Alfonso V of Portugal and built by Manetti 1461 – 1466. As a space with a central plan it is strongly oriented to Brunelleschi's Old Sacristy in San Lorenzo. The interior decoration combines Christian and ancient ideas. Thus Antonio Rossellino's conception of the sarcophagus is reminiscent of Roman models; a Mithras sacrifice as well as putti decorate the tomb niche. The reclining figure of the deceased faces an empty judge's seat as a reminder of the Last Judgement. The terracotta figures are by Luca della Robbia.

Crypt: To the left and right of the marble ciborium, steps lead down to the crypt with frescoes (14th century) by Taddeo Gaddi.

Presbytery and apse: The marble screens and the marble pulpit (2nd half 12th cent.) are among the most valuable late Romanesque decorations of the church. The apse is decorated with a mosaic Christ with Mary and San Miniato, in which Byzantine influence is recognizable. It was originally made in 1297 and in the second half of the 19th century almost completely renewed.

Sacristy: From the apse go right into the sacristy, where Spinello Aretino created his masterpiece, the Legends of St Benedict, in 1387, then through to the cloister with frescoes by Andrea del Castagno and Paolo Uccello.

❶ daily 8am – 12.30pm, 3pm – 5.30pm; free admission, sacristy/frescos €1

*Museo Stibbert

The English officer Frederick Stibbert, a well-travelled and wealthy man, collected weapons, art, but also religious items, clothing and utensils all over the world. In his villa in the hills north of Florence (Bus 4) this gigantic collection fills 60 rooms.

❶ Via Federico Stibbert 26; Mon – Wed 10am – 2pm, Fri – Sun 10am – 6pm, admission €6, www.museostibbert.it.

AROUND FLORENCE

The former Carthusian monastery 5km/3mi lies south of Florence at the outskirts of Galluzzo (Bus 37). Niccolò Acciaiuoli, a Florentine statesman and friend of Petrarch, had the fortress-like Carthusian monastery built in 1341. The complex was later expanded several times and is used by Benedictine monks today. In the monastery church of San Lorenzo is the famous grave of Cardinal Agnolo II Acciaiuoli, which is attributed to Francesco da Sangallo. The monastery picture gallery includes lunette frescoes by Pontormo to designs by Albrecht Dürer and a *Madonna with Child* by Lucas Cranach.

*Certosa del Galluzzo

❶ Winter Tue – Sat 9am – 11am, 3pm – 4pm, Sun 3pm – 4pm, summer until 5pm; admission: donation

*Villa la Petraia (not signposted) lies on the right above the Florence – Sesto road. Ferdinando de Medici acquired the estate in 1575 and had it converted by Buontalenti, but the defensive tower was preserved. In the 19th century the estate served as the summer residence of the Italian kings. It is still owned by the state and open to the public. The charming park offers a good view all the way to Florence. Only a few hundred metres to the west of Villa la Petraia lies **Villa Medicea di Castello**, which dates from the 16th century in its present form. It was the country residence of Cosimo I de' Medici, Grand Duke of Tuscany. As the today seat of the Accademia della Crusca it is not open to the public, but the extensive park with its elaborate waterworks, grottoes and statues is. In the sculptural group on the central fountain Hercules battles against the giant Antaeus.

**Medici villas

Villa la Petraia: Via della Petraia 40; June – Aug 8.15am – 7.30pm, Apr, May, Sep , Oct until 6.30pm, Mar until 5.30pm, Nov – Feb until 4.30pm, closed 2nd and 3rd Mon of the month; last admittnace 60 min. before closing; tours every 45 min.; free admission
Villa Medicea di Castello: Via Castello 47; opening hours like Villa la Petraia; no tours are offered but the staff will show the Giardino Segreto; free admission

The two Medici villas west of Florence, Poggio a Caiano and Artimino, can be found under ▶Prato and ▶ Borgo San Lorenzo, Surroundings.

Other Medici villas

In Coverciano east of Florenzce Museo del Calcio shows the history of Italian soccer through jerseys, memorabilia, game scenes and stars like Riva, Maldini, Cannavaro or Riviera.

Museo del Calcio

❶ Viale Aldo Palazzeschi 20, Mon – Fri 9am – 1pm, 3pm – 7pm, Sat 9am –1pm; admission €5; www.museodelcalcio.it

★★ Giglio / Isola del Giglio

——————————————————— ✦ P/Q 8

Province: Grosseto (GR)
Area: 21 sq km/8 sq mi
Population: 1,470

11 nautical miles west of Monte Argentario lies the green and mountainous Giglio. The second-largest tuscan island, which made the headlines in January 2012 when the cruise ship Costa Concordia rammed a rock on its east coast and started to sink, is otherwise a small paradise for holidaymakers and divers looking for peace and quiet.

Giglio has a few small, attractive sandy coves for **swimming and snorkelling** north and south of Lazzaretto Peninsula (Arenella beach and Caletta cove, Cala delle Canelle and Cala degli Alberi beaches). The biggest beach is **Campese Bay**; the smaller beaches can only be reached on footpaths. The underwater world with a sandy or sea-grass bottom offers lots of variety for divers.

❶ RAMA busses: circular route Porto – Castello – Campese; summer 5.15am – 2.30am; www.ramamobilita.it

Giglio Porto   The ferries from the mainland arrive at Giglio Porto on the east coast. In the busy harbour old houses cluster around the quay on a narrow coastal strip, restaurants, bars and shops await customers. The massive Torre del Porto was built in 1596 by Grand Duke Ferdinand I.

*Giglio Castello   A steep winding road leads up to the main town of the island, Giglio Castello, which lies at an elevation of 400m/1,312ft. The fortress, which was begun under Pisan rule and later strenghtened by the Genoese and the Medici grand dukes has the small island museum. Within the enclosing wall **tiny streets** and typically narrow outside steps give the picturesque town its character. The church of San Pietro Apostolo (15. cent.) is worth a visit.

Campese   This modern town has a beautiful location and a long sand beach. The former fishing village has long since become a holiday resort with a considerable tourist infrastructure (including diving schools).

Isola di Giannutri   The flat island of Giannutri with an area of 2.6 sq km/1 sq mi. lies about 15 nautical miles south-east of Giglio. Because of its half-moon shape the Greeks called it Artemisia; the Romans called it Dianum (Diana's bow). Ferries connect it to Maregiglio and water taxis to Porto Santo Stefano (in the summer half of the year only with a guide). Giannutri is a tip for keen **divers**. On the north-west side of

Giglio

INFORMATION
Via Provinciale 9, Giglio Porto (at the
harbour)
Tel. 05 64 80 94 00
www.isoladelgiglio.it

FERRIES/EXCURSION BOATS
Ferries to Giglio depart from Porto Santo
Stefano (► Monte Argentario; shuttle
busses from Grosseto railway station)
and from San Vincenzo (►Livorno). Boat
excursions from Elba.

Shipping companies
www.maregiglio.it
www.toremar.it
www.aquavision.it

WHERE TO EAT
Da Maria €€€
Via della Casamatta 12, Giglio Castello
Tel. 05 64 80 60 62
Closed Wed. and Jan. – Feb.
Restaurant with family tradition. Fresh
fish daily.

La Paloma €€
Via Umberto I 48, Giglio Porto
Tel. 05 64 80 92 33
Sept. – June closed Mon., July/Aug.
open daily.
Claudio Bossini serves unusual speciali-
ties from the sea.

WHERE TO STAY
Castello Monticello €€€
Via Provinciale, Giglio Porto

Tel. 05 64 80 92 52
www.hotelcastellomonticello.com
Open Easter to the end of September.
Beautiful hotel in a 1920s villa with a
terrace and a sea view above Giglio Porto; 29 rooms.

Arenella €€€
Via Arenella 5
Giglio Porto
Tel. 05 64 80 93 40
www.hotelarenella.com
Family-friendly hotel with 27 rooms.
There is a large terrace for sunbathing
with a bar, but the beach is only a few
minutes' walk from the house.

Hotel Bahamas €€
Via Cardinale Oreglia 22
Giglio Porto
Tel. 05 64 80 92 54
www.bahamashotel.it
Solid and traditional. The hotel is located
above the harbour, some rooms have a
view of the sea and the harbour; 28
rooms.

CAMPING
Baia del Sole €
Cala Sparavieri, Campese
Tel. 05 64 80 40 36
www.campingbaiadelsole.net
The only campground on Giglio; with
about 50 pitches – some right above the
sea – and a few bungalows. It has a
rocky beach for swimming.

the island above Cala Maestra cove are the remains of a Roman settlement (1st/2nd cent.), including baths and the stately villa of the
patrician family of Domizi Aenobarbi (not accessible) There are only
apartments and simple rooms available of Giannutri.

✴ Grosseto

✴ **N 9**

Province: Grosseto (GR)
Altitude: 10m/33ft above sea level
Population: 82,300

150 years ago it was still a sleepy village, but now the provincial capital is growing more and more attractive. The location, good shopping and pretty old city make the bicycle-friendly city just as interesting as its art and cultural attractions.

History Grosseto grew in the Middle Ages from a small castle which guarded the Via Aurelia, the old Roman road that connected Pisa and Rome. After the Etruscan town of Rusellae was destroyed in the year 935 by the Saracens, Pope Innocent II moved the bishop's seat to Grosseto in 1138. The Medici had the fortifications strengthened and new irrigation canals built. The grand dukes of Tuscany also made improvements which brought modest prosperity to the town. Only after 1930 when the ▶Maremma was finally completely drained did the town grow to be a wealthy centre of agriculture with some industry.

Grosseto's main square: cathedral on the left, city hall on the right

What to See in Grosseto

The historic city centre is surrounded by an irregular six-sided wall with six bastions, which was begun by Baldassare Lanci in 1574 under orders from the Grand Duke Francesco I and completed in 1593 under Ferdinand I. In 1835 Leopold II had the fortifications converted into a **public wall garden**.

*Medici fortifications

The main square of the old city is Piazza Dante Alighieri with a monument to Leopold II (1797 – 1870), the last Habsburg hereditary grand duke of Tuscany. The north side is marked by the red-and-white marble façade of the cathedral of San Lorenzo. Of the original building, which Sozzo di Rustichino built around 1300 on the foundations of an older church, only the south doorway remains, its architrave adorned with figures of Christ and the evangelists. Inside the left transept is an *Assumption of the Virgin* (1474) by Matteo di Giovanni.

*Piazza Dante Alighieri, Duomo

The museum of archaeology and art north of the cathedral holds finds from Roselle (see below) and its more and more complex city infrastructure, types of houses and wall techniques are documented. The exhibits include Etruscan black ceramic vases, terracottas and ceramics of the Hellenistic period as well as imperial Roman statues. The art museum has works from the 13th – 19th century, including Sassetta's masterly *Madonna delle Ciligie* (1450), majolicas and a collection of coins from the Middle Ages and Renaissance. The diocese museum shows sacred objects, including *Last Judgement* (14th cent.) attributed to Guido da Siena from Grosseto's church of San Leonardo.
❶ Musei di Maremma: Piazza Baccarini 3; Oct – June Tue – Sat 10am – 7pm, Sun 10am – 1pm and 4pm – 7pm; July – Sep Tue – Sat 10am – 8pm, Sun 10am – 1pm and 5pm – 8pm; admission €5; www.museidimaremma.it

*Museo Archeologico e d'Arte della Maremma

A hominide is the symbol of the Museum of Natural history: Oreopithecus Bambolii was discovered in 1872 by the palaeontologist Paul Gervais in the Montebamboli mine near Massa Marittima. In 1996 the body was reconstructed in three dimensions by Ronald Clarke from south Africa. Life on earth is presented in the museum by means of a Tree of Life, among other things. The museum includes an aquarium and astronomical observatory in Roselle.
Natural History Museum: Strada Corsini 5, June 15 – Sep 15 Tue, Wed 10am –1pm, Fri – Sun 6.30pm – 11.30am; Sep 16 – June 14 Tue, Wed and Fri 9am – 1pm, Sat 9am – 1pm, 4pm – 8pm, Sun 4pm – 8pm; admission: €5; www.museonaturalemaremma.it
Aquarium: Via Porciatti 12; July/Aug Tue – Sat 5pm – 11pm, Apr – June, Sep – Dec Tue – Sat 9.30am – 12.30pm, 3pm – 7pm; free admission
Observatory: Fri 9.30pm; free admission

Museo di Storia Naturale della Maremma, Aquarium

** PARCO ARCHEOLOGICO DI ROSELLE

Remains of the Etruscan city Rusellae

A must for everyone with an interest in ancient times lies on the hill flank of Poggio di Moscona, 9km/5.5mi north-east of Grosseto: the remains of the Etruscan city of Rusellae, a member of the twelve-city league. In ancient times it was separated from Vetulonia by a lake, while a trade road secured the connection to northern and southern Etruria. According to Livy, Rusellae was conquered by the Romans in 294 BC and expanded under Augustus. The city declined after the fall of the western Roman Empire. Parts of the 3km/1.8mi-long wall made of limestone blocks 2m/6.5ft high, which presumably enclosed the two hills of the city from the 7th century BC, have been preserved. The oldest part of the settlement is the northern area **with Etruscan houses** made of unfired brick, which come from the 7th century BC. The regularly ordered rows of stones on the western side date from the 2nd century BC. The quarters of the craftsmen were sited on the southern hill from the Hellenistic period until the end of the 2nd century BC. Several wells and cisterns ensured the water supply, and a **sewer system** disposed of waste water. Excavations have exposed three city gates, and the existence of four more is supposed because of the access roads. Along these roads remains of graves from archaic and Hellenistic-Roman times can be seen. Within the walls Roman buildings were excavated, including an amphitheatre and an imperial forum, as well as remains of a villa from imperial times and a Roman road paved with flagstones.

Grosseto

A Piazza Dante Alighieri
B Piazza del Duomo
C Piazza Baccarini
D Piazza dell'Indipendenza
E Piazza del Popolo
F Piazza Frateli Rosselli
G Piazza Palma
H Piazza del Mercato
J Piazza De Maria
K Piazza Esperanto
1 Prefettura
2 San Francesco
3 Museo Archeologico e d'Arte della Maremma
4 Municipio

Where to eat
❶ Buca di San Lorenzo
❷ Antico Borgo

Where to stay
❶ Grand Hotel Bastiani
❷ Maremma

250 m
820 ft

©BAEDEKER

* VETULONIA

Remains of a once flourishing Etruscan city were found here. More than 10,000 people lived in Vetluna or Vatluna. Gold, silver and iron were the basis of the wealth in the 7th/6th cent. BC; it was lost at the end of the Roman civil war (1st cent. BC) when the city was sacked and looted. The doctor and amateur archaeologist Isidoro Falchi rediscovered the site around 1896 in Poggiarello Renzetti, today »Scavi Città«. The **＊Museo Archeologico I. Falchi** is named after him. It exhibits gold jewellery, finds from Villanova culture, finds and a frieze from the Medea House. The highlight is a gold scarab ring that was discovered in 2007 in Tomba dello Scarabeo (Casenovole necropolis, Civitella Paganico). The signs read »Scavi Città« and there is parking right at the entrance. The museum is completely barrier free and adapted to the needs of the sight impaired.

Etruscan stronghold Vetluna

❶ Oct – Feb daily 10am – 4pm, Mar, May Tue – Sun 10am – 6pm, June, Sep Tue – Sun 10am – 2pm, 4pm – 8pm, July/Aug daily 10am – 2pm, 4pm – 8pm; admission: €4.50; www.parcodeglietruschi.it

Grosseto

INFORMATION
Viale Monterosa 206
Tel. 05 64 46 26 11
www.turismoinmaremma.it

EVENTS
International jazz festival in July

WHERE TO EAT
❶ *La Buca di San Lorenzo da Claudio* €€€
Viale Manetti 1
Tel. 056 42 51 42
Closed Sun, Mon and 2 weeks in Jan. and July. Luciano Nonnini's gourmet restaurant in the medieval fortress wall serves creative regional cuisine. and is known for its seafood.
Reservations recommended.

❷ *Antico Borgo* €€
Via Garibaldi 52
Tel. 0 56 42 06 25
http://anticoborgogr.altervista.org

Closed Mon. Small trattoria in the historic centre. Try the ravioli with porcini from Monte Amiata and ricotta tarts with lemon cream for dessert!

WHERE TO STAY
❶ *Grand Hotel Bastiani* €€€
Piazza Gioberti 64
Grosseto
Tel. 0 56 42 00 47
www.hotelbastiani.com
Elegant palazzo ambience in 48 rooms with tradition and charm in the heart of the city

❷ *Maremma* €€
Via F. Paolucci de Calboli 11
Grosseto
Tel. 056 42 22 93
www.hotelmaremma.it
This classic hotel with its own parking lot is in the middle of the pedestrian zone. 30 rooms with air conditioning, WiFi, TV

*Etruscan
necropoli

The Etruscan graves lie below the ancient city. The characteristic graves of Vetulonia are the **circoli**, stones set in a circle with a burial chamber covered by an earth mound. Along Via dei Sepolcri – the »grave route« which runs toward Grilli – lies first the Tomba del Belvedere, a chamber grave with a short passage.

Tomba della Pietrera: The two-storey Tomba della Pietrera is an architecturally interesting grave (2nd half 7th cent. BC) to the north-east of the settlement. The tomb looks like the domed graves of Mycene in Greece – an artificial hill bordered by a circular base with a diameter of more than 60m/65yd. The grave is 14m/46ft high and the entry is 22m/24yd long. A pillar in the middle of the lower chamber supported the limestone ceiling. When it caved in, presumably already during construction, the grave was mounded up and a more stable sand-lime structure was used in order to make the upper chamber with the artificial dome.

Tomba del Diavolino: The square chamber of the Tomba del Diavolino, further to the north and 15m/50ft high, dates from the same period. It also has an artificial tumulus, which is bordered by a circular base. The base of the central pillar in the middle of the burial chamber has been preserved. The dome grave got its name from a bronze statuette of Charon, the god of death, which was found here and was first thought to be a devil (can be seen in Museo Archeologico, Florence).

Livorno

✳ H 4/5

Province: Livorno (LI)
Altitude: Sea level
Population: 161,150

The provincial capital 20km/13mi south of ▶Pisa is the most important harbour of Tuscany. No wonder then that the modern container harbour, ferry traffic and fishing industry dominate life in the second-largest Tuscan city. The city quarter Venezia Nuova and the Riviera degli Etruschi are pretty.

Old town,
youthful
looks

In view of the industrial complexes and modern buildings it is easy to forget that Livorno is a city rich in tradition. It was Pisa's harbour for a long time, but after the defeat of the Pisans was taken over in 1405 by Genoa, which then sold Livorno to Florence in 1421 for 100,000 gold florins. The Medici founded a new harbour in 1571 and built a **city on a five-sided plan**, which they surrounded with a water channel, the Fosso Reale. This pentagon is the centre of Livorno today.

WHAT TO SEE IN LIVORNO

The oval Piazza della Repubblica at the edge of the town centre covers part of the Fosso Reale. Statues of Grand Dukes Ferdinand III and Leopold II, both from the 19th century, face each other on the large historic square.

Piazza della Repubblica

The modern Via Grande, Livorno's main shopping street, begins at Piazza della Repubblica. At the intersection with Via Cairoli it broadens into Piazza Grande where the cathedral is located. The cathedral was built between 1594 and 1606, and rebuilt exactly like the original after being destroyed in 1943. Museo di Santa Giulia has a panel picture from the school of Giotto of St Julia, patron saint of Livorno, standing with eight episodes from her life.

Via Grande, Piazza Grande, Duomo

❶ Mon – Fri 9am – 1pm; free admission; www.santagiulia.org

On Piazza Micheli, which opens up to the harbour, the Monumento dei Quattro Mori shows Grand Duke Ferdinand I (1587 – 1609) as the liberator of the seas and successful fighter against piracy and the Saracens. This is shown by the four slaves who writhe in chains at the foot of the monument . The old harbour is called the Porto Medicea after its founders.

Quattro Mori, Porto Medicea

At the northern end of the old harbour stands the Old Fort, built in 1521 – 1523 by Antonio da Sangallo on orders from Cardinal Giulio de Medici. The complex has a high tower, a survival from an older fortification of the 11th century. Between the Old Fort and the New Fort on the northern edge of the old city the merchants' quarter Venezia Nuova grew after 1629. The **quarter is characterized by canals and bridges** and is one of the prettiest parts of Livorno. The oil warehouse Bottini dell'Olio, built in 1705, is now a hand some venue for exhibitions. In the church of Santa Caterina a Coronation of the Virgin by Giorgio Vasari is the artistic highlight. Follow Fosso Reale eastwards to get to the New Fort, a fortification surrounded by water channels that was built in 1590 and is a park today.

Fortezza Vecchia *Venezia Nuova, Fortezza Nuova

The synagogue, which was considered to be one of the most beautiful in all of Europe, was destroyed at the end of World War II by bombs; the roots of the Jewish community are Spanish-Portuguese (16th/17th cent.). From 1958 to 1962 architect Angelo di Castro built a spectacular rationalist concrete structure. Form and shape are reminiscent of a desert tent to symbolize the Exodus of the Jews from Egypt. Photos of the old synagogue are displayed in the basement.

* Synagogue

❶ Piazza Benamozegh 1; visits by appointment only via Amaranta Service; admission: €5; www.amarantaservice.it

Livorno

INFORMATION
Piazza Cavour 6
Tel. 05 86 89 81 11
www.costadeglietruschi.it

FERRIES
From Porto Medicео ferries run back and
forth to Elba and to the islands of the
Arcipelago Toscano. The ferries to Sardinia and Corsica start from Porto Mercantile. Ferry schedules: tel. 05 86 20 29
01, www.portolivorno2000.it.

BOAT TRIPS
Boat trips on the Medici canals can be
booked in the tourist information office
(depart from Scali D' Azeglio)

SHOPPING
Shops in Mercatino Americano (Via della
Cinta Esterna) carry Italian designer fash-
ions, among other things.

WHERE TO EAT
❷ *Il Sottomarino* €€
Via Terrazzini 48
Tel. 058 61 88 70 25
Closed Thu and Sun evenings. Friendly
trattoria where everything revolves
around seafood. Try the famous
Livornese fish soup cacciucco.

❶ *La Perla* €€€
San Vincenzo, Riviera degli Etruschi
Via della Meloria 9
Tel. 05 65 70 21 13
www.laperladelmare.it
Summer open daily, winter only open
Sat, Sun. Restaurant right at the beach
with a sophisticated fish cuisine. Our tip:
tonno rosso alle erbe e riso basmati.

❸ *Osteria del Mare* €€
Borgo dei Cappuccini 5
Tel. 05 86 88 10 27
Closed Thu, all of Sept.
The Mazza family runs a popular fisher
taverna in two rooms. Try the clam dish-
es or the gnocchi with scampi with one
of the good house wines.

WHERE TO STAY
❶ *Gran Duca* €€€
Piazza Micheli 16 -18
Tel. 05 86 89 10 24,
www.granduca.it
This hotel with 80 rooms lies opposite
the harbour in an ideal location. It was
completely renovated in 2007 and has a
parking lot, fitness centre and spa. It
also owns an apartment house on
Capraia.

❷ *Hotel Al Teatro* €€€
Via Mayer 42
Tel. 05 86 89 87 05
www.hotelalteatro.it
19th cent. palace with a small garden
near the Teatro Goldoni. The 8 rooms
are named after composers and musicians.

❸ *Villa Tramonto* €€ – €€€ *Insider Tip*
San Vincenzo, Riviera degli Etruschi
Via Sirena 16
Tel. 05 65 70 18 58
www.hotelvillatramonto.com
The absolutely beautiful location right
on the sea and with its own beach
makes this small family hotel a top address for seaside holidays. Lounges and
sunshades are included with the room.
The hotel has a fish restaurant. Rental
bikes and vespas available. Boat trips.

No walking tour of the city should leave out one of the most beautiful market halls in Italy: Mercato Centrale from 1894 even has a kosher butcher.

* Market hall

The Teatro Goldoni with a spectacular glass roof offers opera friends an exhibit on the life and work of the composer Pietro Mascagnano, who was born in on Dec. 12, 1864 in Livorno (works include *Cavalleria rusticana*). The **Museo Mascagnano** with photographs, music instruments etc. can be discovered in three tours.

* Teatro Goldoni

❶ Via Goldoni 83; Mon – Fri 9am – 1pm, 3pm – 7pm; www.goldoniteatro.it

Museo Fattori on Via San Jacopo in Aquaviva exhibits work of the Macchiaioli group of artists around Giovanni Fattori (1825 – 1908). The Macchiaioli cast off the academic style and oriented themselves to the upcoming Impressionist movement. Amadeo Modigliani (▶Famous People) studied with the Macchiaioli before he went to Paris. The house where he was born, **Casa Natale Amadeo Modigli-**

Museums

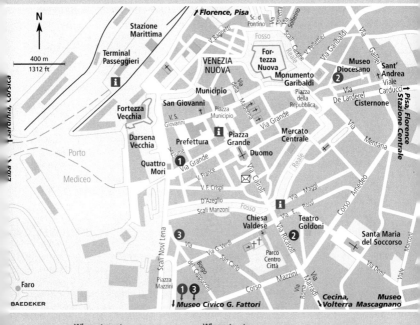

Livorno

Where to eat
❶ La Perla
❷ Il Sottomarino
❸ Osteria del Mare

Where to stay
❶ Gran Duca
❷ Hotel Al Teatro
❸ Villa Tramonto

? *Spot painters*

The »Macchiaioli« were in their time the most progressive artists in Tuscany. But they were not taken seriously in the established art circles, as you can easily see by their name: they were called »spot painters«.

ani is open to visitors. The Villa Henderson from the 18th century houses the **museum of natural history** with a garden, ampitheatre and planetarium. Museo Diocesano further to the north exhibits liturgical implements (17th – 19th cent.) and two panel pictures from the school of Giotto.

Museo Fattori: Tue – Sun 10am – 1pm, 4pm – 7pm; admission: €4; http://pegaso.comune.livorno.it

Casa Natale Amadeo Modigliani: Via Roma 38; only Sat 4pm – 7pm; tours: €5

Natural History Museum: Via Roma 234; Tue, Thu, Sat 9am – 1pm, 3pm – 7pm, Fri 9am – 1pm, Sun 3pm – 7pm; admission: €4

Museo Diocesano: Via del Seminario 61; Mon – Fri 9am – 1pm, Tue, Fri 4pm – 7pm; free admission

Aquarium	At Terrazza Mascagni the **third largest aquarium in Italy** presents the wonders of the Mediterranean underwater world on 3000m2/ over 32,000 sq ft.

❶ daily 11am – 7pm, July/Aug until 10pm, sometimes until 12am; admission: €12; www.acquariodilivorno.it

*Viale Italia	Along the sophisticated Viale Italia, which follows the coast to the south, there is a succession of green areas, art nouveau villas and some beaches.

* RIVIERA DEGLI ETRUSCHI

Coast south of Livorno	The Riviera degli Etruschi (Etruscan coast) begins south of Livorno. The section around Rossignano Marittimo has the most interesting scenery, since the mountains come right up to the coast here. In the interior there are small villages with in part excellent wine selections. South of Rossignano the beaches are wider and bordered by pine forests, ideal for swimming and water sports.
*Quercianella	After Calafuria the coastal road passes Quercianella, a likeable beach resort with many private holiday homes under shady pines and a stony beach which can be reached over steep steps.
*Castiglion-cello	About 8km/5mi further is the pretty and very leafy seaside resort Castiglioncello, where the wealthy took their holidays in the 19th century. The continuing popularity of Castiglioncello can be seen not

Venezia Nuova, city quarter of Livorno

least in the **wide selection of hotels and bed & breakfasts** and the comparatively high prices. In Castiglioncello bathing areas are lined up along the small sandy bay. The archaeological museum in Poggetto shows finds from Castiglioncello (Etruscan necropolis) and Cecina.

ℹ Via del Museo 8; July/Aug Tue – Sun 9am – 1pm, 4pm – 8pm, Sep – June Tue – Sun 9am – 1pm; free admission

The old mountain village of **Rosignano Marittimo** is beautifully situated below a castle on the top of a hill about 3km/2mi inland. From here it can easily be seen how the landscape gets flatter and the hills withdraw into the interior. Further to the south the towns become less attractive, the beaches broader and there are more camp grounds. The pines of the »Pineta«, which is a protected nature reserve, grow all the way to the fine-grained sandy beach and stretch from Cecina to Marina di Bibbona near Bolgheri. Sun worshippers can be found above all at ***Vada beach**, as this is one of the most beautiful beaches on the Etruscan Riviera.

Rosignano
Marittimo,
Vada

Cecina, Marina di Cecina The town itself attracts less attention than the bathing resort Marina di Cecina, where holiday-makers swim in the sea or the Aquapark and have a choice from a wide range of accommodation, including six camp grounds. In the part of Cecina called La Cinquantina the **archaeological museum** in Villa Guerrazzi and the beautiful **park** in the grounds, as well as the **archaeological park** of Villa Romana di San Vincenziano (1st. cent. BC) are worth visiting.
Archaeological Museum and Park: Feb 1 – May 31, Sep 13 – Nov 30 Sat, Sun 3.30pm – 7pm, June 1 – Aug 31 Tue – Sun 6pm – 10pm, Sep 1 – 12 Tue – Sun 4pm – 7.30pm; admission: €4
Archaeological Park: Via Ginori 33; Feb 1 – May 31, Sep 13 – Nov 30. Sat, Sun 2pm – 5.30pm, June 1 – Aug 31 Tue – Sun 5pm – 9pm, Sep 1 – 12 Tue – Sun 4pm – 7.30pm; admission: €3.50; www.comune.cecina.li.it

Bolgheri The **cypress-lined road**, straight as an arrow, runs 5km/3mi from San Guido to Bolgheri. The poet and **Nobel laureate Giosué Carducci** described the avenue in his ode *Davanti a San Guido* and thus immortalized this pretty old village. In nearby **Castagneto Carducci** the literary park »Giosuè Carducci« and the museum his house commemorate the author. **Museo dell' Olio** on Piazzetta della Gogna is dedicated to Italy's favourite crop. Bolgheri offers galleries, crafts shops, restaurants and wine shops that sell the »Super Tuscans« Sassicaia and Ornellaia. The local farms sell fruit, wild boar and Chianina beef. Dr. Taffis' perfume from the shop »Acqua di Bolgheri« makes a unique gift. The shady country roads around Bolgheri are ideal for biking.
Literary park: Mon – Fri 10am – 1pm; www.parchiletterari.com/parchi/carducci
Museo dell' Olio: Tue – Sun 10am – 12.30pm, 5.30pm – 7.30pm; free admission

*San Vincenzo San Vincenzo, just 30km/19mi south of Cecina, is famous for wide, white sandy beaches – those south of the town are accessible to the public – and a dense pine forest that runs right up to the beach. Biking trips in the natural park »Costiero di Rimigliano« as well as the »Etruscan« biking tour to Populonia, Piombino and Campiglia Marittima (40.5km/24mi) are also popular.

*Parco Archeologico Mineraio di San Silvestro The extensive **San Silvestro Park**, which is also great for a walk, documents the long history of metal mining in this region from Etruscan times to 1976. The mine **Miniera del Temperino** invites on a »Journey to the centre of the earth«; the mine train of the Galleria Lanzi-Temperino makes underground tours. The high point is the medieval miners' town of **Rocca San Silvestro** from the 10th and 11th cent., which was built by the noble family Gherardesca. Parts of the medieval town wall and the church have been preserved. In **M Musei della Rocca di Campiglia** there is a whole museum of archaeology. The castle history began in AD 1004 with the noble family Gherardesca.

Parco Archeominerario di San Silvestro: Mar 1 – May 31, Oct 1 – 31 Sat, Sun 10am – 6pm, June 1 – 30, Sep 1 – 30 Tue – Sun 10am – 7pm, July 1 – Aug 31 daily 9.30am – 7.30pm, Dec 27 – Jan 6 daily 10am – 5pm; admission: €9 – 15; www.parchivaldicornia.it

Musei della Rocca di Campiglia: June/Sep Sat, Sun 10am – 1pm, 3pm – 7pm, July/Aug Tue – Sun 10am – 1pm, 4pm – 8pm; admission: €4

✳ POPULONIA AND SAN CERBONE

Populonia was important as one of the twelve cities of the Etruscan league. It became wealthy through its production of iron ore and had a population of about 25,000 at its zenith. The necropolis of Populonia, San Cerbone, is one of the best-preserved Etruscan excavation sites and thus a popular attraction on the Etruscan Riviera.

Earliest traces of Etruscan **Pupluna** go back to the 9th century BC. The Etruscans smelted the copper ore of the Colline Metallifere and the iron ore of the island of Elba at an early date. The wealthy iron industry brought prosperity to the harbour; its ships sailed to Greece and Asia Minor. The city was destroyed in the 1st cent. BC in the confusion of the civil war between Sulla and Marius.

The ancient **acropolis** of today's upper city Populonia Alta is preserved from Roman-Etruscan times. In the 14th/15th cent. Populonia was fortified with a castle; its towers give a view of the fantastic Gulf of Baratti. In the medieval town centre the **private Gasparri collection** exhibits Etruscan finds.

Private collection Gasparri: Via do Sotto 8, Tue – Sun 10am – 1pm, 3pm – 7pm, winter only Sat, Sun 10am – 1pm, 3pm – 7pm; admission: €1.50

Populonia's necropolis, San Cerbone, lay outside of the city to the east. It was in use from the 9th until the 2nd century BC. Until the beginning of the 20th century the burial site was covered with slag from the smelting ovens of Populonia – and so was well preserved. From 1908 the slag was smelted to extract ore again and the grave sites were exposed. Most of the finds went to the archaeological museum in Florence, but the graves can still be viewed locally. There are three types of grave: the oldest are chamber graves which were carved out of tuff stone and the so-called tumuli, burial mounds that are covered with grass today and have a »false« vault made of overhanging stones. Aedicula graves are newer. These constructions of ashlar

*San
Cerbone

Island in sight: ferries run from Livorno to Corsica and Elba
and to the smaller islands of the Tuscan Archipelago

stone with saddle roofs made of flagstones look like small free-standing houses or temples.

Parco Archeo-
logico Baratti
e Populonia

The 80ha/200ac Archaeological Park of Baratti and Populonia includes the Necropoli di San Cerbone and the Necropoli delle Grotte,
also Etruscan iron ore smithies and smelteries. The park also includes
the present village of Populonia Alta with the acropolis. The signposted parking lot is located on the street along the Gulf of Baratti.
Shuttle busses run up to Populonia Alta and back. The park visitor's
centre with a book shop, café and snackbar is about 300m/1,000ft
from the parking lot in a former manufacturer's villa.

Colour-coded tour paths start from the visitor's centre. Plan on 4 – 5
hrs. for the two necropoli. Guided tours that include the inside of
Tomba dei Carri (tomb of the chariots, 7th cent. BC; only accessible
in a tour) are recommended; the tumulus grave has a diameter of 28
m/90ft. The highlight of the tour are the semicircular tuffstone burial chambers of the **Necropoli delle Grotte**. The blue path »Via del

Ferro« (iron path) leads to other tumuli graves and an excavated iron smeltery.

❶ Mar – May, Oct Tue – Sun 10am – 6pm, June, Sep Tue – Sun 10am – 7pm, Jula/Aug daily 9.30am – 7.30pm, Nov Sat, Sun 10am – 5pm, Dec – Feb Sat, Sun 10am – 4pm

ISLANDS OFF LIVORNO

Gorgona, a good 18 nautical miles from Livorno and only a little more than 2 sq km/0.7 sq mi in size, is the northernmost and smallest of the islands of the Tuscan archipelago. Since it is still used as a prison colony only organized guided tours are allowed on the island, which are occasionally organized from Portoferraio (▶ Elba).

Isola di Gorgona

Capraia, 35 nautical miles from Livorno, was also a prison colony until 1986. Now the 19 sq km/7.3 sq mi island is in the hands of water sports fans, especially **divers and snorkellers**. Monte Castello is its highest peak at 447m/1,467ft. The only town on the island is Capraia on the northern coast above the harbour. Its fortress San Giorgio was carved out of the cliff in the Pisan era and strengthened in the 14th century by the Genoese. South-east on Monte Campanile common buzzards and kestrels can be seen, while sea birds nest in the steep cliffs of the unapproachable west coast. In the summer many private yachts set their course for the island. A guided tour informs on the history of the penal colony.

Isola di Capraia

❶ Agenzia Viaggi e Turismo Parco; daily ferries from Livorno/Porto Mediceo, travel time 2.5 hrs., www.toreMarit; boats excursions also from Elba; www.isoladicapraia.it

** Lucca

———————————————————— ✦ F/G 5/6

Province: Lucca (LU)
Altitude: 19m/62ft above sea level
Population: 84,900

For many people Lucca is the definitive Tuscan city – open, lively and with an agreeable atmosphere. The romantic old city streets are an attractive ambience for browsing in traditional shops. Lucca is also a city for lovers of good pastries. The delicacies are produced according to old recipes; castagnaccio, for example, a sweet chestnut cake, or buccellato, a yeast cake with aniseed and raisins, best eaten warm from the oven.

History   The name of the city is thought to derive from the Etruscans, who called a swamp between the tributaries of the Serchio River »luk«. The name was passed on to the Roman colony Colonia Luca, where Julius Caesar, Gnaeus Pompeius and Marcus Licinius Crassus met in 56 BC to form their triumvirate. The Holy Roman emperors favoured Lucca, so that it was the largest community in Tuscany into the high Middle Ages, more important even than Florence and Pisa. The **production of soap and brocade** as well as gold leaf brought wealth. The self-confident Lucchese fought and won their independence as early as 1117. Under the rule of condottieri (mercenary leaders), Lucca temporarily regained its independence from Emperor Charles IV in 1369.

FROM PORTA VITTORIO EMANUELE TO PIAZZA SAN MICHELE

A walk on the city wall   On the park-like city fortifications walkers and cyclists have a wonderful view of the old city and the silhouette of the Apennines. The first wall with four gates of massive limestone blocks already stood in Roman times. In the 12th – 13th centuries the new parts were also enclosed in a wall. In the 14th century on the order of Castruccio Castracani another fortification, the Augusta, was built within the city walls. Today the old city is surrounded by a 4.2km/2.6mi long **wall with eleven bastions and six gates. This fortification, 12m/40ft high with foundations 30m/100ft thick, was built between 1504 and 1645 by Flemish engineers and defended with 126 cannons. The massive wall did not protect the city from attacks but from the floods of the Serchio River. In the first half of the 19th cent. a tree-lined avenue was built on the broad wall. Thus the fortification became a **park**.

Porta Vittorio Emanuele   The following walking tour begins on the west side of the old city at Porta Vittorio Emanuele with the tourist information office at Piazza Verdi. In the casemates of San Donato the **Antico Uffizio della Zecca di Lucca** lets the history of Lucchese coin-making come alive. The Pinocchio zechine is a popular souvenir. Via San Paolino leads from here into the city centre.
Antico Uffizio della Zecca di Lucca: Tue – Fri 10am – 1pm, 3pm – 6pm; admission: €5; www.zeccadilucca.it

Museo Nazionale di Palazzo Mansi   The outwardly simple Palazzo Mansi (16th cent.), Via Galli Tassi 43, was altered in the 18th century in ornate Baroque; today it is the home of the state picture gallery. The largest part of the collection was a gift of Grand Duke Leopold II on the occasion of Lucca's incorpora-

Lucca by night: atmospheric city streets

Lucca

INFORMATION
Piazza Guiccioni 2
Tel. 05 83 91 99 31, www.lucca.tourist.it
Office also on the Piazzale Verdi

TRANSPORT
Lucca is the city of bicycles. Rental:

Cicli Bizzarri
Piazza Santa Maria 32
www.ciclibizzarri.net

Biciclette A. Poli
Piazza S. Maria 42
www.biciclettepoli.com

Vespa or Ducati rental and tours:

Speciality Tours
Via della Cavallerizza 21
Tel. 05 83 95 41 39.

PUCCINI FESTIVAL
The »Puccini e la sua Città« festival
(www.puccinielasualucca.it) honours the
city's famous son. Music by Puccini and
Verdi can be heard all year in the Basilica
San Giovanni, Via del Duomo, daily at
7pm; admission: €15

SHOPPING
In Lucca the shops are traditional and
have been run by families for generations. Most of them are in Via Fillungo.

Vineria Marsili Costantin
Piazza San Michele
Shop for spirits and gourmet foods with
an absolutely enticing selection.

Buccellato Taddeucci
Piazza San Michele 34

Wonderful, old-fashioned pasticceria
founded in 1881.

Carli
Via Fillungo 95
A little paradise for lovers of old jewel-
lery and fine table silver.

Caffè Casali
Piazza San Michele 40
Here are authentic Toscani cigars made
in Lucca – by hand of course.

Camiceria Cerri
Via Fillungo 178
Lucca has a long tradition of producing
fabric. Dressing in good-quality cloth is
here – as in Florence – a matter of
courtesy. A special service of this cultured shirt shop: have shirts mono-
grammed – within a few minutes, your
own shirts as well.

Enoteca Vanni
Piazza S. Salvatore 7
www.enotecavanni.com
In Enoteca Vanni good wines, olive oil
and grappa have been sold since 1965.

WHERE TO EAT
❶ Antica Locanda dell'Angelo €€€
Via Pescheria 21
Tel. 058 34 77 11
www.locandadellangelo.it
Open daily. Food has been cooked and
eaten here since 1414. Once simple now
stylish family-run business. Very good
wines.

❷ Da Giulio in Pelleria €
Via delle Conce 45
Tel. 058 35 59 48

Closed Sun, except for 3rd Sun of the month. Popular trattoria with cheerful staff *Insider Tip* where you can try the best of Lucchese cuisine. The lentil and bean soups are especially good.

❸ *Gigi* €

Piazza del Carmine 7
Tel. 05 83 46 72 66
www.gigitrattoria.it
Open daily
In his friendly restaurant Carmine Mariniello serves a tasty seafood risotto or roast beef with rocket and mushrooms and wonderful homemade desserts, for example tiramisu »alla Gigi«. Inexpensive lunch menus available.

❹ *Da Leo* €

Via Tegrini 1
Tel. 05 83 49 22 36
www.trattoriadaleo.it
Open daily
A classic! In 1949 wine was decanted here, in 1974 it became a osteria. In 1980 the Buralli family took over from »old Leo«! Speciality: spelt or bean soup.

WHERE TO STAY

❶ *La Luna* €€€

Via Fillungo
Corte Compagni 12
Tel. 05 83 49 36 34
www.hotellaluna.com
The hotel is right in a 12th cent. palace is located centrally near Piazza Anfiteatro. Some of the 30 rooms still have 17th cent. frescos!

❷ *San Marco* €€ – €€€

Via San Marco 368
Tel. 05 83 49 50 10
www.hotelsanmarcolucca.com
Located near the city wall; San Marco was once a factory, later a church and then a cinema. Today it is a fully air-conditioned hotel with 42 rooms, terrace and garden.

tion in the Grand Duchy of Tuscany in 1847. The highlights include works by Domenico Beccafumi (*Abstinence of Scipio*, 1520 – 1530) and the Mannerist Pontormo (*Portrait of the Young Alessandro Medici*, 1525), as well as *Peter the Hermit before the Doge* by Paolo Veronese and Andrea del Sarto's *St Anne with Mary and Jesus*. On the second floor there are works from the neo-classical period to the 20th cent. (Eclecticism) as well as a portrait of Giacomo Puccini by Luigi de Servi. In the former palace kitchen the hand weaving shop shows the local traditional weaving with authentic implements.

❶ Tue – Sat 8.30am – 7.30pm, Sun 8.30am – 1.30pm).; admission: €4; www.luccamuseinazionali.it

Continue on Via San Paolino to the only Renaissance church in Lucca, built 1522 – 1539. There was probably already a Roman temple on this site. In the presbytery an early Christian sarcophagus in which St Paulinus is interred bears a depiction of the Good Shepherd. Both of the choir lofts are works of Nicolà and Vincenzo Civitali. A few steps further on the left is the little Piazza Cittadella. Here the ice-cream

San Paolino, Piazza Cittadella

Lucca

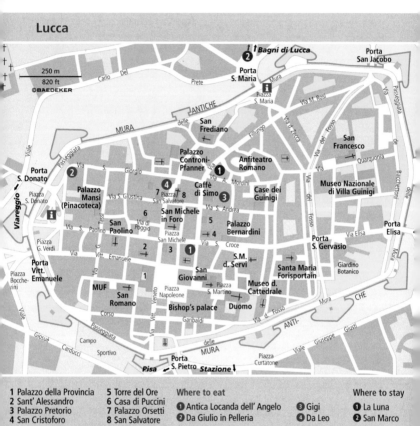

1 Palazzo della Provincia	5 Torre del Ore
2 Sant' Alessandro	6 Casa di Puccini
3 Palazzo Pretorio	7 Palazzo Orsetti
4 San Cristoforo	8 San Salvatore

Where to eat
1 Antica Locanda dell' Angelo
2 Da Giulio in Pelleria
3 Gigi
4 Da Leo

Where to stay
1 La Luna
2 San Marco

parlour Gelateria Santini and Café Cittadella are tempting places to take a break.

AROUND PIAZZA SAN MICHELE

*Piazza San
Michele,
Palazzo
Pretorio

Piazza San Michele, dominated by the white façade of the church of San Michele, is the **pulsating heart of the city**. The most striking building next to the church is Palazzo Pretorio on the south side of the square, which was begun in 1492 to designs by Matteo Civitali and completed in 1588 in the Renaissance style by Vincenzo Civitali. Its loggia on the ground floor is adorned by a statue of the architect.

In 800 there was already a chapel on the site of the former Roman forum. A new building, in the form of a columned basilica, was begun in the 12th century. The five-storey west façade was conceived for a larger building, which was never built. The dwarf galleries in the top storeys have columns that are clad with stone of different colours; a larger-than-life-size statue of the archangel Michael crowns the gable. The Romanesque character of the building remained until 1512, when a vault roof replaced the flat wooden ceiling. The large crucifix created by local artists around 1200 shows the body of Christ in stucco without a wound in his side, in a triumphant posture surrounded by painted scenes such as the entombment and a fine ornamental border. The white and blue terracotta figure (*Madonna with Child*) on the first side altar on the right is by Andrea della Robbia, while a panel from around 1480 – 1500 *St Roch, St Sebastian, St Jerome and St Helen* by Filippino Lippi adorns the east wall of the right transept.

*San Michele in Foro

❶ daily 7.40am – 12pm, 3pm – 6pm, winter 9am – 12pm, 3pm – 5pm

In a side street south-west of Piazza San Michele, the church of Sant'Alessandro stands on the piazza of the same name. It is thought to date from the mid-11th century. The relief of Pope Alexander was not added until the 13th century. Blind arches from the 12th century decorate the apse; the baldachin portal in the side aisle is from the late 15th century. The columns and capitals of the austere interior are partly Roman spolia.

Sant' Alessandro

The birthplace of the celebrated composer Giacomo Puccini (▶Famous People) is in Corte San Lorenzo 9. He was born here on 22 December 1858. A small museum with personal memorabilia tells the story of his life; concerts are also held here.

Casa natale di Giacomo Puccini

❶ Apr – Oct Wed – Mon 10am – 6pm, Nov – Mar Wed – Mon 11am – 5pm; admission: €7; www.fondazionegiacomopuccini.it

NORTHERN OLD CITY AND VIA FILLUNGO

North of Piazza San Michele on Piazza San Salvatore stands a beautiful classical fountain and – dominated by a 12th cent. residential tower – the simple church of San Salvatore. It goes back to the 12th century and is framed, also from the 12th century. At the right side door is a richly decorated architrave with a miracle of St Nicholas by the master Biduino (1180).

Piazza San Salvatore

The church of Santa Maria Corteorlandini (entrance on Via del Loreto) was built at the end of the 12th century. It is also called Santa Maria Nera because a copy of the Madonna of Loreto is revered here. A side portal with inscribed architrave, the bell tower and two choir

Santa Maria Corteorlandini, Palazzo Orsetti

San Michele in Foro with its five-story façade which was
designed for a larger church

apses remain from the Romanesque building, whose interior was
given a Baroque facelift around 1719 with frescoes and stucco, col-
umn-framed altars and an **ornate organ loft**. Opposite the church
lies the office of the mayor, Palazzo Orsetti, a Renaissance building
from the early 16th century with two beautiful round-arched entrances. In Via Santa Giustina 16 is the **Puccini Opera**, dedicated to
the composer, with exhibits, shop etc.

*Palazzo
Controni-
Pfanner

This palazzo at Via degli Asili 33, which was built around 1667, has a
pretty Baroque garden with statues and fountains. In the accessible
part of the palace that is often used as a film setting and that belonged
to the brewer dynasty Pfanner there is a permanent exhibit of old
medical instruments. Pietro Pfanner (1864 – 1935) was a surgeon
and mayor of Lucca in 1920 – 1922.

❶ Apr 1 – Oct 31 Tue – Sun 10am – 6pm; admission: €4;
www.palazzopfanner.it

Basilica San Frediano, which is dedicated to an Irish pilgrim monk and later bishop of Lucca who died in 588, was built between 1112 and 1147 in place of a 6th-century church. The fact that the church faces west is unusual and remarkable. The reason is that when the building was extended in the 13th century, and the existing baptismal chapel and Cappella della Santa Croce were integrated, the city walls already stood in the place where the church entrance would have been. The entrance was therefore placed on the east side and the apse with the altar on the west. A **gold mosaic** with Christ in an aureole dominates the façade, flanked by two angels with the twelve apostles in a row underneath. The design is attributed to Berlinghiero Berlinghieri (around 1230). Next to the apse is a tall, crenellated bell tower. In the Romanesque **interior** the unusually high nave with a flat ceiling stands out. In the first chapel of the right-hand aisle there is an especially beautiful **Romanesque baptismal font** (mid-12th cent.). The round lower basin has reliefs of the life of Moses. The depiction of Christ as the Good Shepherd with apostles or prophets shows Byzantine influences. The upper basin is shaped like a small temple. The fourth chapel of the left aisle, the Cappella Trenta (1413), contains a rich Gothic marble polyptych with bas-reliefs by Jacopo della Quercia (*Madonna with Child and Saints*, 1422). The same artist made the memorial for the merchant Lorenzo Trenta and his wife. A Roman sarcophagus from the 3rd century contains the remains of St Richard of Wessex, who died in Lucca in 722 while on a pilgrimage. The frescoes in the chapel of St Augustine include a depiction of how the revered Byzantine cross is transported from the harbour of Luni to the cathedral of Lucca.

*San Frediano

The oval Piazza del Anfiteatro gains its atmosphere from the perimeter houses with bright façades and the typical green shutters. From the 2nd century the **amphitheatre** stood here – hence the oval shape. In the Middle Ages houses were built over the walls of the arena, and their entrances or passages made use of the arches of the ancient spectators' stands. Until the beginning of the 19th century the square was completely covered by buildings. Only in 1830 – 1839 were the houses inside the oval torn down to create the square.

*Piazza del Anfiteatro

Fine old façades line Via Fillungo which runs north to south. Its many traditional shops, some of them extremely elegant, make it the main shopping street of Lucca. There are plenty of cafés here, too. The **Torre delle Ore** (clock tower), which can be climbed, stands on Via Fillungo.

**Via Fillungo

A short detour from Via Fillungo leads east to Via S. Andrea, where a 44m/144ft-high tower with holm oaks growing from the top catches the eye. It is part of the Case and Torre Guinigi group of buildings,

*Case and Torre Guinigi

city houses of the noble family under whose rule Lucca flourished peacefully in the early 15th century. The two palaces which face each other were built in the 14th and 15th centuries and later rebuilt. The Loggia dei Guinigi on Via Sant' Andrea was once the centre of family festivities, but is walled up today.

❶ Nov – Feb daily 9.30am – 4.30pm, Mar/Oct 9.30am – 5.30pm, Apr/May 9.30am – 6.30pm, June – Sep 9.30am – 7.30pm; admission: €3.50

EASTERN OLD CITY

Via Santa Croce, Santa Maria Forisportam

Via Santa Croce is the main axis at right angles to Via Fillungo. The broad, three-storey Palazzo Bernardini on Via Santa Croce was built around an elegant inner courtyard in the early 16th century. The ground floor has flat pilasters, the upper floors round-arched windows. The church of Santa Maria Forisportam (13th cent.) is further to the east, set back a little on a piazza. The name Forisportam means »in front of the gate« – the church was built outside the city gate and Roman walls. The **façade is Pisan Romanesque** and was never finished, but possesses three beautiful portals with decorations in an antique style. The early Christian sarcophagus inside the three-aisled church is now used as a baptismal font (with depictions of the Good Shepherd and Daniel in the lions' den). The right aisle has a Baroque ciborium as well as two 17th-century altar panels, St Lucia and Assunta by Guercino.

**Museo Nazionale di Villa Guinigi

It is undoubtedly worth paying a visit to Villa Guinigi. It was built in 1420 for the Lucchese patrician Paolo Guinigi and houses the national museum today (barrier-free entrance on Via Quarquonia). On the ground floor the collection has Etruscan grave finds, Roman mosaics and marble urns (2nd cent.), frescos from Late Antiquity from the church of Santi Giovanni e Reparata (5th cent.), early medieval capitals and Roman stone masonry. The showpieces of the art treasures from the High Middle Ages in the department »From Gothic to Renaissance« are three superb crucifixes: a panel cross from the Servite church of Lucca (around 1150), a famous cross signed by Berlinghiero Berlinghieri (after 1220) and a cross from the Convento di San Cerbone (1288). One of the two terracotta Madonnas (with child) is ascribed to Donatello. The department »From the Renaissance to the Counter-Reformation« exhibits include a painted terracotta *Madonna with Child* (1490) by the Lucchese Matteo Civitali. Among the works by Fra Bartolomeo the monumental *Appearance of God the Father to Mary Magdalene and Catherine of Siena* (1509) stands out.

❶ Tue – Sat 8.30am – 7.30pm Sun 8.30am – 1.30pm; admission: €4
www.luccamuseinazionali.it

In the year that Francis was canonized (1228) the construction of the aisle-less Franciscan church was begun in Lucca opposite Villa Guinigi. The interior was renovated in the 14th and 17th centuries.

San Francesco

Lu.C.C.A. (Lucca Center of Contemporary Art) in the Palazzo Boccella (16th cent.) holds high quality rotating exhibits. Eight rooms are reserved for the permanent exhibition, which includes works by Balzano, Pulcinelli and Maranghi.

Lu.C.C.A. museum

❶ Via della Fratta 36, Tue – Sun 10am – 8pm; admission: €7; www.luccamuseum.com

To look at and relax: street art object on Piazza del Anfiteatro

✦✦ DUOMO SAN MARTINO / PIAZZA SAN MARTINO

Building history As early as the 6th century Bishop Frediano of Lucca probably established the church that became the cathedral in the 8th century. Bishop Anselmo da Baggio, later Pope Alexander II (1061 – 1073), had the church rebuilt. Now dedicated to St Martin, it was completely renovated from the 13th to the 15th century.

Façade The richly decorated Romanesque façade is the work of the Lombard architect Guidetto da Como – an inscription in the first dwarf gallery bears the date of completion: 1204. The portico is the dominant feature of the ground floor. Above it are three floors with dwarf galleries which were probably intended to be crowned by a gable. The right side of the façade has two fewer arcade arches than the left due to the campanile. The slender six-storey bell tower, which is 69m/226ft tall, is made of brown stone at the bottom and light travertine at the top, and crenellated. The portico was decorated in the mid-13th century by Lombard artists with high-quality **sculptural decoration**. Four reliefs with scenes from the life of the church patron adorn the main portal. The right-hand portal shows St Regulus with the Apostle's Creed, disputing with the Arians; his beheading is depicted in the tympanum. On the lintel of the left portal are the *Annunciation, Nativity,* and *Adoration of the Magi.* In the tympanum the *Deposition from the Cross* can be seen, excellent works from the period around 1260 – 1270; the last two are attributed to Nicola Pisano.

> **MARCO ⊕ POLO TIP**
>
> ❗ *Combination ticket*   **Insider Tip**
>
> Anyone on the cultural circuit in Lucca can save some money: there is a combination ticket that is valid for the cathedral sacristy, the cathedral museum and the baptistery of San Giovanni and it only costs €6.

Interior The interior, which largely acquired its present form in the 14th and 15th centuries, holds several important works. The famous sculpture group of St Martin and the Beggar, dated about 1300, was originally on the west façade but is now on the inside wall. The statue of a rider, which is almost a free-standing figure, exemplifies the transition from Romanesque to Gothic style. In the right transept is the tomb of Pietro da Noceto, the secretary of Pope Nicholas V (1447 until 1455); it faces the grave of the patron Domenico Bertini. Both are by Matteo Civitali and are important examples of 15th-century funerary sculpture. To the right of the apse is the tomb of St Regulus (1484) with a Renaissance reclining figure. The free-standing marble **✦✦Tomb of Ilaria del Carretto**, second wife of Paolo Guinigi, is by Jacopo della Quercia of Siena. It is a major work of the early Renaissance and stands in the sacristy. Ilaria died young in 1405 and is portrayed lying with a peaceful expression, as if she were only sleeping. Even though the robe is artistically draped in folds, her delicate form beneath can be recognized – a clear break with the »bodiless« Gothic rendering of figures. At her head is the coat of arms shared by the powerful Guinigi and Carretto; at her feet a dog watches as the symbol of marital fidelity.

The most important religious and artistic work in the cathedral is the ****Volto Santo** (Holy Face). The crucifix stands in a small eight-sided marble temple that was especially made for it in 1484 by Matteo Civitali. The miraculous image probably dates from the 13th century. According to legend it was carved by Nicodemus from the wood of a cedar of Lebanon and had an adventurous journey to Lucca. It is still carried through the streets of Lucca every year on 13 September.

The **sacristy** is part of the Complesso Monumentale e Archeologico della Cattedrale, which has been turned into a museum.

❶ Mar 28 – Oct 30 Mon – Fri 9.30am – 5.45pm, Sat 9.30pm – 6.45pm, Sun 9.30am – 10.45am, 12pm – 6pm, Oct 31 – Mar 27 Mon – Fri until 4.45pm, Sun until 5pm; admission sacristy: €2; www.museocattedralelucca.it

In the cathedral museum opposite the cathedral, the cathedral treasure, altars, illustrated codices, silk robes and sculpted decorations are on display.

Museo della Cattedrale

❶ i Mar – Nov daily 10am – 6pm, Nov – Mar daily 10am – 2pm, holidays 10am – 5pm; admission: €4; www.museocattedralelucca.it

Bikes will get you everywhere in Lucca and also make it easy to stop for a chat

Duomo San Martino

There are unique masterpieces in the cathedral of Lucca: the grave of Ilaria del Carretto, a finely sculpted figure in marble that seems to be made of porcelain, Tintoretto's Last Supper which he painted in 1592, as well as the wooden crucifix Volto Santo, which is supposed to have been carved from cedar wood by St Nicodemus and angels.

❶ Portico
Sculptors from Lombardy decorated it with reliefs in the mid-13th century.

❷ St Martin on a horse
The sculpture, which was made around 1300, shows the patron saint of the Franks, to whom the church was dedicated in 774 after Charlemagne conquered the Lombards.

❸ Interior
Inside visitors are greeted by colourful marble and several high quality works of art, including Presentation of Mary in the Temple by Alessandro Allori in the right-hand aisle.

❹ Sacristy
In the sacristy on the right-hand aisle are the sarcophagus of Ilaria del Carretto dei Marchesi di Savona, the wife of Paolo Guinigi and who died in 1405 and the altar painting Sacra Conversazione by Domenico Ghirlandaio in living colours.

❺ Significant altar pictures
Federico Zuccari's Adoration of the Magi (1595) and Tintoretto's Last Supper (1592) are above the second and third altar respectively on the right side.

❻ Grave of Pietro da Noceto
It is considered to be Matteo Civitali's first work; he modelled it on the Florentine grave monuments of Santa Croce in the late 15th century.

The Festival of Lights on September 13 is considered to be a high point. All of the buildings in the historical centre are illuminated with candles and a procession through the old city begins at 9pm at San Martino cathedral.

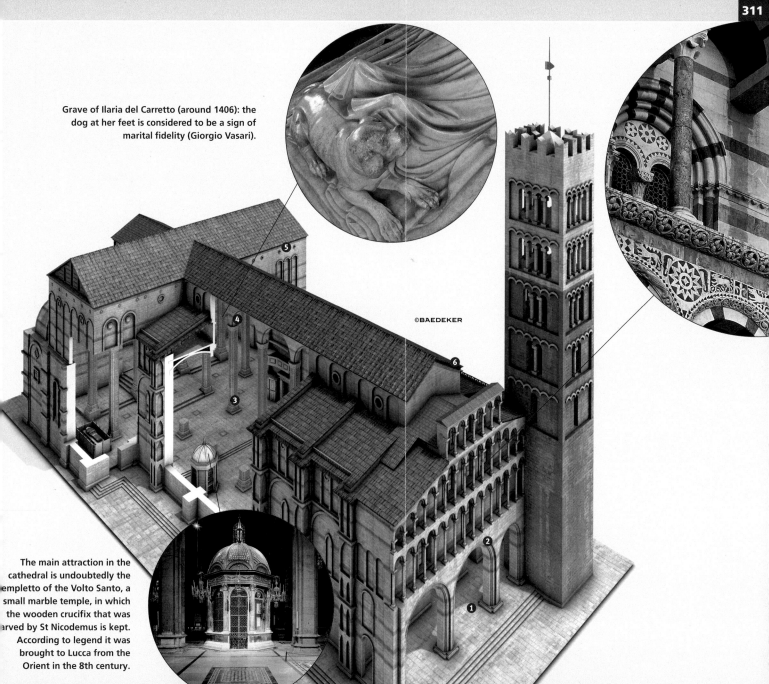

Grave of Ilaria del Carretto (around 1406): the dog at her feet is considered to be a sign of marital fidelity (Giorgio Vasari).

©BAEDEKER

The main attraction in the cathedral is undoubtedly the empletto of the Volto Santo, a small marble temple, in which the wooden crucifix that was arved by St Nicodemus is kept. According to legend it was brought to Lucca from the Orient in the 8th century.

Palazzo Micheletti, San Giovanni The little Mannerist-style Palazzo Micheletti on the west side of the cathedral square was built around 1556 for the Bernardi family. A few steps further is the Basilica San Giovanni, which consists of two churches, Santa Reparata and the baptistery San Giovanni. The **baptistery San Giovanni** from the 4th cent. is considered tbe the first episcopal structure, thus the predecessor of the cathedral. The façade of **Santa Reparata**, a 12th-century construction, was completely rebuilt in the 17th century – only the middle door and part of the south façade were preserved. In the right transept of the church the funerary monument of Countess Matilda of Tuscany (1046 – 1115) can be seen. Emperor Henry IV and Pope Gregory VII met in 1077 in her castle of Canossa to resolve their dispute, the so-called investiture controversy about the powers of church and state; the penance of the emporer before Gregory VII was a high water mark of the influence of the papacy. The left transept gives access to the domed baptistery, which was renovated in the 14th century. Interesting discoveries were made under the floor of the double church. The remains of Santa Reparata (4th/5th cent.) were discovered 2.2m/7ft below street level. The lower church is accessibly and has frescos that show holy relics being brought from Palestine. A total of five building phases from 1,200 years of city history were identified. The oldest finds document a Roman residential house (1st cent.), also thermal baths (2nd cent.), the first Christian baptistery, constructed with four apses (4th/5th cent.), foundations of the square baptistery from the High Middle Ages as well as the 12th century baptistery.

❶ Mar 28 – Oct 30 daily 10am – 6pm, Oct 31 – Mar 27 Mon – Fri 10am – 2pm, Sat, Sun 10am – 5pm; admission: € 2.50

PIAZZA NAPOLEONE

*Piazza Napoleone A few steps further to the west the street opens into Piazza del Giglio with the classical theatre on the south side. The square merges almost without a break into the expansive tree-lined Piazza Napoleone, where there are several cafés. In the middle is a **monument for Maria-Luisa of Spain**, duchess of Lucca (Maria Luigia di Lucca), who was very popular among the citizens of Lucca.

Palazzo della Provincia The whole west side of Piazza Napoleone is taken up by the stately façade of Palazzo della Provincia. construction began in 1578 on plans by the Florentine Bartolomeo Ammanati; from 1805 Napoleon's sister Elisa Baciocchi lived here.

MUF (Museo Nazionale del Fumetto e dell' Immagine) In the restored Caserma Lorenzini (Piazza San Romano 4) there is the national comic museum, which grew out of the annual and very successful comic exhibition in Lucca. It documents the close relationship between the city and the Fumetti (comic drawings). The museum shows rare documentation of the history of comics and three dimensional comic figures.

❶ Tue – Sun 10am – 7pm; admission: €4; www.museoitalianodelfumetto.it

AROUND LUCCA

Villa Reale, also called Villa Orsetti or Villa Pecci-Blunt, lies about 6km/3.5mi west of Lucca in Marlia. The decorative residence was built at the beginning of the 18th century for the Orsetti family and expanded in the course of the century. In 1806 Napoleon's sister **Elisa Baciocchi** acquired it and had it decorated in the style of her time. The illustrious guests included Prince Metternich and the virtuoso Paganini. The wonderful park was originally modelled after the Baroque garden of Versailles but was transformed into an English park in the 19th century.

Villa Reale

Park: Mar 1 – Nov 30 Tue – Sun 10am – 1pm, 3pm – 6pm; admission: €7; www.parcovillareale.it
Tours: 10am, 11am, 12pm, 3pm, 4pm, 5pm, 6pm

* **Villa Mansi** (16th/18th cent.) in Segromigno in Monte is 14km/9mi north of Lucca (signposted). It is not open to the public but the **extensive garden with some very rare, old trees** is the biggest attraction.   **Villa Torrigiani** is also surrounded by a wonderful old park; it lies a few miles to the east in Camigliano (signposted). The furnishings, stucco work and ceiling frescoes from the 18th century can only be viewed as part of a guided tour.
Villa Grabau (16th cent.) with an old park, a hedge theatre from 1814 and a luxurius accommodation (www.villagrabau.it) is located in San Pancrazio 7 km from Lucca. **Villa Oliva** is also in San Pancrazio. It goes back to the year 1042 and the family of the imperial adviser Buonviso di Corrado (Buonvisi family). Concerts have been held here regularly for 40 years.

Other villas by Lucca

Villa Mansi: Apr 1 – Oct 31 Tue – Sun 10am – 1pm, 3pm – 7pm; admission: €5
Villa Torrigiani: daily Mar 1 – May 31, Oct 1 – Nov 30 10am – 1pm, 3pm – 5pm, June 1 – Sep 30 until 6.30pm; admission: park €7, including villa €10
Villa Grabau: Apr 1 – June 30 , Sep 1 – Oct 31 daily 10am – 1pm, 2pm – 6pm, Jul 1 – Aug 31 daily 10am – 1pm, 3pm – 7pm, Nov 1 – Mar 31 only Sun 10am – 1pm, 2.30pm – 5.30pm; free admission
Villa Oliva: Mar 15 – Nov 5 daily 9.30am – 12.30pm, 2pm – 6pm; admission: €6; www.villaoliva.it

The »smallest theatre in the world« with an area of 70m²/750sq ft and 99 seats can be found in Vetriano north of Lucca (between Pescaglia

Teatrino di Vetriano

In Parco di Pinocchio everything revolves around the famous puppet

and Borgo a Mezzano). It was started after a donation and an initiative by local villagers in 1890. In the past visitors would nring their own chairs. In the summer stars from the Scala in Milan perform.

❶ Tours on appointment (custodian Cristina, tel. 05 83 35 81 31); admission: €4

Collodi, Parco di Pinocchio

About 5km/3mi further on the SS 435 toward Pistoia is the pretty mountain village of Collodi. Here, under the pseudonym Carlo Collodi (▶Famous People), Carlo Lorenzi wrote in 1878 the *Story of a Mannikin*, later known as the *Adventures of Pinocchio* (Avventure di Pinocchio). Collodi's book later became an international bestseller. A remarkable sculpture trail with figures from the book leads through **Parco di Pinocchio** (Pinocchio recreational park). There are also attractions like drawing and mask-making, fairy magic in a circus wagon or a pirate ship to entertain guests.

The architects Emilio Faroldi and Maria Pilar Vettori created the **Collodi Butterfly House**, a tropical setting for butterflies from all over the world. Along with the Florentine office of Gurrieri they also restored the maze, the waterworks and the outdoor theatre in the **Giardino Garzoni**, one of Italy's most beautiful Baroque gardens. The »villa of the 100 windows« was built from 1652 for the Margrave Romano Garzoni and is not open to the public.

❶ Parco di Pinocchio Feb 27 – Nov 1 daily 8.30am until sunset, Nov 2 – Feb 26 Sat, Sun 9am until sunset; admission: Feb 27 – Nov 1 €11, otherwise €10; www.pinocchio.it

Collodi Butterfly House/Giardino Garzoni: opening times see Parco di Pinocchio; admission: Feb 27 – Nov 1 €13, otherwise €8

* Maremma

M 5 – P 13

Province: Grosseto

The southern part of the Tuscan coast between Piombino and ▶Monte Argentario is called Maremma, which means »belonging to the sea, by the sea«. In fact the area was part of the sea – as were the coasts to the south and north – before lagoons and fertile alluvial land gradually formed and finally a swampy plain developed.

In order to preserve the typical Maremma landscape as such an area of about 70 sq km/44 sq mi south of ▶Grosseto was set aside as a nature reserve – the Parco Naturale della Maremma. Long beaches of fine-grained sand, edged with dense pine forests and Mediterranean macchia, crystal-clear water, quiet coves constitute the charms of this coastal region. There are particularly beautiful beaches on the southern Gulf of Follonica around the luxury holiday resort **Punta Ala** and the fishing village **Castiglione della Pescaia**.

Biking tourism has begun to boom in the Maremma recently. Anyone interested in exploring the region on a bike will find many offers. Vacationers also enjoy the well-equipped campsites.

Maremma

INFORMATION
Castiglione della Pescaia
Piazza Garibaldi 6
Tel. 05 64 93 36 78
www.turismoinmaremma.com

WHERE TO EAT
Pierbacco €€€
Piazza della Repubblica 24
Tel. 05 64 93 35 22
www.pierbacco.it
Oct. – May closed Wed, otherwise open daily; closed Jan. Pierpaolo Rotoloni and the cook Valentino have an excellent fish restaurant in the centre of Castiglione

della Pescaia with a very good wine selection.

WHERE TO STAY
Hotel Capo d' Uomo €€€€
Talamone
Tel. 05 64 88 70 77
www.hotelcapoduomo.com
A real dream of a hotel, with a view down onto the sea and of Rocca Senese, as well as direct access to the sea. Sun terraces and lots of greenery make for a restorative atmosphere; 22 rooms, 2 suites.

Italy's Wild West

*Life in the Maremma is far from the romantic image of the Wild West.
Yet there are a few parallels: sparsely populated land, horses and cattle
roaming free, and cattle drovers.*

The Maremma is actually **swamp-land**. The Etruscans were the first to drain and settle it. They constructed drainage channels and founded the cities of Rusellae and Vetulonia. In Colline Metallifere, the hilly, ore-rich landscape south of Cecina , they mined minerals. The Romans took over this Etruscan heritage and distributed the fertile land to veterans, but when their empire fell apart the drainage channels decayed. The land became swampy again and **malaria** was rife. The settlers fled from the deadly illness into the hills, where they built their spiritual and secular centres of power. During the Middle Ages and under the Habsburg grand dukes there were repeated efforts to drain the land, but the Maremma remained a poor and unpopulated region with a high crime rate until well into the 19th century – Italy's »Wild West«. While most of the Maremmani had to work in the fields of the estate owners, the romantics in distant Livorno and Florence developed an idealized picture of the life of the Maremma farmers in the middle of **unadulterated nature**.

Typical for the Maremma are the white long-horned cattle that are kept in free ranging herds

Landscape painters captured on canvas idyllic scenes of cattle herds and half-wild horses. The building of the railway line along the coast in 1860 created new jobs, but also caused more malaria – the water-filled pits that were excavated for the railway were ideal breeding places for the dreaded mosquitoes. Large parts of the Maremma were completely drained only from the 1930s. The land reform twenty years later also contributed to changes in the landscape. Today barley, maize, fruit, vegetables and wine are grown in the fertile plains.

Cowboys of the Maremma

The Maremma has its characteristic way of breeding cattle. White longhorn cattle are raised here on the open range. They are particularly robust, resistant towards disease and very undemanding. The half-wild Maremma horses, Maremmanos, are more rare. Both the Maremmanos and the Maremma cattle are herded through the swampy plains by »butteri«, cattle drovers on horseback – with the reins in one hand and the long drover's staff, the uncino, in the other. Day in, day out the butteri tend their herds, which are gradually decreasing year on year. Anyone interested in a closer look at the day-to-day life of the Maremma cowboys and their skill on horseback should go either to the »torneo dei butteri« in Albarese in August or to one of the large cattle drives that take place several

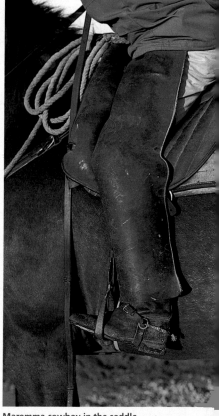

Maremma cowboy in the saddle

times a year. The following addresses have information on equestrian events and excursions: Azienda Regionale Agricola di Alberese, Loc. Spergolaia, Alberese, tel. 05 64 40 71 80; www.alberese.com and the 50-member consortium Naturalmente Toscana, Via del Bersagliere 7/9, Alberese, Tel. 05 64 40 72 69, www.naturalmentetoscana.it .

WHAT TO SEE IN THE MAREMMA

Golfo di Follonica

Sun worshippers are attracted to the broad beaches of the Golfo di Follonica. In Follonica, which was already known in antiquity for iron smelting, there is a sign of the early industrialization of the area. In the 18th century the grand dukes of Tuscany promoted the foundry Fonderia di Ghisa at the eastern edge of town. In the mid-19th century Carlo Reishammer designed the typical iron architecture of the plant, which is used today as a museum (Museo del Ferro e della Ghisa).

In Scarlino in the interior the museum **»Portus Scabris« (MAPS)** exhibits ancient underwater finds that were discovered in 2001 when a tourist harbour was being built. The museum and theatre in **Parco Minerario Naturalistico di Gavorrano**, also in the interior, gives insight into local mining.

Museo del Ferro e della Ghisa: June 15 – Aug 31 daily 5.30pm – 10.30pm, Sep 1 – June 14 Wed, Fri – Sun 9am – 1pm, 3pm – 6pm; free admission

MAPS: Via delle Collacchie 1; June/Sep Sat, Sun 10am – 1pm, 4pm – 7pm, Jul 1 – Aug 31 Tue – Sun 10am – 1pm, 4pm – 7pm; free admission

Parco Minerario Naturalistico di Gavorrano: June 16 – Sep 30 daily 9.45am – 1.15pm, 2.45pm – 6pm, Mar, Oct 1 – Jan 6 only Sun, Apr 1 – June 15 only Sat, Sun; admission: €8; www.parcominerario.it, www.teatrodellerocce.it

*Castiglione della Pescaia

This fishing town 22km/14mi west of Grosseto is the pearl of the Maremma coast; in the summer it is often booked up. The privately owned medieval **Rocca Aragonese** (14th – 15th cent.; privately owned) dominates the town. The climb through pretty narrow streets is rewarded with a beautiful view. The area around the canal harbour, where the town grew, is much busier. The fish here is guaranteed to be fresh since fishing, along with tourism, is still an important source of income for the residents of Castiglione. Long, clean sand beaches stretch to the left and right of the mouth of the Bruna River. A little further away the beaches can be used free of charge.

> **!** MARCO POLO TIP
>
> *Cowboys close up* Insider Tip
>
> The mounted cattle drovers of the Maremma are known as »butteri«. They tend the free-ranging cattle and drive them over rough territory. Anyone who wants to watch can make a date to visit at Equinus di Adriano Peloso, Via dell' Unione 37, Grosseto, (tel. 0 56 42 49 88, www.cavallo maremmano.it).

Punta Ala

15km/9mi further to the north on a tongue of land lies **Punta Ala**, an elegant bathing resort. This is the exclusive part of the Maremma: first-class hotels, orderly campsites, beautiful villas, elegant shops and

a large yacht harbour. Sports are important in Punta Ala – from wa-
ter sports to polo, everything is available. The 18-hole course of the
Punta Ala Golf Club is among the most beautiful in Italy (▶MAR-
CO POLO Tip p. 127).

The coast between Principina a Mare and Talamone with the parallel
mountain range Monti dell'Uccellina was declared a nature reserve
in 1975. It is best to come in the spring or fall when the park is open
daily between 9am and sunset and visitors can move about freely in
the park. From June 15 – Sept. 15 the park is only accessible as part
of a guided tour by one of the 50 members of the consortium »**Naturalmente Toscana«**. Various kinds of tours are offered – on horseback, in a horse-drawn coach, in canoes or on bikes. Shuttle busses
run from the park centre Alberese to the starting point for hikes. A
gourmet shop in the visitor's centre sells fresh specialities as well as
Maremma beer.

****Parco
Naturale
della
Maremma**

❶ Via del Bersagliere 7/9, Alberese; park opening times: daily 9am until
1 hour before sunset; www.naturalmentetoscana.it
Guided tours: by canoe (2 hrs., €14), coach (4 hrs., €19), on horseback
(2 hrs. €40, 4 hrs. €60), island expeditions (€25 – €35) on foot and by bike
(rental: 4 hrs. €7, 1 day €11)

Eight beautiful hiking trails of various levels of difficulty (3 – 6 hours,
mid June – Sept only with guide) cross the 100 square kilometres (40
square miles) of the nature reserve, the home of wild boar, red deer,
badgers, stone martens, Maremma horses and the characteristic
white Maremma cattle. On the banks of the Ombrone storks, small

Hiking trails

Pine-tree-lined road in flat Maremma landscape

A sandy beach in Parco Naturale near Marina di Alberese

egrets and cormorants can be seen. One trail leads past ancient oaks to the ruins of San Rabano Abbey (10th century). On the so-called »forest trail« the most important species of tree and bush are marked. The »tower trail« passes the olive route and two of the eight old lookouts. There is an interesting variety of landscape features, including wave-eroded cliffs and lonely beaches further to the north. The vegetation here, which can grow in a salty environment, gives way to Mediterranean macchia with garrigue and evergreens further away from the shore. North of the mouth of the Ombrone in the swampy **Padule di Trappola**, little coastal lakes alternate with flat dunes; the inland areas have been drained. The characteristic sight in this area are the half-wild **Maremma cattle** which graze all year on the fertile pastures of the former malaria swamps. In the winter the inland bodies of water harbour countless migrating birds. South of the Ombrone lies a compact area of dunes, interrupted by small marshy low-lying areas and extended groves of shady stone pine.

Talamone The beautiful fishing village Talamone is now the Mecca of surfers, kite surfers and snorkellers. The Sienese, who once ruled Talamone, built the castle above the harbour in the 15th cent. Talamone has an **aquarium** with a rescue station for sea turtles.

❶ Via Nizza 24; June 12 – Sep 15 daily 9am – 12pm, 2pm – 5pm, Apr 1 – June 11 only Fri – Sun; admission: €3; www.acquario-posidonia.com

** Massa Marittima

◆ L 8

Province: Grosseto (GR)
Altitude: 380m/1,247ft above sea level
Population: 8,800

Marittima means »on the sea«, and Massa Marittima possibly really lay on the coast in earlier times. Today, however, this wonderful town now lies almost 20km/12mi inland at the edge of the ▶Maremma on a hill in the southern foothills of the Colline Metallifere. Torre del Candeliere, at the highest point in Massa Marittima, commands a fantastic view over the beautiful surroundings.

The Etruscans and Romans exploited the lead, copper and silver deposits of the Colline Metallifere. Massa's rise to be the main centre of the Maremma began in the 8th century. Around the year 1300 the mining town had about 10,000 residents; in 1310 the first mining law passed in the free town, the Codice Mineraio, determined mining rights, royalties and profit distribution. Under Sienese rule mining stopped from the middle of the 14th century and resumed only in the 19th century. Malaria caused a decline in the population and the economic importance of Massa until the 19th century. After the swamps were drained the city enjoyed new prosperity, but mining ceased once again.

Mining town

WHAT TO SEE IN MASSA MARITTIMA

The centre of the old town is the broad, irregular Piazza Garibaldi, a square completely surrounded by medieval buildings that possesses both individuality and charm.

***Piazza Garibaldi*

A broad flight of steps on the south side of the piazza leads to the cathedral, which was begun in 1228 in Romanesque style on the model of Pisa cathedral and completed in 1304 in the Gothic style. Round-arched blind arcades – the lower parts continue on the walls of the church – adorn the façade, which was built in the mid-13th century with the help of Giovanni Pisano. On the lintel of the main portal a carefully worked relief recounts five episodes from the life of the church patron St Cerbone. The church possesses outstanding works of art such as the baptismal font in the right aisle, which was made from a single block of travertine (1380) with reliefs by Giroldo da Como of scenes from the life of John the Baptist. The altar painting Madonna delle Grazie in the left choir chapel, which was execut-

Duomo San Cerbone

Massa Marittima

INFORMATION
Via Todini 3/5
Tel. 05 66 90 27 56
www.turismoinmaremma.it

EVENT
Balestro del Girifalco, the town festival
with archery contest in medieval costume, every year on 20 May or the following Sunday.

WHERE TO EAT
Osteria da Tronca €€
Vicolo Porte 5
Tel. 05 66 90 19 91
Only open evenings, closed Wed and
January to March. Comfortable osteria
with typical dishes from the Maremma
and regional wines.

Enoteca Balestracci €
Via Ximenes 5
Tel. 05 66 90 35 46

www.massamarittima.info/balestracci/
index.htm
Excellent wine shop with 1,000 wines;
daily menus and light dishes.

WHERE TO STAY
Duca del Mare €€
Piazza Dante Alighieri 1/2
Tel. 05 66 90 22 84
www.ducadelmare.it
Location very central but quiet (28
rooms), popular with bikers. There is a
pool in the garden.

Il Girifalco € – €€
Via Massetana Nord 25
Tel. 05 66 90 21 77
www.ilgirifalco.com
Family hotel at the edge of Massa Marit-
tima in restful surroundings with garden,
pool and sauna. Large breakfast buffet.
Mountain bikes available at no charge.

ed around 1316, is attributed to the workshop of Duccio di Buoninsegna or Simone Martini. Another treasure is behind the high altar:
the **sarcophagus of St Cerbone** (493 – 575), who was born in Africa and later became bishop of Populonia. Eight reliefs carved in
1324 by the Sienese sculptor Goro di Gregorio relate the life of the
»Apostle of the Maremma«: Totila, king of the Goths, throws Cerbone into a cage of bears, but they set the saint free; Cerbone reads
the mass, is the victim of libellous reports to Pope Virgilius and has
to face trial in Rome, where geese prove his innocence; the saint
milks a deer for emissaries of the pope and heals the sick.

Palazzo Pretorio On the south-west corner of Piazza Garibaldi stands Palazzo Pretorio
or Palazzo del Podestà (around 1230), which is built entirely of travertine stone. Its façade is decorated with the city coat of arms of
Massa Marittima and Siena and the arms of the podestà. Today it
houses the ***Museo Archeologico** with finds from the excavation of
Etruscan sites in Poggio Castiglione and Lago dell'Accesa. The painting collection in the **Museo di Arte Sacra** includes the greatest art

Small town with a grand square: Piazza Garibaldi in Massa Marittima is one of the most fascinating places in all of Tuscany

treasure of Massa, *Maestà* painted by Ambrogio Lorenzetti around the year 1335. The panel painting shows Mary as a loving mother with her child, seated on a throne to which lead steps personified as faith (*fides*), hope (*spes*) and love (*caritas*), while numerous apostles, doctors of the church and angels kneel devoutly at the feet of the mother of God.

Museo Archeologico: Jul 20 – Aug 20 daily 10am – 1pm, 4pm – 10pm, Apr 1 – Jul 19, Aug 21 – Oct 31 Tue – Sun 10am – 12.30pm, 3.30pm – 7pm; Nov 1 – Mar 31 Tue – Sun 10am – 12.30pm, 3pm – 5pm; admission: €3; www.museidimaremma.it

Museo di Arte Sacra: Corso Diaz 36; Apr – Sep Tue – Sun 10am – 1pm, 3pm – 6pm, Oct – Mar 11am – 1pm, 3pm – 5pm; admission: €5

For the neighbouring travertine palace three Romanesque residential towers of the 13th and 14th centuries were joined together. The office of the mayor is decorated with 16th-century frescoes. **Palazzo Comunale**

The narrow Via Moncini, a street of craft workshops, leads up to the fortezza, fortifications that were strengthened by the Sienese in the 14th century. The Arco dei Senesi (1337), the connecting arch to the ***Fortezza, Torre del Candeliere**

massive Torre del Candeliere (1228) has been well-preserved; a visit to the observation platform leads up steps that are extremely narrow and dizzily steep.

❶ Apr – Oct Tue – Sun 10am – 1pm, 3pm – 6pm, Nov – Mar Tue – Sun 11am – 1pm, 2.30pm – 4.30pm; admission: €2.50

*Museo dell'Arte e Storia delle Miniere

Opposite in the 16th-century Renaissance Palazzo delle Armi (1442), Museo di Arte e Storia delle Miniere explains the golden age of iron-ore and mineral mining, with information on mining techniques and the composition of the rock. Tours go to the 700m/765yd-long mine on Via Corridani, now no longer in operation (Museo della Miniera). The museum is also the information point for **Parco Colline Metallifere**.

Parco Colline Metallifere: www.parcocollinemetalifere.it
Museo di Arte e Storia delle Miniere: Apr 1 – Jul 15 Tue – Sun 3.30pm – 5.30pm, Jul 16 – Aug 31 Tue – Sun also 10.30am – 1pm; admission: €1.50
Museo della Miniera: Apr – June, Sep /Oct hourly Tue – Sun 10am – 12.45pm, 3pm – 5.45pm, Jul 1 – Aug 31 half-hourly Tue – Sun 10am – 12.30pm, 3pm – 5.30pm, Nov – Mar Tue – Sun half-hourly 10am – 12pm, 3pm – 4.30pm; admission: €5

One of the narrow streets in the old mining town

Museo degli Organi is Italy's only museum for mechanical organs. It shows portable organs from 1686 as well as the development of the pianoforte by means of a Bösendorfer piano from 1840.

Museo degli Organi

❶ Corso Diaz 28; Mar 1 – May 31 daily 10am – 1pm, 3pm – 6pm, June 1 – Sep 30 daily 10am – 1pm, 4pm – 7pm, Oct 1 – Jan 15 daily 10am – 12.30pm, 3pm – 6pm; admission: €4; www.museodegliorgani.it

Museo di Arte Sacra in the adjacent Complesso di S. Pietro all' Orto is dedicated to Massa's art historical competence in the 14th/15th cent. On display are original sculptures by Giovanni Pisano of the cathedral façade and a wooden crucifix by the same artist as well as works by Pietro and Ambrogio Lorenzetti (1319 – 1347). The same entrance leads to the *** Collezione Angiolino Martini** with 750 works from the 20th cent., including ones by Guttuso, Schifano, Nespolo or Bueno.

Museo di Arte sacra

❶ Apr – Oct Tue – Sun 10am – 1pm, 3pm – 6pm, Nov – Mar Tue – Sun 11am – 1pm, 3pm – 5pm; admission: €5

In **Giardino dei Suoni**, the sound garden by the Bavarian artist Paul Fuchs in Boccheggiano north-east of Massa Marittima, metal and wind make for a unique atmosphere. It is well worth a visit. The **aquarium Mondo Marino** in Valpiana south-west of Massa informs on subjects including biodiversity.

Attractions near Massa

Giardino dei Suoni: appointments: tel. 05 66 99 82 21; www.paulfuchs.com
Aquarium Mondo Marino: June/Sep Tue – Sun 10.30am – 12.30pm, 3pm – 7.30pm, July/Aug Tue – Sun 10am – 8pm, Oct – May Tue – Sun 10am – 12.30pm, 3.30pm – 6.30pm; admission: €6; www.aquariummondomarino.com

* Montalcino

✳ **L 11**

Province: Siena (SI)
Altitude: 564m/1,850ft above sea level
Population: 5,300

Montalcino can be seen from far off because of its location on the hill above the rivers Ombrone and Asso. A castle towers over the town, which is surrounded by vineyards where the grapes for the famous Brunello di Montalcino grow. The town must have been surrounded by forests originally – thus the name »holm-oak mountain« (Mons Ilcinus). But the ground and the climate here were especially good for growing grapes, and the best wines from this area are world famous.

Brunello di Montalcino, which is produced only from Sangiovese Grosso grapes, was developed by the Bondi-Santi family in 1842. 140

years later the garnet-red wine was the first in Italy to receive the highest classification D.O.C.G. If the vines are younger than ten years, ruby-red Rosso di Montalcino is pressed from the grapes. This is the more affordable version of the costly Brunello, which is indisputably one of the best wines in Italy.

WHAT TO SEE IN MONTALCINO

*Fortezza

It is best to park at Piazza Fortezza on the parking lot in front of the castle that was built in the mid-14th century under Sienese rule. Between 1555 and 1559 it was the refuge of 600 Sienese who had fled from their home city when it was besieged by Emperor Charles V and formed a kind of government in exile here. The castle has an excellent **enoteca** with all sorts of Brunello, pecorino cheese, wild boar ham and olive oil.

*Museo Civico e Diocesano

From the castle go the former Augustinian monastery at Via Ricasoli 31 (pedestrian zone). The cloister and 12 other rooms are an **atmospheric setting** for the sacred art in the city and diocesan museum. The late Gothic altar pictures, painted in sumptuous colours on a gold ground by Sienese masters like Simone Martini, Giovanni di Paolo and Bartolo Fredi, are all the more impressive for their simple and modest presentation. The museum's wood carvings from the 12th to 17th centuries are of high quality, as are two volumes of a 12th-century Biblia Atlantica from the neighbouring monastery Sant'Antimo and the terracottas from the della Robbia atelier.

❶ Apr – Oct Tue – Sun 10am – 1pm, 2pm – 5.50pm, Nov – Mar Tue – Sun 10am – 1pm, 2pm – 5.40pm; admission: €4.50

*Piazza del Popolo

The two squares Piazza Garibaldi and Piazza del Popolo a little further down, both on a slope, are the centre of the walled town. The slender high tower of the Palazzo Comunale, which is decorated with coats of arms, dominates Piazza del Popolo. Today it is the seat of the local administration and the Brunello and Rosso di Montalcino consortium. **Caffè Fiaschetteria** with its small marble tables, bentwood chairs and two large mirrors on the wall, has been a popular meeting place on this square since it opened in 1888.

City walls

For a view over the town take a walk on the medieval city walls. They are well preserved, have six gates and originally had 19 towers.

Museo del Vetro Giovanni F. Mariani

The **Brunello winery** south-west of Montalcino offers wine tasting in its Balsameria and Enoteca. The adjoining Museo del Vetro Giovanni F. Mariani shows the development of glass-making from antiq-

Montalcino

INFORMATION
Costa del Municipio 1
Tel. 05 77 84 93 31
www.prolocomontalcino.it

EVENTS
The Sagra del Tordo takes place on the 2nd Sunday in August (parade in historic costumes and archery contest). In July there is a popular jazz and wine festival.

WHERE TO EAT
Trattoria L' Angolo € – €€
Via Ricasoli 9
Tel. 05 77 84 80 17
Closed Tue. Cosy trattoria with regional specialities. The homemade pasta and spicy ragout of wild boar are recom-mended.

WHERE TO STAY
Vecchia Oliviera €€€ – €€€€
Porta Cerbaia / Via Landi 1
Tel. 05 77 84 60 28
www.vecchiaoliviera.com

10 rooms and 1 suite in an old oil mill outside of the city gates. All rooms are named after flowers. There is a beautiful panorama terrace and a pool.

Castello di Velona Resort & SPA €€€€
Loc. Velona
Tel. 05 77 80 01 01
www.ehc.it/castello-di-velona-montalcino
The old castle on the Frank pilgrimage route to Rome was converted into a 5-star hotel with 28 rooms and 18 suites. With pool, vineyard and restaurant.

Porta Castellana €€   Insider Tip
Via S. Lucia
Tel. 05 77 83 90 01
www.portacastellana.it
This is the place for everyone who likes unique accommodation. The three dou-ble rooms – Lavender, Saffron and Daf-fodil – have been carefully restored, and Annalisa Mancini personally sees to it that her guests are comfortable.

uity until the 20th cent., including **Murano glass** and rare examples by Picasso, Cocteau and Dalí.
❶ Poggio alle Mura, S. Angelo Scalo; Apr – Oct daily 10am – 7pm, Nov – Mar until 6pm; admission: €4.50

AROUND MONTALCINO

The former Benedictine abbey Sant'Antimo and its church, a jewel of Romanesque architecture, stand among meadows and olive groves in the gentle Starcia valley, 10km/6mi south of Montalcino. According to legend Charlemagne had the foundation stone of the monastery laid in 781 – out of gratitude for the end of a plague epidemic. Nu-merous donations enlarged the lands of the abbey to a princely fief and made Sant'Antimo one of the **wealthiest and most powerful monasteries in Tuscany** in the high Middle Ages. After the demise

**Abbazia Sant'Antimo

Set in idyllic landscape: Abbazia Sant' Antimo

of the Staufer imperial dynasty, but presumably also because of the high costs of building the church, the monastery lands diminished towards the end of the 13th century, the convent declined and in 1462 was dissolved by Pope Pius II, who gave the ruins to the newly founded diocese of Montalcino. At the beginning of the 20th century the architect Giuseppe Partini initiated the restoration of the monastery, of which only the church, part of the chapter house and the refectory remained.

Since 1992 Premonstratensian monks have occupied Sant'Antimo and it is open to the public. The abbey was begun in 1118 and was constructed entirely of travertine stone. The architecture clearly exemplifies the **style of the Romanesque period**. Construction of the three-aisled church stopped in 1260, leaving it without a transept. The aisles continue into and around the choir with its radiating chapels reminiscent of French churches. The shortened campanile stands to the north of the church; it was added in the 12th century. To the south stands the Carolingian chapel which is now used as the sacristy. The side doors are adorned by fine **reliefs with Lombard leaf ornament and animal motifs**. Columns and compound piers divide the interior of the 42m/138ft-long basilica into three aisles. The rich ornamentation of Burgundy-influenced Romanesque is uniquely evident in the capitals: eagles, griffons, sheep, rams and other animal motifs alternate with chequer and braided patterns. The depiction of Daniel in the lions' den (second column on the right), which is attributed to the Maître de Cambestany, is especially worthy of note.

Church: daily 6.45am – 9pm
Open for visitors: Mon – Sat 10.15am – 12.30pm, 3pm – 6.30pm, Sun 9.15am – 10.45am, 3pm – 6pm
Tours: Guido Burlando, tel. 34 94 79 63 74
Devotions/mass with Gregorian chanting: Mon – Sat 5.45am, 7am, 9am, 9.15am, 12.45pm, 2.45pm, 7pm, 8.30pm, 9pm; Sun 12am (July/Aug 1am), 7.30am, 9am, 11am, 12.45pm, 2.45pm, 6.30pm, 8.30pm, 9pm

North of Montalcino is the romantic brick-built town of Buonconvento (population 3,200). It rose in the 13th century over the remains of the Roman fort Percenna. In the 14th cent. it got a wall modelled on that of Siena. On 24 August 1313, Emperor Henry VII died here on the way from Rome to Pisa; he is buried in the cathedral of ▶Pisa. In Via Socini 18 is the Museo d' Arte Sacra. In the Art deco rooms panel and altar pictures of the Sienese school are exhibited, including a Madonna by Duccio di Buoninsegna.

*Buonconvento

❶ Apr – Oct Tue – Sun 10am – 1pm, 3pm – 6pm, Nov – Mar Sat, Sun 10am – 1pm, 3pm – 5pm; admission: €3.50

** MONTE OLIVETO MAGGIORE

❶ daily 9.15am – 12pm, 3.15pm – 5pm, summer until 6pm; liturgical services (with Gregorian chanting): Mon – Sat 8am, 6.15pm, 9pm, Sun 8.15am, 11am, 6.30pm, 9pm; www.monteolivetomaggiore.it

The mother house of the Olivetan congregation of Benedictines lies 10km/6mi north-east of Buonconvento on a cypress-lined rise in the middle of of the Sienese Crete landscape. The »Abbey of the Great Mount of Olives« is visited particularly for its famous fresco cycle on the life of St Benedict of Nursia, a masterpiece of Italian mural art.

Main seat of the Olivetans

In 1313 the Sienese nobleman Bernardo Tolomei bid the world farewell and withdrew to this place with two friends in order to live an ascetic life according to a strict interpretation of the rule of St Benedict. In 1320 the foundation stone for the monastery was laid. It soon developed into a centre of spiritual and cultural life. Bernardo Tolomei died in a plague epidemic in August 1348 while nursing the sick.

Monastery and church A shady avenue of cypresses leads to the entrance of the monastery complex with a crenellated gate tower (around 1393). Above each side of the monastery gate is a terracotta sculpture by Luca della Robbia. The monastery buildings were built of red brick between 1387 and 1514. The early 15th-century church was given a Baroque makeover in 1772. It has choir stalls decorated with early 16th-century intarsia and a large lectern that was designed by a member of the order in 1520. In the refectory (1387 – 1390) are 17th-century frescoes by the lay brother Paolo da Alfidena.

Fresco cycle of St Benedict The large two-storey cloister, built between 1426 and 1443, is the main attraction of the monastery. Abbot Domenico Airoldi of Lecco commissioned the murals, which were executed by the famous Renaissance painter **Luca Signorelli after 1495 and the Piedmontese Giovanni Antonio Bazzi, better known as **Sodoma**, after 1505. The cycle consists of 35 scenes, episodes from the life of the founder of the order, St Benedict (around 480 – 547). Numbers 1 – 19 and 29 – 35 were painted by Sodoma, numbers 21 – 28 by Signorelli and his assistants.

Frescoes on the east side The 35 episodes from the life of St Benedict begin on the east side of the cloister. First his childhood in Nursia is shown, and his taking leave of his family in order to study in Rome (1). Hedonistic and epicurean teachings do not convince Benedict, so he leaves the school in Rome (depicted in the background as Castel Sant'Angelo and Tiber River), in order to leave an ascetic life (2). In the following scene Benedict prays in the village of Affile and a broken wooden trough is mended miraculously (3) – the young man on the right of the spectators is a self-portrait of Sodoma. In the hermitage in Subiaco Benedict gets the robes for his order from the monk Romanus (4), who also supplies him with bread in his hermit's cave (5) despite all attempts of the devil to hinder this. At Easter Christ appears to a diocesan priest, who then brings his feast-day meal to the fasting Benedict (6). In front of his cave Benedict teaches the farmers of the area about God (7). When the spirit of unchastity haunts the isolated monk in a paradise-like landscape with erotic visions, Benedict castigates himself in a thorn bush (9). At the request of several hermits Benedict becomes their abbot, but his strict teachings find little response and the monks plan to kill him (10). When he crosses himself over the poisoned cup it breaks. Finally Benedict leaves the monastery (11). The saint now has 12 monasteries built to honour God.

Sodoma's fresco depicts the meeting between Benedict and two Roman boys, Maurus and Placidus, in a colourful and lively manner (12). Benedict liberates a possessed brother in the faith by physical castigation (13). He invokes a spring on a mountain top to supply three monasteries with water (14) and causes the axe-sheath of a fellow monk that had fallen into a lake to return miraculously to its place (15). When the monk Placidus falls while fetching water Benedict has the boy Maurus walk across the water to save him from drowning (16). Benedict tells a messenger who gave him only two jugs of wine and intended to keep the third one for himself that the jug would be transformed into a snake (17). In order to kill his op-

Frescoes on the south side

The frescos by Sodoma in the monastery's large transept depict scenes from the life of St Benedict

ponents the jealous priest Florentius sends Benedict a poisoned loaf of bread, which is then taken away by a tame crow (18). The attempt to seduce the monks with seven pretty courtesans also fails – the monks remain chaste (19). The following fresco (1540), where Benedict sends the monks Maurus to France and Placidus to Sicily (20), is by Sodoma's son-in-law Bartolomeo Neroni, called Riccio, who is supposed to have depicted himself as the king of France in the painting to the left of Maurus. On the first of Signorelli's pictures a monk tells of God's punishment: Benedict's opponent Florentius was killed by the collapsing walls of his palace (21). Benedict moves on to Monte Cassino and preaches the gospel to the residents – on the right of the picture monks take down a pagan statue of Apollo (22); he also removes idols and drives Satan out of a stone (23). When the devil causes a monk to fall from a wall during the construction of the new monastery, Benedict brings the dead man back to life (24). Against the rules of the order two monks eat outside the monastery in an inn with two pretty maids, whereupon Benedict confronts them (25). He also reprimands the brother of the monk Valerianus for not keeping the fast (26). The king of the Goths Totila, too, cannot deceive the pious man: when Totila sends his shield bearer Riggo in shiny armour to Benedict, the saint orders the servant to take off the robes that he is not entitled to (27). In the background Riggo reports to the king. The magnificent clothing of the courtiers and knights is especially remarkable. Then Totila comes himself in order to pay his respects to the saint (28). Benedict also stands up to honour the king.

Frescoes on the north side The following frescoes are by Sodoma. The first picture shows how Benedict prophesies to the noble Theoprobus the destruction of Monte Cassino by the Lombards, which is depicted in the foreground (29). Benedict feeds his monks with flour supplies that were multiplied miraculously – the fish on the table symbolize Christ's miracle of the loaves and fish in the New Testament (30). The saint appears to two monks in a dream and tells them to build a monastery in Terracina (31). The monk with the plumb line is probably a self-portrait of the Olivetan Fra Giovanni da Verona, who designed the choir stalls in Monte Oliveto Maggiore.

Two noble women who cannot find peace for their souls after death and rise out of the grave to attend a mass for the dead are redeemed by Benedict's alms (32). A young monk who has died cannot find peace in the grave until Benedict lays a consecrated host on him (33). When a monk wants to leave the monastery he meets a horrible monster just outside the walls; he sees this as a sign from heaven and returns penitently (34). With just a glance Benedict frees a chained farmer in the last scene from the hands of the thieving Goth Zalla (35).

** Monte Amiata

— M 12

Province: Siena (SI) and Grosseto (GR)
Altitude: 1,738m/5,738ft above sea level

Between the river valleys of the Orcia, Fiora and Paglia, the massif of Monte Amiata rises above the hills of southern Tuscany. Chestnut, oak and beech forests cover the slopes, where there are trails for long hikes. Porcino mushrooms and chestnuts can be found in the fall; in the winter skiers populate the slopes. At the foothills of the extinct volcano, there are opportunities to bathe in warm springs.

From the in part steeply ascending road around Amiata, a side road leads up to the peak (Vetta) with restaurants and shelters. This popular excursion site is topped by a radio tower and a cross of steel mesh (1910).

*Vetta
Amiata

WHAT TO SEE AROUND MONTE AMIATA

The tiny thermal bath at 524m/1,719ft elevation owes its name to the Servite Prior Filippo Benizi (1233 – 1285), who fled from the conclave of Viterbo in 1269 and thus escaped being elected as pope. he found a refuge here and was canonized in the 17th cent. The spa hotel Terme San Filippo (www.termesan-filippo.com) has an outdoor thermal pool (37°C/98°F) that is open to the public. The natural pool of **MFosso Bianco** in the nearby wooded valley even offers a pleasant swim for free under the waterfall that got its name from its white limestone sediments. The water is so warm that bathing is possible even in cool weather! A little further on is the Balena Bianca (white whale), a natural stream with hyperthermic water.

Bagni San
Filippo

Howl with the wolves **Insider Tip**

MARCO POLO TIP

The visitor's centre of Parco Faunistico e delle Riserve Naturali Amiata in Arcidosso presents the six natural reserves of the park and the ecosystem on Monte Amiata. Excursions to the wolves are also offered. The path to the observation deck in the middle of the wolf compound is protected by a high fence (Jun. 16 – Sep 15 Tue – Sun 10.30am – 1pm, 3.30pm – 7pm, Apr 1 – July 15, Sep 16 – June 6 only Fri afternoon, Sat, Sun; admission: €2; www.sistemamusealeamiata.it).

The former mining town lies on the eastern flank of Monte Amiata, at the edge of the Paglia valley between chestnut forests and pine groves. In the 8th century the Lombards built a Benedictine monastery here.

Abbadia San
Salvatore

Monte Amiata

INFORMATION
APT Amiata
Via Adua 25
Abbadia San Salvatore
Tel. 05 77 77 58 11
www.amiataturismo.it

WHERE TO EAT
Ainole €€
Loc. Bivio (turn-off Aiuole)
Arcidosso
Tel. 05 64 96 73 00
Closed sun evening, Mon. This restaurant lies on the road Arcidosso – Santa Fiora. Lionella and Ugo Quattrini spoil their guests with country minestrone, pork roast in Brunello or roast lamb.

WHERE TO STAY
Kappa Due – K2 € – €€
Via del Laghetto 15
Abbadia San Salvatore
Tel. 05 77 77 86 09
www.hotelk2.net
Small family hotel with 16 rooms a short distance outside town in a chestnut forest. In the restaurant mother Mariella cooks traditional, regional cuisine.

Its church has survived and is the town's main attraction. From the abbey (see below) walk through the northern gate (Porta del Castello or Porta della Badia) to the historic town centre, which has preserved its medieval character quite well. Near Porta del Torrione are **the remains of a fort** which was passed in 1347 from the counts of Santa Fiora to the city of Siena and from them to the Medici.

The **mining park** on the upper edge of town has a museum (Via Hamman) and another attraction: the **Galleria livello VII**. In an underground passage tools and machines show how mercury was mined into the 19th cent.

Mining park: June 15 – Nov 1 daily 9.30am – 12.30pm, 3.30pm – 6.30pm; admission: €3

Galleria: (tours only) July 1 – Aug 31 daily 10am, 4pm; admission: €4

*Abbazia di San Salvatore The »Abbey of the Holy Redeemer« is one of the oldest monasteries in Tuscany. Historians still dispute over the establishment of the monastery: according to a charter of donation from the 8th century mentions the year 743 and the Lombard king Rachis. Another version claims that the founder and first abbot was Erfo, a Lombard from Friuli and 762 as the founding year. In the year 800 an epidemic presumably forced Charlemagne's troops to rest here while on the way to Rome to his coronation. As thanks for the healing qualities of their herbs, the monks received generous privileges and lands a short while later. In the 11th and 12th centuries the monastic properties extended to Monte Cetona and from the Orcia River to Monte Argentario. The high point of their power was achieved under Abbot Winizzone who built a new church, dedicated in 1036. In 1228 the

Gently rolling landscape in the foothills of Monte Amiata

abbey passed to the Cistercians, and finally to Siena. The monastery was closed in 1782, but since 1939 it has belonged to the Cistercian order again.

The fact that the abbey church was built in the Romanesque style can still be seen clearly despite several reconstructions. In the aisle-less interior of the upper church **17th-century frescoes** tell the legend of King Rachis. Next to it four Latin inscriptions describe a hunting trip of the king to Monte Amiata, where the Redeemer is supposed to have appeared to him – Rachis then took the vows of a monk and founded the abbey. The late 12th-century wooden crucifix to the right of the entrance, which is similar to the cross of the abbey of Sant'Antimo (▶Montalcino), was presumably made in Siena and based on Burgundian models. There is an impressive crypt with five aisles from pre-Romanesque times, whose vaults are supported by 28 trachyte columns with richly decorated capitals.

From Abbadia San Salvatore it is about 16km/10mi (via Piancastagnaio and Pietralunga) to the village of Santa Fiora (population 3,000), which occupies a 687m/2,254ft-high bluff south-west of Monte Amiata. The main square, Piazza Garibaldi, was built over the remains of an Aldobrandeschi castle. In the church of Santa Fiora e Lucilla **terracotta works**, attributed to Andrea della Robbia, can be seen. Below the village at Fiora Spring, Count Sforza had a fish pond built in his park where trout still swim today.

*Santa Fiora

*Arcidosso On the western slope of Amiata at 660m/2,165ft lies the romantic mountain village of Arcidosso with a castle of the Aldobrandeschi family, which was occupied in 1331 by the Sienese under their commander Guidoriccio from Fogliano and handed over to the Medici in 1559. In the mid-19th century the charismatic waggoner Davide Lazzaretti (1834 – 1878) lived in the village. In 1872 he founded a brotherhood with about 80 poor farmer and shepherd families in order to »make the kingdom of God real«. Since the »prophet of Amiata« was a thorn in the flesh of both the church and owners of latifundia, he was shot on 18 August 1878 by carabinieri during a peaceful procession. His grave is in the cemetery of Santa Fiora.

*Giardino di Daniel Spoerri About 10km/6mi to the north, just before Seggiano, the artist Daniel Spoerri, created a small paradise with the »art garden« on a 15ha/37-acre property on the slopes of Monte Amiata. More than 50 sculptures, many by internationally known artists, are spread over the area so that they form a symbiosis with the landscape. In the woods, for example, he hid a hotel room cast in bronze with all its furnishings and personal props (Chambre no. 13 de l'Hotel Carcassonne Paris); on the grassy parking lot in front of the entrance Susanne Runge's *Escalator Bench* stands as if by chance. The botanical nature trail is a wonderful complement to the works of art.

❶ Easter – June 30, Sep 16 – Oct 31 Tue – Sun 11am – 8pm, July – Sep 15 daily 11am – 8pm; admission: €10; www.danielspoerri.org

Monte Argentario

✦ P 9/10

Province: Grosseto (GR)

Three small spits of land connect the mainland with the »silver mountain«, the peninsula Monte Argentario, which reaches into the Tyrrhenian Sea 35km/21mi south of Grosseto. Macchia, hills, grottos and rough rocks characterize the landscape. In between beaches and bays invite swimmers, yacht harbours and palatial summer residences testify to wealthy holidaymakers; no mass tourism developed here.

Once the Promontorio dell'Argentario was an island off the coast. A spit 4km/2.5mi long and 500 – 600m (550 – 660yd) wide developed when the channel sanded up in the place where the town of Orbetello is situated today. Later the two outer sandbanks, the Tombolo di Feniglia in the south and the Tombolo di Giannella in the north, were formed and with them the Orbetello lagoon, which covers an area of 26 sq km/10 sq mi.

WHAT TO SEE ON MONTE ARGENTARIO

The heart of Monte Argentario is the bustling Porto Santo Stefano. Just a few decades ago it was a small fishing village. Today it is a bathing resort where luxury yachts anchor next to fishing boats in the harbour and ferries depart to ▶Giglio. In the 17th century the harbour was an important base for the Spanish merchant fleet and protected by the fortress on higher ground. An aquarium shows life under water (www.acquarioargentario.org) and a sea museum is being planned.

Porto Santo Stefano

The highest elevation of Monte Argentario is Monte Telegrafo (635m/2,083ft), 17km/10.5mi to the south-east. On a clear day the view extends seawards all the way to Corsica and landwards to ▶Monte Amiata.

Monte Telegrafo

Porto Santo Stefano, the lively resort town and the most important harbour on Monte Argentario

Monte Argentario

INFORMATION
Porto Santo Stefano
Piazzale Sant' Andrea
Tel. 05 64 81 42 08
www.turismoinmaremma.it

WHERE TO EAT
Il Cantinone €€€
Capalbio, Piazza Porticina 4
Tel. 05 64 89 60 73,
www.cantinone.it
Closed Mon (not from July – Sept). Elegant restaurant in Capalbio castle vaults. Regional cuisine of excellent quality is served here, also organic dishes. In the summer there are tables on a terrace with a wonderful view.

Il Gambero Rosso €€€€
Porto Ercole, Lungomare Doria 62
Tel. 05 64 83 26 50
Closed Wed and mid-Nov. until mid-Feb. Exquisite fish restaurant that is considered to be the best place in town. In summer food is served on the terrace with a view of the harbour.

Trequarti (3/4) €
Piazzale del Valle 11
Porto S. Stefano
Tel. 05 64 81 06 70
www.bartrequarti.com
First class gelateria and bar, including a family-run trattoria/pizzeria. diver's meet at the harbour (Cala Galera Diving Center). Very friendly service.

WHERE TO STAY
Il Pellicano €€€€
Porto Ercole
Tel. 05 64 858 11
www.pellicanohotel.it
This exclusive hotel (32 rooms, 15 suites) near Porto Ercole is one of the best in the Maremma. The villa is covered with wild grapevines and nestles into the steep cliffs of Monte Argentario. Antique furniture and paintings of the 18th and 19th century give the rooms a personal touch. There is a small private beach for sun-seekers and the top class restaurant is known for miles.

La Palma €€€
Capalbio, Via di Chiarone 5
Loc. Chiarone Scalo
Tel. 05 64 89 06 60
www.albergolapalma.com
Well-kept hotel and apartment complex with lounge-bar in the garden, pool and whirlpool. About 1km/0.5mi from the fine sandy beach Chiarone.

Vecchia Maremma €€
Orbetello
Statale 1 – Aurelia km 146
Quattrostrade
Tel. 05 64 86 30 05
www.vecchiamaremma.it
This comfortable house in the middle of the Maremma has a nice family atmosphere. Restaurant, pool and garden on premises.

Port'Ercole The main settlement on the east coast is the former fishing village Port'Ercole, which goes back to ancient Portus Herculis. The holiday resort has a picturesque location **on a small cove** bordered in the south by a mountain spur with an old fortress called Forte Stella. The parish church in the pretty old town holds the grave of the painter

Michelangelo da Caravaggio, who died of his wounds here on 18 July 1610.

Forte Stella: Easter until June 30 and Sep Sat, Sun 10.30am – 12.30pm, 6pm – 8pm, July/Aug daily 6pm – 10pm; admission: €2; www.portoercole.org

The spit of land reaching out from the mainland, on which the town of Orbetello (population 15,000) is situated, was presumably already **settled by the Etruscans** in the 8th century BC. The city changed hands often during the Middle Ages. At first the Aldobrandeschi ruled, then the Orsini family before Siena took over in the period 1414 – 1455. From the mid-16th century the Spanish temporarily ruled Monte Argentario and made Orbetello the capital of their little »Stato dei Presidi«. In 1815 the peninsula was annexed to the Grand Duchy of Tuscany; in 1842 the spit was extended to Monte Argentario by means of a dyke and the lagoon was divided. Orbetello has considerable remains of the Etruscan sea wall from the 4th century BC as well as the fortress begun in 1557 under King Philip II of Spain and completed in 1620 under Philip III. The cathedral was built in 1376 and enlarged in the 17th century with two aisles. The Gothic travertine façade is decorated with a beautiful portal and a bust of St Benedict. The valuable **Frontone di Talamone**, which is on display in the ground floor of a powder magazine built in 1692 (Polveriera Guzman), is worth seeing . The terracotta frieze of a temple from Etruscan-Hellenistic times, which was found near Talamone, was made around 150 BC. It shows the heroic-mythical battle of the »seven against Thebes«.

Orbetello

MARCO POLO TIP

Organic farm »LaSelva« **Insider Tip**

In Albinia Karl »Carlo« Egger, a pioneer of organic agriculture, has been working his organic farm »LaSelva« since 1980. Olive oil, organic wine »Morellino di Scansano«, fruit, vegetables are produced and also sold here. Along with the farm shop there are 7 rooms and apartments (Strada Provinciale 81, www.laselva-bio.eu; double room €58 to €78).

❶ Frontone di Talamone: Jan 1 – June 30, Oct 1 – Dec 31 Fri, Sat 2.30pm – 5.30pm, Sun 10am – 1pm, otherwise only Sat, Sun; free admission

AROUND MONTE ARGENTARIO

The ruins of the ancient city of Cosa lie 7km/4.5mi south-east of Orbetello above the residential town Ansedonia. Cosa was founded in 273 BC by the Romans as a colony. However, the town was abandoned already in the 1st cent. AD – probably because of malaria. For a long time the remains of Cosa were thought to be Etruscan until an excavation by American archaeologists showed that the city was

*Ruins of Ansedonia-Cosa

Giardino dei Tarocchi is a world of fabulous creatures

founded by Rome and was used as a defence against the Etruscans. The 1.5km/1mi-long **enclosing wall from the 3rd to 1st centuries BC**, which has a polygonal form and is fortified by 18 crenellated towers and three gates, in part still visible, is impressive. The Porta Romana in the north-east is best preserved. It is the entrance to the ancient quarters, which are spread over two hills. Outside the old city is the forum with a basilica, two temples and the walled acropolis on higher ground (upper city) with the 2nd-century capitol. Despite the unevenness of the terrain, the streets in the city centre are laid out in a grid. In the museum **Museo della Città di Cosa** in Via delle Ginestre exhibits include torsi from the Julian-Claudian era, amphora, bronze and silver coins.

❶ daily May 1 – Sep 30 9am – 7pm, Oct 1 – Apr 30 9am – 5pm; admission: €2

Tagliata Etrusca
Walk downhill past the Torre San Biagio built by the Saracens to the so-called Tagliata Etrusca (Etruscan cut), a drain cut into the tuff stone. The name is misleading: the drain was dug by the Romans who, however, largely owe their knowledge of waterway construction to the Etruscans. The channel, which is 2 – 2.5m/6-8ft wide, not only prevented the ancient harbour from silting, but also drained the low-lying interior and kept the small lake Burano from becoming swampy. WWF offers guided tours of the Lago di Burano nature reserve.

Tours: Sep – May Sun 10am and 2.30pm, July/Aug Mon, Wed, Sat 6pm

***Capalbio**
About 18km/11mi east of Ansedonia lies Capalbio, with a well-preserved wall that can be walked on. Giacomo Puccini already visited the Castello Aldebrandesco Collacchioni. Art exhibits are held here regulary.

❶ daily 10am – 12.30pm, 5.30pm – 11pm

15km/9mi east of Orbetello lies Pescaia Fiorentina on the border to ****Giardino**
Latium. The fantasy figures of the artist **Niki de Saint Phalle**, who **dei Tarocchi**
died in May 2002 at the age of 72, can be seen from far away. She ful-
filled her lifelong dream in a former quarry in the village Garavicchio.
Giant mythical creatures, winged monsters and shining towers rise up
out of the olive grove where the sculptress worked from 1979 to 1997
to create her unique fantasy landscape. Niki de Saint Phalle began the
tarot garden with her life partner Jean Tinguely. Tinguely built skele-
tons of steel mesh based on his wife's models, which were then covered
with a 15cm/6in- thick layer of cement and decorated with glittering
mirror fragments, colourful Murano glass and ceramic tiles. Every tile
had to be formed and baked individually for the larger sculptures. The
model for the 22 figures was the ancient card gametarot or tarock.

❶ Apr 1 – Oct 15, daily 2.30 – 7.30pm, admission €10.50;
www.nikidesaintphalle.com

✱ Montecatini Terme

✦ F 7

Province: Pistoia (PT)
Altitude: 27m/88ft above sea level
Population: 21,400

**Montecatini is the largest and most elegant spa in Tuscany
and one of the most famous thermal spas in Europe. In the
magnificent facilities many members of European royal families, world-famous writers and Hollywood stars have sought
remedies for their aches and pains. Montecatini has plenty to
offer the 800,000 annual guests, including horse races (on the
local sulky track), fashion shows,
high quality concerts and exhibitions.**

The healing springs were known already in antiquity, as finds of Roman
devotional offerings from the 1st
century prove. In his book on Italian
baths the doctor Ugolino Simoni
mentions three bathhouses in the
town and the efficacy of the water for
curing liver disease in 1417. The water was drunk under the Medici,
the owners of Montecatini after 1583, but the importance of the spa
was only rediscovered in the 18th century. At the initiative of Grand
Duke Leopold I the town was modernized and adorned with the
glamorous establishments Regina, Terme Leopoldine, Tettuccio and

> **!** *Cialde di Montecatini* **Insider Tip**
>
> **MARCO⊕POLO TIP**
>
> Montecatini's famous »Cialde«
> taste best with a dessert wine and
> ice cream or dipped in hot choco-
> late. Top address for a »Cialde«
> gift is Paolo Bargilli's shop,
> Viale P. Grocco 2.

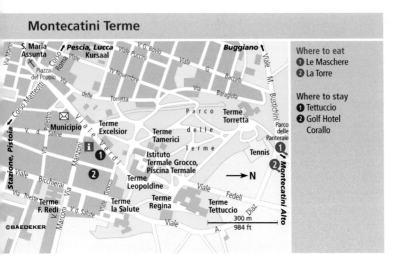

Montecatini Terme

Where to eat
1 Le Maschere
2 La Torre

Where to stay
1 Tettuccio
2 Golf Hotel
Corallo

Palazzina Regia after 1773. When European spas became the meeting place for high society at the turn of the 19th to 20th century, **illustrious guests** came to Montecatini. Verdi completed his opera *Otello* here, and Puccini composed *La Bohème* in Montecatini in 1895.

WHAT TO SEE IN MONTECATINI TERME

*Spa district
The centre of Montecatini Terme is the expansive spa park and with it the main axis Viale Verdi. The tourist information office and the finest hotels are here. The vibrancy of the bagniaioli, as the residents of Montecatini Terme are called in the midst of stately villa and Art nouveau architecture can be experienced in the bars and liberty cafés. Caffetteria Carlotta or the New York Bar on Corso Roma are popular. The Neo-Renaissance town hall (1911), Viale Verdi 46, has valuable Art nouveau decorations by Galileo Chini. Joan Miró's monumantal painting (1975 – 1978) *Woman Wrapped in a Flight of Birds* caqn be seen inside the building.

*Spas
The fact that a cure in Montecatini is a rather exclusive pleasure can be seen in, among other things, the architecture of the baths. Impressive buildings on Viale Verdi include the **Stabilimento Excelsior**, which was expanded in 1968 with an eccentric but insensitive annex, and the **Terme Leopoldine** in the classical style, which was opened in 1775. The neo-Baroque **Terme Tettuccio** dating from 1927 at the end of a tree-lined avenue decorated with flowerbeds is also imposing.

Montecatini Terme

INFORMATION
Viale Verdi 66
Tel. 05 72 77 22 44
www.montecatini.turismo.it

WHERE TO EAT
❶ *Le Maschere* €€€
Piazza Giusti 21, Montecatini Alto
Tel. 05 72 77 00 85
www.ristorantelemaschere.com
Closed Mon. Popular restaurant in Teatro dei Risorti. Tables outside in the summer. Try the salami with dried porcini!

❷ *La Torre* €€€
Montecatini Alto, Piazza Giusti 8/9
Tel. 05 72 706 50
Closed Tue.
Restaurant in Toore Signorelli right on the main square of the atmospheric little borgo. The less expensive restaurant La Rughetta and the enoteca Il Torrino are also located here.

WHERE TO STAY
❶ *Tettuccio* €€€ – €€€€
Montecatini Terme,
Viale Verdi 74
Tel. 057 27 80 51
Elegant house from the turn of the century (70 rooms) directly opposite the Excelsior Therme.

❷ *Golf Hotel Corallo* € – €€
Montecatini Terme
Viale Cavallotti 116
Tel. 05 72 78 288
www.golfhotelcorallo.it
A comfortable house (65 rooms) with very helpful staff and an excellent restaurant.

Even visitors who are not here for treatment should take a look inside this elegant facility. Beyond the colonnades there are wonderful pump rooms where the guests pick up their daily water ration. The monumental architecture opens up to a beautiful park behind the baths.

Take either the funicular railway (funicolare) or the winding road (past Terme Tettuccio) up to Montecatini Alto. The lower station of the funicular is at the north-east corner of the spa park. The old town on the 290m/951ft high hill above the spa has a **wonderful view of the plain**. The centre is closed to cars, and the centrally located, somewhat sloping Piazza Giuseppe Giusti has been almost completely taken over by welcoming cafés and restaurants, although a small theatre from the period around 1900 has hung on. For a view of the surroundings go to the terrace of Gran Caffè Il Giardino.

*Montecatini Alto

Funicolare: Mar – Oct daily 9.30am – 1pm, 2.30pm – 12pm on the half and full hour; ticket: €4; www.funicolare1898.it

Grotta Maona lies on the way to Montecatini Alto; it is Italy's only stalactite and stalagmite cave with two shafts.
❶ Viale Fedeli, tours: Apr 1 – Oct 31; admission: €6; www.grottamaona.it

AROUND MONTECATINI TERME

Monsumma-
no Terme

An old city on the hill and spas below it are also the attractions of Monsummano Terme, about 5km/3mi to the east. The large **MGrotta Giusti Terme** dripstone cave with an underground lake was discovered here in 1849. Giuseppe Verdi called it the eighth wonder of the world. The water temperature in the connected grottoes is as high as 34°C/93°F and creates highly effective atmosphere for steam baths, which are especially good for arthritis, metabolic disorders and bronchial illnesses. The therapy areas are called »Paradise«, »Purgatory« and »Hell«. The satirist Giuseppe Giusti, who born in 1809 in Monsummano and who helped to prepare the way for the Risorgimento, is the subject of the **Museo Nazionale di Casa Giusti**. **Museo della Città e del Territorio**, on the other hand, in Monsummano's old pilgrimage hostel on Piazza F. Martini presents the history of the locality and the spa

Grotta Giusti Terme: Mar – Nov

Museo Nazionale di Casa Giusti: Viale Vincenzo Martini 18; May 1 – Oct 31. Wed – Mon afternoon, Nov 1 – Apr 30 also morning; free admission

Museo della Città e del Territorio: summer Mon 9am – 12pm, Wed – Sun 4pm – 7pm, winter Mon 9am – 12pm, Wed – Fri 3.30pm – 6.30pm, Sat, Sun 9am – 12pm, 3.30pm – 6.30pm; admission: €3; www.museoterritorio.it

Marble basins and cultured water faucets in the Tettucio Terme

Between Montecatini Terme and Pescia a steep road leads up to the **Buggiano**
medieval mountain village Buggiano. Palazzo Pretorio (13th cent.) is
most noteworthy; its façade is decorated with coats of arms (15th/16th
cent.). The Romanesque parish church was established in 1038 for a
Benedictine abbey and in part renovated in the 13th to 16th centuries.

PESCIA

About 10km/6mi north-west of Montecatini Terme, the town of **Provincial**
Pescia is situated in Valdinievole on both banks of the Pescia River, **town on the**
which supported the town's paper mills, silk weaving and leather tan- **river**
ning industry for centuries. Asparagus fields, olive trees and flowers
characterize the surroundings of Pescia. 200 citrus plants flourish in
Giardino degli Agrumi in nearby Castellare di Pescia (www.giardi-
nodegliagrumi.it). The river divides
Pescia into two different parts. The
bustling centre of the **west bank** is
the oblong **Piazza Mazzini**, where
there is a market every Saturday. The
northern end of the square is dominated by the Palazzo del Vicario, em-
bellished with coats of arms (13th –
14th cent.) and used as a town hall
today. The **cathedral** attracts the eye
on the **east side** of the river. The
people who live on this side call
themselves »Domaioli« after it. The
church was built in the late 17th century on Romanesque foundations

? MARCO ◉ POLO INSIGHT

Ivo Livi's career

Did you know that Ivo Livi was
born in 1921 in Montesummano
Terme? He is better known under
the name Yves Montand. When
the future actor and singer was
three years old he had to flee
with his father to Marseilles from
the Fascists. In 1944 Montand began his career in Paris. The film
The Wages of Fear (1953) made
him world famous.

and became the seat of a bishop in 1726. The façade dates from the
late 19th century, the massive campanile possibly from the previous
Romanesque building. For art lovers the simple Franciscan church
San Francesco is far more interesting. It holds a famous panel from
1235 by Bonaventura Berlinghieri from Lucca with a depiction of St
Francis and six scenes from his life. This painting of a man who had
lived only shortly before and was canonized soon after his death
– the figure in the centre surrounded by scenes from his life story
– employed a pictorial composition that had previously been reserved for Christ and the Virgin.

5km/3mi north of Pescia in the little town of Pietrabuona the **Museo** **Pietrabuona**
della Carta di Pescia documents the long tradition of the paper industry in the Pescia valley.
❶ Mon – Fri 9am – 1pm, tours Mon and Fri 9.30am – 12.30pm, Sat 9.30am
– 1.30pm; free admission; www.museodellacarta.org

** **Montepulciano**

✦ **L 13**

Province: Siena (SI)
Altitude: 605m/1,985ft above sea level
Population: 14,600

A steep tuffstone hill between ▶Val di Chiana and Val d'Orcia is the site of a charming architectural gem: stately Renaissance palaces and well-maintained medieval brick houses in a labyrinth of narrow streets make Montepulciano one of the best-preserved historic towns in Tuscany. Music lovers come here for the festival every summer, wine lovers for the many enoteche and the Vino Nobile di Montepulciano, one of the best-known Italian wines.

History
According to legend Montepulciano was founded by the Etruscan king Porsenna. Montepulciano probably owes its existence to the Roman dynasty of the Publicii. Today the residents of Montepulciano still call themselves **Poliziani** – from Mons Politianus, the Roman name for the town. In the Middle Ages this independent community was allied with Siena and Florence in alternation until 1511, when it submitted finally to Florence.

WHAT TO SEE IN MONTEPULCIANO

Sant'Agnese
When approaching from the north the church of Sant'Agnese lies outside the town wall opposite Poggifanti Park. Remnants of the first church in this location are the Gothic doorway and the fresco of the Madonna from the school of Simone Martini in the first chapel on the right. The marble reliquary of St Agnes is at the main altar.

! MARCO POLO TIP
Caffè Poliziano **Insider Tip**

The café with an Art nouveau interior, which first opened in 1868, and a small panorama terrace offers lunch with »vampire« menus, dinner, along with tea – 40 varieties are available – and concerts, exhibitions and theatre as well as a free library for guests (Piccola libreria). Via Voltaia del Corso 27-29, www.caffepoliziano.it.

Enter the walled old city through the **Porta al Prato**. It was built in the 14th century and incorporated into the new Medici fortification by Antonio da Sangallo the Elder around 1520. He was active as a master builder in Montepulciano in the early 16th cent. The gate is decortaed with the Tuscan coat of arms and the Florentine lion. From here the slightly winding corso leads through the city to the south-east gate, the 14th-century Porta delle Farine.

Honourable old Renaissance palaces line the Piazza Grande

A few yards along, Piazza Savonarola appears with the Baroque church of San Bernardo and Palazzo Avignonesi (no. 91), whose design is attributed to Giacomo da Vignola. The late Renaissance façade, in the lower part made of so-called cushion masonry, was designed with a row of windows, each with alternating triangular and segmented pediments, on the two upper floors.

Piazza Savonarola

On Palazzo Bucelli, further along on the right side, Etruscan urns with mythical creatures are set in the wall, as are Etruscan and Latin inscriptions.

Palazzo Bucelli

The showpiece of Piazza Michelozzo a few steps further uphill is the elegant façade of the church of Sant'Agostino. Michelozzo di Bartolomeo designed it in 1427, skilfully combining Gothic forms with early Renaissance elements. The terracotta relief in the tympanum over the portal depicts the Virgin, John the Baptist and St Augustine. Inside the aisle-less church, which was reconstructed in the late 18th

Sant'-Agostino, Torre di Pulcinella

Montepulciano

INFORMATION
Piazza Don Minzoni 1
(below Porta Al Prato)
Tel. 05 78 75 73 41
www.prolocomontepulciano.it

SHOPPING
Consorzio del Vino Nobile di Montepulciano
Piazza Grande 7, Tel. 05 78 75 78 12
www.consorziovinonobile.it
54 wines from producers in the region can be tasted, and some can be also bought here.

EVENTS
Bravio delle botti
is the name of the Montepulciano city festival on 29 August, when wine barrels weighing 80kg/176lb are rolled through the city (www.braviodellebotti.com).

Cantiere Internazionale d'Arte
At the annual music festival, classical and modern music is performed (last week in July; www.fondazionecantiere.it).

WHERE TO EAT
❶ *Le Logge del Vignola*
€€€ – €€€€
Via delle Erbe 6
Tel. 05 78 71 72 90
www.leloggedelvignola.com
Closed Tue, mid-Nov. until mid-Dec.
In a former bakery in the middle of Montepulciano three friends opened this stylish restaurant. The tourist menu at noon is worthwhile; candlelight atmosphere in the evenings. Aperitif and amuse-gueule are served as complimentary starters.

❷ *Ristorante Borgo Buio* €€ – €€€
Via di Borgo Buio 10
Tel. 05 78 71 74 97, www.borgobuio.it
Closed Thu and all of Jan. In a medieval vaulted cellar Elda and Pier spoil theri guests with typical Tuscan dishes and homemade pasta. After the kitchen closes (10.30pm) Pier invites his guests to the cocktail bar Caffé degli Archi next door.

WHERE TO STAY
❶ *Il Borghetto* €€€
Via di Borgo Buio 7
Tel. 05 78 75 75 35
www.ilborghetto.it
Centrally located small hotel in a 15th-century house with a wonderful view of the old city, 15 rooms.

❷ *Il Marzocco* €€
Piazza Savonarola 18
Tel. 05 78 75 72 62
www.albergoilmarzocco.it
Traditional family business in a 16th-century palazzo. The 16 rooms are simple but tastefully furnished, some with balcony.

century, are a 15th-century wooden crucifix and paintings by Alessandro Allori and Federico Barocci from the 16th and 17th centuries. A curiosity can be seen on the clock tower opposite, the Torre di Pulcinella (16th-cent.): a masked **Pulcinella** figure dressed in white, which a monk is said to have brought back from Naples, strikes the hours (access: donation towards upkeep of the tower).

The Baroque church of Santa Lucia, which was completed to designs by Flaminio del Turco, stands in Via Saffi. In the Ceppari chapel there is *Madonna della Misericordia* by Luca Signorelli.

Santa Lucia

Follow Via del Poggiolo to the travertine-clad Palazzo Benincasa and the church of San Francesco, which owes its present appearance to a reconstruction in the 18th century. The terrace next to the church offers a wonderful view of the surroundings and of Chiesa San Biagio.

Palazzo Benincasa, San Francesco

Palazzo Neri Orselli (Via Ricci 10) in late Gothic-Sienese style houses the city museum; its collection goes back to a donation by Francesco Crociani in 1859. The exhibits from the 15th–18th centuries include several terracottas by Andrea della Robbia, Madonna paintings by Jacopo di Mino del Pelliccaio and Raffaelino del Garbo, Filippo Lippi's *Crucifixion* as well as works by Carlo Cignani and Antonio Coli. The second and third floor also have some Etruscan urns from ▶Chiusi and San Casciano.

*Museo Civico, Pinacoteca Crociani

❶ Summer Tue – Sun 10am – 1pm, 3 – 7pm, winter until 6pm; admission: €4.15

At the highest point of the walled old city is the centre of Montepulciano: Piazza Grande – officially Piazza Vittorio Emanuele – surrounded by dignified Renaissance palaces. At the corner of Via Ricci stands the 14th-century Palazzo del Capitano del Popolo, one of the few remaining examples of Gothic architecture in Montepulciano. Palazzo Tarugi, set back a little, is attributed to **Antonio da Sangallo the Elder**, although the upper storeys were probably executed by Baldassare Peruzzi. The open loggia on the ground floor corresponds to a similar one on the second floor which is walled up today. The fountain in front of the palace with the two griffins and two lions holding the Medici coat of arms was built in 1520 using two Etruscan columns.

**Piazza Grande

Palazzo Contucci, also a work of Antonio da Sangallo the Elder, stands on the east side of the square. It was commissioned in 1519 by Cardinal Giovanni Maria del Monte, the later Pope Julius III. When Sangallo died in 1534, Baldassare Peruzzi took over the construction of the piano nobile; the upper mezzanine storey was only added in 1690 by the Contucci family. The main hall has frescoes by the Baroque painter Andrea Pozzo.

*Palazzo Contucci

In 1561 the bishop of Chiusi moved his seat to Montepulciano in 1561 because the Chiana valley was becoming increasingly swampy. The new cathedral was built on Piazza Grande, at that time the location of a 15th-cent. parish church. Ippolito Scalza designed the plans for the early Baroque structure and had it built 1592 – 1630 The building was never finished; there is no cladding and the façade is in

*Duomo

brick. The lower storeys of the campanile come from the previous building. Inside the church to the left of the main portal is the reclining figure of Bartolomeo Aragazzi, a secretary of Pope Martin V (1417–1431). The tomb, created in 1437 and later dismantled, is an early Renaissance work by Michelozzo di Bartolomeo. Other parts of the tomb are displayed elsewhere in the cathedral: on the first two piers in the nave are reliefs of the Virgin and members of the Aragazzi family; on the south-east pier of the crossing is a statue of St Bartholomew, and the base of the tomb is the slab of the high altar. The late Gothic triptych over the high altar was painted by the Sienese master Taddeo di Bartolo in 1401.

Palazzo Comunale

The west side of Piazza Grande is bordered by the massive Palazzo Comunale. Its tower offers a **wonderful panorama** over the city and as far as ▶Monte Amiata. The palace was begun at the end of the 14th century; it got its present form in 1424 to plans by the Florentine Renaissance architect Michelozzo, as the architect's plans which were discovered in 1965 show. The simple façade with crenellations and the tower with a crown are reminiscent of the Palazzo Vecchio in ▶Florence.

❶ Mon – Sat 9am – 1pm; free admission

Via S. Donato, Santa Maria dei Servi

From the cathedral follow Via S. Donato southwards past the fortress rebuilt around 1880 in historicizing style to the church of Santa Maria dei Servi with its Gothic façade outside the city walls. The foundation stone for the church was laid in the 14th century, the aisle-less interior was converted to Baroque in the late 17th century by the Jesuit Andrea Pozzo. The panel painting on the third altar to the left by a pupil of Duccio di Buoninsegna is worth noting.

Via dell'Opio

Follow Via del Poliziano further along into Via dell'Opio in the eastern part of the old city. The house at Via dell'Opio no. 5, built around 1400, is the birthplace of the poet **Poliziano** (1454–1494), whose real name was Agnolo Ambrogini. After his father was murdered the 15-year-old Agnolo left his home town for Florence, where he later became a friend of Lorenzo de Medici. A little further – the street is now called Via di Voltaia – is the Church of Jesus built between 1702 and 1714 by Andrea Pozzo.

*Via di Voltaia, Palazzo Cervini

In Via di Voltaia there are many shops selling ceramics and wine, as well as the city's traditional café, Caffè Poliziano (no. 27 – 29). Palazzo Cervini (no. 21) is occupied by the Banca Populare dell'Etruria. The massive three-wing palace was commissioned by Cardinal Marcello Cervini, later Pope Marcellus II, and built by Antonio da Sangallo the Elder between 1518 and 1534, but was never completed. On Piazza delle Erbe the Logge del Grano (or Logge del Mercato) by Vignola are worth a look.

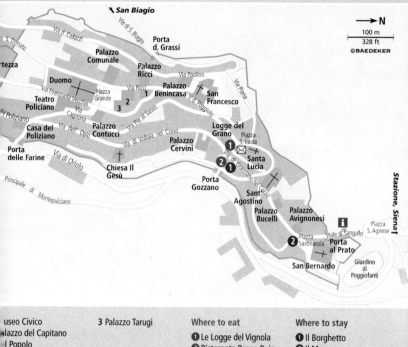

	3 Palazzo Tarugi	Where to eat	Where to stay
useo Civico		❶ Le Logge del Vignola	❶ Il Borghetto
alazzo del Capitano		❷ Ristorante Borgo Buio	❷ Il Marzocco
l Popolo			

AROUND MONTEPULCIANO

About 1km/0.5mi north of Piazza S. Agnese is the church of Santa Maria delle Grazie, built in the 16th century to plans by Ippolito Scalza. It holds a valuable organ, which was probably donated to the church at Christmas 1600 by the patrician Vincenzo Salimbeni. The organ has pipes made of cypress wood that produce the variety of tone characteristic of Italian Renaissance organs.

Santa Maria delle Grazie

One of the most significant late Renaissance buildings in Tuscany is located 2km/1.2mi south-west of Montepulciano: the impressive church of San Biagio at the end of a avenue of cypresses. It was built to designs by Antonio da Sangallo the Elder between 1518 and 1545 as a **pilgrimage church for a picture of the Madonna**. The ground

*San Biagio

Renaissance church of San Biagio was built on the outline of a Greek cross. Montepulciano rises up in the background.

plan has the shape of a Greek cross. A high tambour dome rises above the central crossing. Of the two free-standing towers planned by Giuliano di Baccio only one was completed. The building, which was conceived in the tradition of Bramante and built of yellow-gold travertine, is not only interesting on the outside: the frescoes in the presbytery are probably 16th-century works of the Zuccari brothers, and the marble altar retable (1584) behind the main altar is attributed to Lisandro and Giannozzo Albertini. The carefully restored 18th-century organ includes parts of its predecessor.

Therme di Montepulcia-no, Sant 'Albino About 4km/2.5mi out on the road to Chianciano Terme lies the little spa of Sant' Albino. Its two carbonated springs were already known in antiquity and are used in a modern thermal spa today. The current wellness spa (Sat, Sun 8am – 12.30pm) offers reiki, ayurveda, aroma therapy, massages and treatments for bronchial and pulmonary problems or rheumatism. The house own cosmetic line »Renaissance« contains a wine extract with anti-oxydants (www.termemontepulciano.it).

The Etruscan king Porsenna and Horace already raved about the healing hot springs 10km/6mi south of Montepulciano. Chianciano's oldest thermal pool (1st cent.) is one of the largest in Antiquity. Charlemagne stayed here as well. Pirandello dedicated two stories to the hot springs, Fellini used the setting for his masterpiece *Eight and a Half* (www.termechianciano.it). The news about their successful treatment of kidney, liver and bronchial ailments spread after the spa was expanded in 1915. **Parco Acqua Santa** with the spa house and the larger **Parco di Fucoli** east of Viale delle Terme with tennis courts, roller-skating track and boccia court form the centre of the spa resort. **Parco Sorgente Sant' Elena**, thanks to the mineral water of the same name, is also very popular.

The pretty * **Centro Storico** with romantic houses and arches is located 3km/2mi north of the spa district. **Museo Civico Archeologico delle Acque** shows the life of the Etruscans and Romans from the 6th/5th cent. BC up to the 4th cent. AD in its departments »World of the Dead«, »Sanctuaries«, »Settlements«, »Spas from Roman Times«. * **Museo d' Arte di Chianciano**, whose exhibits come from private collectors, shows Asian art, drawings of Tiepolo and 20th cent. works by Renato and Guercino Guttuso, René Magritte and Edvard Munch.

*Chianciano Terme

MARCO POLO TIP

Frantoio La Macina Insider Tip

Don't let the rather sober atmosphere put you off: Dora Forzioni and her team produce wonderful olive oil! Chianciano Terme, Strada Cavine e Valli 34 (below Chianciano Terme), www.frantoiolamacina.it

Parco Acqua Santa: June 1 – Sep 30 admission: €9.50; Oct 1 – May 31 admission: €7.50

Parco di Fucoli: only Apr – Oct ; admission: €5.50

Parco Sorgente Sant' Elena: Apr – Nov; www.termesantelena.it;

Museo Civico Archeologico delle Acque: Viale Dante 80; Easter – Oct Tue – Sun 10am – 1pm, 4pm – 7pm, Nov – Easter Sat, Sun 10am – 1pm, 4pm – 7pm; admission: €5; www.museoetrusco.it

Museo d' Arte di Chianciano: Via della Libertà 280; Tue – Sun 10am – 1pm, 4pm – 7.30pm; admission: €5

5km/3mi west of Chianciano Terme in enchanting scenery lies the old estate La Foce. The former owners Antonio and **Iris Origo** had a garden with boxwood hedges, pomegranate trees, lavender beds, lemon trees and a rose garden with a wisteria pergola designed in the 1920s. Iris Origo wrote an impressive diary (▶MARCO POLO Tip p. 42) about her time in La Foce during World War II. The belvedere offers a wonderful view of the magnificent cypress avenue, which winds down from La Foce into the valley and up the hill on the opposite side.

*La Foce

❶ Apr – Sep Wed 3pm – 7pm, Oct – Mar Wed 3pm – 5pm and Sep – Nov first weekend of the month 10am – 12pm, 3pm – 6pm; with B & B/ apartment rental; www.lafoce.com

** Pienza

✦ L 13

Province: Siena (SI)
Altitude: 491m/1,611ft above sea level
Population: 2,180

Corsignano was conceived as a model Renaissance city by its builder, Enea Silvio Piccolomini (1405–1464), the later Pope Pius II. Work on the papal residence began in 1459 and was so far advanced three years later that Pius II elevated the place to a city and seat of a bishop and named it after himself, »city of Pius«. He died before his project was complete, but what remained is a unique ensemble of urban architecture and one of the most popular tourist attractions in southern Tuscany. together with San Quirinco d' Orcia it stands under UNESCO protection.

** PIAZZA PIO II

Heart of town The heart of Pienza is the trapezoid piazza, which – how could it be otherwise – is called Pio II and is framed by important buildings: cathedral, Palazzo Comunale, Palazzo Borgia and Palazzo Piccolomini. Since the tourist information office is here, too, the square is seldom empty.

*Duomo Santa Maria Assunta The cathedral of the Assumption of the Virgin was built in 1459 – 1462 to plans by Rossellino over a Romanesque church dedicated to Mary. Pillars and blind arcades structure its travertine façade. The gable bears the **papal coat of arms of Pius II**: the crown and the crossed keys of St Peter, and the shield with coat of arms of the Piccolomini family. The church was influenced by Gothic architecture. It is a hall church, a relatively rare type in Italy. Because of the sloping ground, elaborate supporting constructions were necessary for the apse; the soft ground still causes problems today. The light interior comes as a surprise. It contains several beautiful Madonnas, including the Madonna with Saints by Matteo di Giovanni on the left wall and the Assumption of the Virgin by Vecchietta in the chapel on the left of the choir.

> **!** *For friends of pecorino cheese* **Insider Tip**
>
> **MARCO ⊕ POLO TIP**
>
> Pienza pecorino is considered the best in all of Italy. Livio Zazzeri at Le Bontà di Pio, Corso Rossellino 6, offers opulent gift packages and will also mail them overseas (www.zazzeripienza.com, www.lebontadipio.com).

Pienza

INFORMATION
Ufficio Informazioni, Corso Rossellino 30
Tel. 05 78 74 99 05
www.comune.pienza.siena.it

SHOPPING
Gourmets and crafts lovers will find everything on Via Rossellino. Tip: Pienza's famous cheese festival always takes place on the first Sunday in September.

WHERE TO EAT
Latte di Luna € – €€
Via San Carlo 2/4
Tel. 05 78 74 86 06
Closed Tue Trattoria with very pretty seating outdoors. Try the fried pork and the semifreddi all' arancio (half-frozen dessert with oranges)!

WHERE TO STAY
Il Chiostro di Pienza €€€ – €€€€
Corso Rossellino 26
Tel. 05 78 74 84 00
www.relaisilchiostrodipienza.com
A 15th-century monastery was converted to this tasteful hotel in the old town of Pienza with 37 rooms, 6 suites, pool and panorama restaurant.

Il Giardino Segreto €
Via Roma 44 Tel. 05 02 90 00
www.intuscany.net/apartments/
giardino_segreto.htm
Friendly accommodation (3 app., 2 double rooms), central but still very quiet in a side street near Piazza Pio II.

Palazzo Borgia

Cardinal Rodrigo Lanzol Borgia, the later Pope Alexander VI and prototype of the clever and unscrupulous Renaissance politician, was known for his excessive lifestyle. He commissioned the bishop's palace on the west side of the square at the end of the 15th century. For this reason the Borgia coat of arms with a bull was placed above the portal.

*Museo Diocesano

In the Renaissance palace next to Palazzo Borgia the diocesan museum shows its treasures, including 14th-century painted panels and 16th-century Flemish needlepoint. The beautiful Madonna picture from the neighbouring Monticchiello by Pietro Lorenzetti on display here, having been stolen twice from its original location. Pienza is also especially proud of the gold-embroidered vestments of Pius II, English work dating from the 14th century, which were given to the pope by Thomas Palaiologos, the brother of the last Byzantine emperor.

❶ Mar 16 – Oct 31 Wed – Mon 10am – 1pm, 3pm – 7pm, Nov 1 – Dec 19, Jan 7 – Mar 15 Sat, Sun 10am – 1pm, 2pm – 5pm, Dec 20 – Jan 6 Wed – Mon 10am – 1pm, 2pm – 5pm; admission: €4.10

*City wall, panorama

Between the cathedral and Museo Diocesano a path leads to the Pienza city wall. The broad wall, which can be walked on, is a wonderful place to view the Val d'Orcia.

Palazzo Comunale

The travertine façade of the city hall (14th cent.) gains lightness from its loggia and seems almost delicate in comparison to the cathedral opposite. The tower is from the 17th century. A fresco of the Madonna (15th cent.) from the Sienese school decorates the council hall.

*Palazzo Piccolomini

To the right of the cathedral stands the three-storey Palazzo Piccolomini, a major work of Rossellino **modelled on the Florentine Palazzo Rucellai**. The façade is made of carefully worked sandstone and travertine. Pilasters and horizontal string courses with windows in between are the main features of its composition. Rossellino also designed the well Pozzo dei Cani (1462). The interior courtyard with its arcades – the two top floors only as tromp l'oeil – are worth a look, as is the garden front on the south side with three loggias one above the other, from which there was a view of the »hanging gardens«. The rooms on the first floor – including a dining room, armoury and library – are open to the public.

❶ Oct 16 – Mar 14 Tue – Sun 10am – 4.30pm, Mar 15 – Oct 15 Tue – Sun 10am – 6.30pm; admission: €7; www.palazzopiccolominipienza.it

San Francesco

The simple church behind Palazzo Piccolomini goes back to the 13th century. The adjacent former monastery with 15th-century cloister now accommodates hotel guests.

A short break under the town hall arcades. The cathedral is opposite on the trapezoid-shaped Piazza Pio II

AROUND PIENZA

About 5km/3mi south-east of Pienza, on a hilltop and surrounded by   ***Monti-**
defensive walls, stands the medieval village of Monticchiello. Every   **cchiello**
year at the end of July / early August street theatre, the popular **»teatro povero«**, is held in Monticchiello – by the residents themselves,
who began this tradition in the 1970s. On the renovated church
square, Piazza Nuovo, TePoTraTos (Teatro Popolare Tradizionale
Toscano) and a museum on the history of the »Teatro povero« have
been established in an old grainery.
❶ Tours: Tue – Sun on the hour 10am – 12pm, 3pm – 6pm, reduced in
winter; admission: €4; www.tepotratos.it

** Pisa

G 5

Province: Pisa (PI)
Elevation: 4m/13ft above sea level
Population: 88,200

**Probably no other city has become as famous as Pisa through
a construction error – the Leaning Tower should never have
been built here because the city stands on alluvial ground. The
capital city of the province of Pisa once stood on a lagoon and
today lies on the banks of the Arno only 10km/6mi from the
Versilia coast. The cathedral and Leaning Tower often cause
the city to be forgotten – unjustly so as Pisa has a beautiful
old city, interesting museums, excellent shopping and the
everyday life of a university city.**

Pisa was probably founded by Greeks in the 7th or 6th century BC.   **Major**
Etruscans later settled on the lagoon. The name Pisa comes from the   **harbour**
Etruscan word for mouth and refers to the delta region of the Serchio
and Arno rivers. The Romans built a harbour in Pisa at the time when it
lay right on the sea. The victory over the Saracens by Messina and Paler-
mo in 1063 initiated the rise of the city to be the pre-eminent commercial power of the western Mediterranean. The maritime republic had
become rich through **trade with the Orient** and dominated the coastal regions of the Near East, Greece, North Africa, Sicily, Sardinia and the
Balearic Islands in the 12th century. However, from the late 12th century Pisa got competition from other cities, including Lucca and Florence, but also from the coastal cities Amalfi and Genoa. The city engaged
in many wars with its rivals: in 1003 Pisa fought the first Italian communal war to gain its independence from Lucca, and in later years did battle with Venice in the Adriatic and Genoa for the control of French trade.

Highlights Pisa

► **Cathedral and baptistery**
Two highlights of Romanesque architecture in Tuscany
►page 360

► **Leaning Tower**
Despite or maybe because of its leaning tendencies the famous tower is
worth climbing.
►page 360

► **Camposanto**
A visit to the cemetery on the Piazza
del Duomo is worthwhile for the excellent fresco decorations
►page 369

► **Museo Nazionale di San Matteo**
One of the great museums of
Tuscany
►page 374

► **Borgo Stretto**
A narrow alley, but Pisa's prettiest
shopping street.
►page 372

► **Piazza Vettovaglie**
The Pisans buy their fruit and vegetables on this atmospheric square.
►page 372

The **defeat of the Pisan fleet by the Genoese on 6 August 1284**
sealed the fate of the Tuscan sea power. Pisa had to give up occupied territory, came under the control of the Milanese Visconti and was taken
over by Florence in 1406. The Medici promoted major construction
plans in the city, such as the regulating of the Arno and Serchio as well
as the building of bridges and canals. From the 16th century to the unification of Italy in 1859 Pisa was part of the grand duchy of Tuscany.

✶✶ PIAZZA DEL DUOMO

Pisa's most popular attractions – the cathedral and the Leaning Tower, the baptistery and Camposanto – are all sited on the cathedral
square, an expansive area on the north-western edge of the old town,
also called the Campo dei Miracoli, «Miracle Square». The monuments were all built of Carrara marble and have been on the UN-
ESCO world heritage list since 1987. Those who want to see the
Campo without the crowds should come early in the morning.

Pisa's »Mirac-le Square«

Baptistery: daily Apr – Sep 8am – 7.30pm, Oct 8.30am – 7pm, Mar 8.30am
– 5pm, Dec/Jan 9.30am – 4.30pm, Feb and Nov 9am – 5pm
Camposanto: daily June – Aug 8am – 11pm, Apr, May, Sep 8am – 8pm,
Oct 9am – 7pm, Mar 9am – 6pm, Nov – Feb 10am – 5pm

**Certainly one of Europe's most famous landmarks: the Leaning Tower
of Pisa, which was closed for years because it had to be stabilised.**

** The Leaning Tower The Torre Pendente, the Leaning Tower, is the city's trademark (▸ MARCO POLO Insight, p. 361). After years of restoration and stabilisation it is accessible again. Groups (max. 40 people) are let in every 30 min.; **children under 8 years of age** are not permitted to climb and older children only when accompanied by an adult. Due to the demand reservations 15 to 45 days in advance are recommended; otherwise expect long waits.

❶ daily June – Aug 8.30am – 10.30pm, Apr/May, Sep 8.30am – 8pm, Oct 9am – 7pm, Mar 9am – 5.30pm, Jan/Dec 10am – 4.30pm, Feb/Nov 9.30am – 5pm; admission: €1€, online €17, online reservation: www.opapisa.it, pick up online tickets at Cashier 2 in Museo delle Sinopie (with ID).

> **!** *Tips for visits* **Insider Tip**
>
> MARCO ⊕ POLO TIP
>
> A ticket office for the sights on Piazza del Duomo has been opened in Museo delle Sinopie. Tickets can be bought or reserved ahead here. Since the demand is great online reservations two weeks in advance are recommended at www.opapisa.it. Reserving by telephone is not possible. Admission prices are staggered according to the number of sights you want to visit (€5 –10).

** DUOMO SANTA MARIA ASSUNTA

❶ daily Apr – Sep 10am – 8pm, Oct until 7pm, Mar until 6pm, Nov – Feb 10am – 12.45pm, 2pm – 5pm; admission: Mar – Oct €2; Nov – Feb free admission, access to masses/devotions in Cappella SS. Sacramento free admission

Building history A naval victory over the Saracens in 1063 made it possible: according to an inscription on the façade the building costs of the large cathedral were covered by the freight »of six richly laden Saracen ships seized off Sardinia«. The unfinished building was dedicated in 1118 already by Pope Gelasius II. The first architect, Buscheto, entered uncharted territory with his plans. There were no precedents in Italy for his double-aisled Romanesque columned basilica with aisles in the transept and a crossing dome. In the mid-12th century the church was extended to the west where Buscheto's successor, Rainaldo, added the façade to the nave.

Façade The magnificent, clearly structured façade was a **model for Romanesque church architecture in Tuscany. The ground floor has a unified appearance with blind arcades and three entrances. Above it are four stepped storeys where rows of arches like loggias stand out from the actual walls. The gable over the nave is crowned with a statue of a Madonna, thought to be by Andrea Pisano. The three bronze doors were made in Giambologna's workshop after a massive fire in 1595. The carefully restored ****Porta di San Ranieri**, the former main entrance to the church, is more important than the doors in the main

The Tilting Monument

Construction failures do not normally attract tourists. But Pisa is different. Probably the first act of every visitor to Pisa is to marvel at the Leaning Tower, which does present the city with some problems due to its extreme angle of inclination, but at the same time is a landmark that overshadows every other local monument.

As is often the case when the unbelievable happens, there is a legend behind it. This states that the Leaning Tower stood **straight as a ramrod** when it was first completed. When the architect wanted to collect his payment from the city fathers, they tried to cheat him. In his anger, the master builder ordered the tower to follow him. And then, to everyone's dismay, the tower began to lean. The city fathers paid him the agreed amount immediately, but the builder left the town with a leaning tower.

Famous Builders

An inscription to the right of the entrance names the year when the foundation stone was laid: 1173. Pisa had risen to be most powerful naval republic in Italy and could invite the most eminent architects and stonemasons to build the campanile. The cathedral architect **Bo-**

After years of stabilising work the Leaning tower is accessible again to those who want to enjoy the view from the top to the Campo dei Miracoli

nanno Pisano, together with Guglielmo from Innsbruck, was responsible for the first three storeys. But before it was completed, the tower began to lean southwards. When counterweights on the north side and supporting walls on the leaning side had no effect, construction was stopped. Almost 100 years passed before another architect dared start on the tower again. **Giovanni di Simone** added another three storeys to the campanile in 1272 and tried to balance the angle by bending the axis of the tower to the vertical. In 1301 the bells were hung, and between 1350 and 1372 **Tommaso Pisano** completed the marble tower with an open belfry.

Up close the 57m/187ft-high, free-standing bell tower leans even more than expected. The base rests on an artificial bed of gravel and is some 4m/13ft high. Above it on the loggia storeys the thickness of the cylinder walls (inner diameter 7.4m/24ft) is reduced to 3.3m/11ft, still enough to hold the circular stairway inside with 294 steps that lead to the top platform. In the more than eight hundred years of its crooked existence Pisa's trademark had tilted 5 degrees and 22 minutes away from the vertical by 1990, a **deviation of 4.86m/16ft**. The foundations had sunk 2.25m/7ft 4in towards the southeast. At an estimated movement of 1mm per year the building would have fallen over in the year 2000: that is, when the vertical axis of the cylinder had moved through the leaning northern edge. When experts discovered that the building was also turning on its own axis, not to mention the unpredictable sudden sinking of the ground, an earthquake or other material fatigue, the tower was closed in November 1990 in order to begin an extensive reconstruction that would keep it from falling over.

The Ground Is Sinking

The reason for the instability of the tower is the soft ground underneath. While the first 10m/30ft of ground was compressed to a stone-like consistency by the weight of 14,450t, the deeper layers consist of clay and sand and are difficult to calculate. The more liquid the clay-sand layer contains, the more it can resist the sinking campanile, which is why the removal of any water in a radius of 1.5km/1mi has been prohibited for over 20 years. When the first recorded attempts at correction were made, little was known about this: in 1839 water was removed to stabilize the ground – with damaging results.

When cement injection was invented the Torre Pendente got its »booster shots« in 1934 and 1959 which appeared only to have accelerated the tilting, since the cement attached itself to the foundation like an anchor and pulled it down. The suggestions for solving the problems were as odd as they were imaginative. Someone from **Japan** suggested building another tower that leaned in the opposite direction; an **Australian** proposed a supporting corset. Others even suggested taking the tower down and rebuilding it later. The method of a **German company** stimulated discussion. The proposal was to push

Campo dei Miracoli with the cathedral, its leaning tower and the baptistery illuminated at night

up the building millimetre by millimetre with the help of hydraulic presses. More than 300 buildings have been adjusted like this in German coal-mining regions. In 1992 the decision was made to wrap 18 steel cables around the base at the lowest arcade in order to keep the walls from breaking apart. At the same time a 600t concrete-and-steel plate was anchored on the north side of the foundations to stabilize the ground and compress it. This suggestion also had its critics, as it was not absolutely certain whether the tower would straighten or turn sideways.

The **good news** came in mid-1994: the sinking had stopped. In 1999 the tower was almost as »straight« as 30 years earlier. A final attempt has straightened the tower by another 400mm/16in. But an inclination of almost 4.5m/15ft remains. Now the campanile just **leans but will not fall over**. The reasons why the Pisans do not want to make their Leaning Tower into a completely normal straight tower are clear …

The Tilting Monument

Shortly after construction began it was already obvious that the monument was leaning. Since then Pisa has been kept busy trying to straighten up the city's attractive problem child. A sheer unending story.

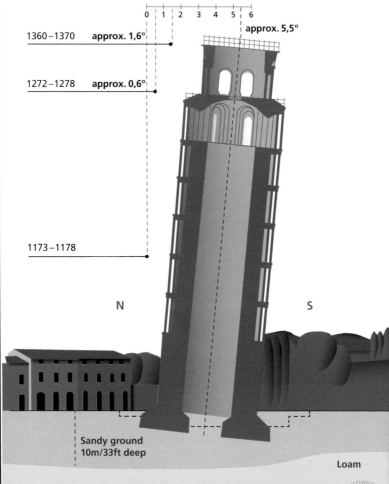

0 | 1 | 2 3 4 5 | 6

1360–1370 **approx. 1,6°**

approx. 5,5°

1272–1278 **approx. 0,6°**

1173–1178

N

S

Sandy ground
10m/33ft deep

Loam

▶ **The Leaning Tower in numbers**

from the ground 55m/180ft high

kg weight 14,500 tonnes

294 steps

12m/40ft diameter

UNESCO Wor' Cultural Heri' since 1987

▶ Problematic tower building

1173 – 1178
Bonanno Pisano

After completing the first three floors construction was stopped because the tower had already begun to lean to the south. The tower consists mainly of marble and limestone. It is at risk of collapsing mainly because of the brittle limestone and the sandy ground.

1272 – 1278
Giovanni di Simone

In order to decrease the tilt southwards heavier building material is used on the north side. In spite of this construction stopped with the seventh floor.

1360 – 1370
Tommaso Pisano

The bell tower was completed almost 100 years later. As an additional measure against tilting towards the south there are only four steps on the south side of the belfry instead of the six used on the north side.

▶ Security measures

In 1990 the tower was closed because the danger of it collapsing was too great.

1993
600 tonnes of lead bars are placed as a counterweight on the north side.

1995
Ground anchors are driven 40m/130ft into the ground. The attempt failed. The reinforced concrete was increased to 960 tonnes.

1998
Steel cable pairs were wrapped around the tower to take the weight off the foundations.

▶ The rescue
1999:

The angle of tilt was reduced by removing the ground on the north side.

The upper layer of sandy mud is brought to light by means of an augur so that the tower could gradually straighten up.

reinforced concrete

Temporary fixation with two steel cables

◄ 103m/340ft ►

▶ Nothing unique: other leaning towers in Europe (selection)

Oude Kerk, Delft
NL

Upper church,
Bad Frankenhausen,
GER

Leaning tower
of Nevjansk,
RUS

Oldehove,
Leeuwarden
NL

Albert Memorial
Clock Tower,
Belfast, IRL

Leaning tower
St-Moritz,
CH

Church tower
Suurhusen,
GER
(supposed to be
the most
leaning tower
in the world)

Pisa

INFORMATION
Piazza Vittorio Emanuele II 16
Tel. 05 04 22 91
www.pisaunicaterra.it
Galileo Galilei Airport
Tel. 0 50 50 25 18

ARRIVAL
Pisa's Galileo Galilei Airport is a destination for cheap flights. Flight info.: tel. 0 50 84 93 00, www.pisa-airport.com (car rental, train and bus connections (LAM rossa) to Pisa's main railway station). Taxi: tel. 0 50 54 16 00..

DRIVING/PARKING
Like Florence Pisa has a ZTL, a traffic-free zone, which is monitored by video cameras. many one-way streets and few parking spaces. Park for a fee at Piazza Manin (200 m from the cathedral; about €1.50 /hour). Free parking on Via Pietrasanta. A bus (»Navetta«; €1) runs from there to Piazza dei Miracoli (5 min.).

EVENTS
On the evening of June 16 the palaces along the Arno are illuminated for the Luminara. On June 17 the Regatta di San Ranieri starts (rowing regatta of the four city quarters). On the last Sat in June at 8pm: the popular Gioco del Ponte parade (bridge players) with 780 costuned participants and 41 horses. The music festivals Musica sotto la Torre (spring/summer) and Anima Mundi (fall/winter) are also engaging. There is a crafts market in the Centro Storico on every second weekend in the month.

WHERE TO EAT
❸ *Antica Trattoria »Da Bruno«*
€€ – €€€
Via Luigi Bianchi 12
Tel. 0 50 56 08 18
http://ristorante.dabruno.it
Closed Tue
Local people come to Piero Cei and the atmosphere is guaranteed. Try the ribollita, pappardelle alla cacciatore or stockfish.

façade. It is in the southern transept on the side facing the Leaning Tower and is named after the patron saint of Pisa. The bronze doors, cast around 1180 by the master Bonannus in one piece each, have four large and 20 small reliefs of the life of Christ and the Virgin. Ivories from Byzantium and Roman bronze doors were models for these doors, which are pioneering works of western sculpture.

Interior   The interior of the cathedral was largely destroyed in the fire in 1595, but a few outstanding pieces were preserved. The most famous work of art in the cathedral is the ****pulpit**, which was made between 1302 and 1312, a **late work by Giovanni Pisano**. The pulpit itself rests on pillars, of which four are shaped like figures: the archangel Michael, Samson or Hercules (a personification of Christian strength), Christ (with the four evangelists at his feet) as well as Ecclesia (a personification of the church with two infants as the Old and New Testament). At the feet of the evangelist John is Pisano's self-portrait and a por-

❶ Osteria La Mescita
€€€
Via Cavalca Domenico 2
Tel. 050 95 70 19
Closed Sat and Sun
Fresh vegetables and herbs feature in
the imaginative cuisine in this stylish res-
taurant. Well-chosen wine list.

❷ Osteria dei Cavalieri
€€ – €€€
Via San Frediano 16
Tel. 050 58 08 58
www.osteriacavalieri.pisa.it
Closed Sat noon, Sun and Aug.
Tasteful restaurant in the university quar-
ter. Typical Pisan dishes such as tripe and
tagliata with porcini.

WHERE TO STAY
❶ Royal Victoria
€€€€
Lungarno Pacinotti 12
Tel. 050 94 01 11
www.royalvictoria.it
A traditional old palace right on the
Arno with a grand staircase and luxurious marble floors, impressive for its old-
fashioned charm and understatement.

❷ Hotel Francesco
€€ – €€€
Via Santa Maria 129
Tel. 050 55 54 53
www.hotelfrancesco.com
Pleasant little hotel in the old city near
the Piazza del Duomo. It has a breakfast
terrace and there are bikes to rent.

❸ Albergo Amalfitana €€
Via Roma 44
Tel. 050 290 00
www.hotelamalfitana.it
Family hotel with 21 rooms – the rooms
facing the back are especially quiet. Simple, clean, good value.

trait of the man who commissioned the work, Burgundio di Tado.
The central support of the pulpit is shaped like three women, presumably representing the cardinal virtues faith, love and hope. Reliefs
on the pulpit show scenes from the New Testament, for example the
birth of John the Baptist, the Annunciation and Assumption of the
Virgin, the Nativity etc. The chandelier from the year 1586 that hangs
in the nave is incorrectly said to have drawn Galileo Galilei's attention to the laws of pendulum movement. At the right front pillar in
the choir the depiction of St Agnes by Andrea del Sarto is remarkable.
The apse mosaic has been restored several times and dates from the
13th and 14th centuries. It shows Christ enthroned between Mary
and John the Evangelist – a work of the Florentine Cimabue from
1302. In the southern transept is another important piece, the fragmentary grave monument of Holy Roman Emperor Henry VII, who
died after a short reign (1308–1313). It was created after 1313 by Tino
di Camaino.

Pisa

← *Viareggio*

← *Lucca*

Camposanto

Battistero

Piazza
Manin

Duomo

Piazza
del Duomo

Campanile

Piazza del Duomo

Porta
Santa
Maria

Museo
delle Sinopie

Via Contessa

Via Roma

Via S. Stefano

Via Luigi Bianchi

V. Marche

Matilde

Strada Statale 12

Porta
a Lucca

San
Zeno

Via Card. Maffi

Museo dell'
Opera del Duomo

Palazzo dei
Cavalieri

Terme Romane

S. FRANCESCO

San Giorgio
d. Tedeschi

Via Capponi

V. S.
Giuseppe

Via S.
Caterina

Santa
Caterina

Orto

Bota-
nico

Piazza
Cavallotti

V. dei
Mille

Pal.
d. Orologio

Piazza
Martiri d.
Libertà

Via San Lorenzo

San
Francesco

Via Savi

Via Derna

Via Nicola

San Sisto

Santo
Stefano
dei Cavalieri

S. Cecilia

Piazza
dei
Cavalieri

Piazza
S. Francesco

S. MARIA

V. Risorgimento

Domus
Galilaeana

San Frediano

Piazza Dante

S. Francesco

Piazza
S. Paolo
all'Orto

San
Paolo
all' Orto

Via Trieste

Università

San
Nicola

Piazza
Carrara

Palazzo
Agostini

Piazza
Vettovaglie

San
Michele
in Borgo

Teatro
G. Verdi

Sant' Andrea
Forisportam

Palazzo
Reale

Palazzo
Upezzinghi
alla Giornata

Piazza
Solferino

Piazza
Cairoli

Ponte di
Mezzo

Piazza
della
Repubblica

Palazzo
della
Giustizia

Prefettura
(Pal. Medici)

Via E. Fermi

Lungarno Gambacorti

Palazzo
BLU

Santa Maria
della Spina

Piazza
Saffi

Municipio
(Pal. Gambacorti)

Logge
di Banchi

San
Sepolcro

Palazzo
Toscanelli

Museo
Nazionale
di San Mat

Lungarno Simonelli

Ponte
Solferino

Lungarno Sonnino

Via S. Paolo

Via Alberto Mario

Casa
Gambacorti

Piazza
Gambacorti

S. Martino

Ponte alla
Fortezza

Via S. Antonio

Corso Italia

Via P. Gori

Piazza
S. Martino

San
Martino

Giar-
dino
Scotto

Via F. Niosi

V. Zerboglio

V. Lavagna

ANTONIO

Via Nino Bixio

Domus
Mazziniana

Sant'Antonio

Autostazione

Palazzo della
Provincia

Piazza
Vittorio
Emanuele II

San Domenico

Viale Benedetto Croce

Piazza
Toniolo

Bastione
di Sangallo

Piazza
Minzoni

Bastione
Stampace

Livorno, Sant
Piero a Grado,
Marina di Pisa

Via
Cesare

Stazione

Piazza
della Stazione

Viale

Viale

F. Bonaini

Piazza
Guerrazzi

Airport ↓

Ponte d
Vittoria

328 ft

100 m

©BAEDEK

Where to eat

① La Mescita
② Osteria dei Cavalieri
③ Antica Trattoria »Da Bruno«

Where to stay

① Royal Victoria
② Francesco
③ Amalfitana

** BATTISTERO

West of the cathedral stands **one of the largest baptisteries of Christendom**, which was begun in 1152 under the architect Diotisalvi and continued by others including Nicola Pisano and his son Giovanni. It is not part of the main church, a common arrangement in Italy. Baptisteries with round or octagonal plans derive from separate, early Christian baptismal churches. Since construction took more than two centuries the building combines elements of the **Romanesque and Gothic** styles. The dome-like roof originally had an elliptical shape; in 1358 the exterior was altered to suggest a semispherical dome. Most of the **outside figures on the galleries and doors** have been replaced by copies. The originals are in the cathedral museum. The main doorway opposite the entrance to the cathedral is striking for its sculptural decoration that recalls ancient sarcophagus art. The baptistery is flooded with light and is almost 55m/180ft high; it is know for its excellent acoustics. At the centre is the octagonal baptismal font (1246). It is a magnificent basin decorated with rosettes and marble inlays by Guido Begarelli from Como. The **pulpit** made in 1260 by **Nicola Pisano** is one of the most important works of Romanesque sculpture. It rests on seven columns and is completely free-standing. The lions are interpreted in the tradition of medieval images; they carry the columns and are intended to express the overcoming of evil. The figure of Hercules or Samson as the personification of strength, which supports the six-sided pulpit along with other figures of virtues, is an epoch-making innovation. The reliefs on the facing include expressive images of the Annunciation and Nativity, Adoration of the Shepherds, Adoration of the Magi, Presentation in the Temple, Crucifixion and Last Judgement.

Pisan tradition has it that Archbishop Ubaldo dei Lanfranchi brought back several shiploads of earth from Golgotha in the fourth crusade so that Pisan citizens could be buried in holy ground. But the construction of the buildings of the Camposanto, the »holy field«, was not carried out until 1278 under Giovanni di Simone. This cemetery on the northern edge of Piazza del Duomo is bordered by monumental arcaded passages with Gothic windows. The gravestones of Pisan patricians are set into the floor of the arcades; ancient sarcophagi stand along the edge including one with the tragic love story of Hippolyte, son of Theseus, who fell in love with his stepmother Phaedra. Until World War II 14th- and 15th-century **frescoes** decorated the walls of the arcades. During a bombing raid on 27 July 1944 they were destroyed by molten lead that ran down from the roof. Parts of the frescoes were successfully restored so that the intense colours can be seen again. *The Triumph of Death*, a large-scale painting which shows the influence of the Great Plague of 1348, is particularly im-

**Camposanto

Interior of the Romanesque cathedral with five aisles

pressive: at the front left three noble horsemen encounter the open caskets of three kings, above them hermits pray. On the other side a wealthy group holds a carefree celebration in the forest. The grim reaper, half devil and half woman, waits for the people, who will either go to eternal damnation or eternal righteousness at the Last Judgement.

*Museo delle Sinopie A visit to the Sinopie Museum is a recommended addition to the Camposanto. The **preliminary sketches for the frescoes** in the Camposanto, which were made with red chalk, are displayed here. The sinopia was the artist's most important contribution because it determined the composition of the work in detail. The actual execution of the frescoes was often done by students and assistants. The museum shows the sinopie of the Camposanto frescoes together with reproductions of the wall paintings.

*Museo dell'Opera del Duomo After the renovation and remodelling work is finished in 2016 the collections of the Museo dell´opera del Duomo, Piazza del Duomo 3, will be given a new look. Palazzo dell'Opera della Primaziale Pisana, Piazza del Duomo 17, on the north side of Piazza dei Miracoli, to the right of Campo Santo, has had a new role since 2014. Exhibitions of contemporary and modern art have been held here since 2014 to great public acclaim. From June 2015 until January 2016 an exhibition of the works of Arnoldo Pomodoro has been running in the Palazzo dell´Opera, the Museo delle Sinopie and on the Piazza dei Miracoli.

Museo dell´Opera del Duomo: Piazza del Duomo 3; Apr – Sep daily 8am – 8pm, rest of the year daily from 9am; www.opapisa.it
Palazzo dell'Opera della Primaziale Pisana: Piazza del Duomo 17; Apr – Oct daily 8am – 8pm, Nov – Mar daily 9am – 5pm, admission €3 or €5, www.opapisa.it

FROM THE CATHEDRAL SQUARE TO THE BANKS OF THE ARNO

The city tour begins at the cathedral square and goes first through Via Santa Maria, which is bordered by beautiful old city palaces, down to the Arno River. At Via Luca Ghini 5, a side street of Via Santa Maria, is the entrance to the Botanical Gardens. It was laid out in 1543 by the physician and botanist Luca Ghini under orders from Grand Duke Cosimo de Medici. It is used today above all for research by the Botanical Institute. Laurel, Californian palm trees, gingko trees and rare medicinal herbs flourish in hothouses and outdoors.

*Via Santa Maria Orto Botanico

❶ Mon – Fri 8.30am – 5pm, Sat 8.30am – 1pm, admission: €2.50

In the house at Via Santa Maria no. 26 Galileo Galilei, (▶ MARCO POLO Insight p. 68) is supposed to have lived – the house where he was born was probably in the eastern part of the city near the church of Sant'Andrea Forisportam. Today the place of memorial, which has a well-stocked library, displays a collection of writings by Galilei and his students.

Domus Galilaeana

Lungarno Pacinotti street along the river was once the finest street in Pisa. The most beautiful of the partially restored magnificent patrician palaces is Palazzo Reale. It was begun in 1559 by the Florentine Baccio Bandinelli and commissioned by Cosimo I. Today it houses the Museo Nazionale di Palazzo Reale. The main attraction of the museum's 14 rooms is an altar panel by Raphael, which he painted when he was only 17 years old. The collection also contains paintings by Francesco Francia, Bernardo Strozzi, Frans van Francken and Joos van Cleve.

*Museo Nazionale di Palazzo Reale

❶ Mon, Wed – Fri 9am – 2.30pm, Sat 9am – 1.30pm; admission: €5; www.ambientepi.arti.beniculturali.it

Walking eastwards toward Piazza Garibaldi and Borgo Stretto past the Renaissance-style Palazzo alla Giornata, today the seat of the uni-

Arno riverbank

versity rector. The 16th-century Agostini palace (Lungarno Pacinotti 27) is noticeable for its trefoil windows and terracotta reliefs. Inside is the oldest café in Pisa **Caffè dell'Ussero**, where supporters of the Risorgimento met in the mid-19th century. The adjacent Hotel Royal Victoria (Lungarno Pacinotti 12) also dates from the 19th century.

BORGO STRETTO AND THE UNIVERSITY

**Borgo Stretto

At Ponte di Mezzo, the oldest bridge over the Arno, the promenade opens up into Piazza Garibaldi, where a monument commemorates the national hero Giuseppe Garibaldi. Borgo Stretto, which does its name proud (»narrow city quarter«), begins to the right of the arcades of the Casino dei Nobili. The pedestrian zone is the most important shopping street and promenade in Pisa. A few yards along on the right is the church of San Michele in Borgo, which was built almost 1000 years ago, presumably over a temple to Mars. It gained its Romanesque-Gothic façade in a renovation in the 14th century. It was severely damaged during a bombing raid in 1944. During the reconstruction afterwards a fresco of St Michael (13th century) was revealed over the left door.

> **MARCO POLO TIP**
>
> **!** Snacks to enjoy   *Insider Tip*
>
> Caffè Salza (since 1898), Borgo Stretto 46, is a popular meeting place that serves outstanding pasticceria. At »Salza Time« from 6pm snacks are served along with aperitifs. www.salza.it. Caffetteria delle Vettovaglie under the arcades of Piazza Vettovaglie 33 is equally popular with businesspeople, students, market sellers and boutique owners: sandwiches, a glass of wine – it doesn't take any more than that to feel good!

*Piazza Vettovaglie

A small covered passage leads from Borgo Stretto into the maze of streets of the old city, first to Piazza Vettovaglie, a square courtyard with arcades where produce is sold every day.

*Piazza Dante Alighieri, University

From there follow Via di Cavalca west to Piazza Dante Alighieri. The **traffic-free square with palm trees in the university quarter** is a wonderful place to take a break in one of the cafés. About 40,000 students are registered at the renowned University of Pisa. It goes back to a law school in the 12th century, which received the papal privilege of teaching theology, jurisprudence and medicine in 1329 and in 1543 was elevated to the status of University of Tuscany by Cosimo I.

San Frediano

To the north-east Piazza Dante Alighieri adjoins the little Piazza San Frediano with the church of the same name. The church, a columned basilica, was already documented in 1077 and completed in the 12th century. Blind arcades with rhombi adorn the Romanesque façade;

Pisa is popular among students – maybe because of the bridges where you can sit and chat for hours?

the interior was reworked in contemporary style during a restoration in the 16th and 17th centuries.

✱ PIAZZA DEI CAVALIERI

Via San Frediano connects to the north with Piazza dei Cavalieri, which is surrounded by stately Renaissance buildings. The »knights' square« was the worldly centre of the old city in the Middle Ages and Renaissance period.

Renaissance square

This magnificent palace, which is decorated with coats of arms, sgraffiti and the busts of six Tuscan grand dukes from the Medici dynasty, is on the north side of the square. Since the 13th century the palace of the city elders has stood here. In 1562 Giorgio Vasari was commissioned to expand it as the seat of the knights of St Stephen who were under the command of the grand duke of Tuscany; Cosimo I de Medici had founded it to commemorate the knights' Florentine victory over Siena on 2 August (St Stephen's day) 1554. The official duty of the Order of Knights of St Stephen was to defend the Tuscan coast against Saracen raids, but unofficially it also served to stabilize the rule of the Medici dukes over Pisa. Since 1810 the palazzo has been the home of the university college named Scuola Normale Superiore, an elite school founded by Napoleon. In front of the building is a statue of Grand Duke Cosimo I (1596) by Piero Francavilla.

✱✱Palazzo dei Cavalieri (della Carovana)

Palazzo dell'Orologio	The palazzo on the north-west side of the square was built in 1607 for the Order of St Stephen. The architect here was also Vasari, who cleverly used this building to connect the prison (Torre delle Sette Vie, after the seven streets that lead to this square) and Palazzetto dei Gualandi (also Torre della Fame, »tower of hunger«). Count Ugolino della Gherardesca is supposed to have died of hunger here in 1288 with his sons. He was accused of abusing his office as Capitano del Popolo of Pisa.
Santo Stefano dei Cavalieri	Giorgio Vasari also designed the church of Santo Stefano, which he built in 1569 for the **order of St Stephen** . In 1606 the building got a marble façade in the late Mannerist style designed by Giovanni de Medici. The two wings were originally changing rooms for knights of the Order of St Stephen who wore the robes of the order for worship. They were not incorporated in the church until the 17th century. The squares of the coffered ceiling, which was added in 1605, depict the history of the order. Paintings on the walls show episodes from the life of St Stephen.
Via Corsica, Piazza Cavallotti	The fact that Pisa is a university city can be seen along Via Corsica, which leaves Piazza dei Cavalieri on the west, and then into Via dei Mille with internet cafés, new and second-hand bookshops.

A WALK TO MUSEO NAZIONALE

San Pierino	Start this walk in Borgo Stretto. A few minutes' walk south-east of the shopping street Via Cavour leads to San Pierino or San Pietro in Vinculis (St Peter in Chains), which was probably built on ancient foundations in 1072–1119. Inside the columned basilica the mosaic floors and some capitals from the Roman period are worth noting, as well as the unusually large crypt, which lies under the whole church.
Palazzo Toscanelli	Toscanelli Palace on the riverside street, which is called Lungarno Mediceo here, is supposed to have been built in the 16th century to plans by Michelangelo. In 1821 / 1822 Lord Byron lived here.
Palazzo Medici	The origins of the palace on Piazza Mazzini are older than the Medici rule in Pisa. The stately building, today seat of the prefecture, was built in the 13th century and remodelled when the Appiano dynasty ruled Pisa in the 14th century. In the late 15th century Lorenzo de Medici lived here when he was in Pisa.
*Museo Nazionale di San Matteo	The national museum is housed in the former Benedictine monastery San Matteo on Lungarno Mediceo. It houses one of the **most important art collections in Tuscany**. Among the numerous exhib-

its are first of all paintings and sculptures of Tuscan schools from the high Middle Ages to the Renaissance. The museum also has valuable textiles, manuscripts and a large collection of ceramics from the 11th to the 15th century.

Pisan paintings from the **12th and 13th centuries** are among the museum's special treasures. Monumental crucifixes painted on wood from the end of the 12th century show the change in depictions of Christ from a divine triumphal interpretation of the Byzantine-Romanesque type to the human, suffering Christ of early Gothic style from the period when the mendicant orders began to preach repentance. Magnificent **panel crosses** by Bonaventura Berlinghiero and Giunta di Capitinio are the highlight of the first half of the 13th century. Along with the Exultet scroll the so-called Maestro di San Martino (possibly Raniero di Ugolino) created the Byzantine-influenced panel painting *Virgin Enthroned with Child*, a masterpiece of the Pisan school from around 1280. *St Catherine of Alexandria* was painted at the same time. In **14th century painting** the 43-part

Arno River at night with its illuminated palaces

polyptych by Simone Martini, which was completed in 1320, takes first place. On a gold background the Madonna and child appear in the centre, to the left the evangelist John, St Dominic and Mary Magdalene, to the right John the Baptist, Peter of Verona and St Catherine of Alexandria. The predella shows Christ as man of sorrows in the middle between the evangelist Mark and the Virgin, surrounded by other saints. Other 14th-century works include panels with the legend of St Galgano (around 1355), a picture of great narrative power from the hand of an unknown master, a charming Madonna depiction by Francesco Traini (around 1350) as well as the Madonna del Latte (around 1370) by Barnaba da Modena. **Renaissance painting** is represented by a panel of St Paul (1426) by Masaccio, an Adoration by Benozzo Gozzoli and a Sacra Conversazione by Domenico Ghirlandaio. Among the **Baroque paintings** *Divine and Earthly Love*, a work from the first half of the 17th century by Guido Reni stands out.

14th-century **sculpture** includes the expressive pulpit relief by Tino di Camaino and the marble, colourfully framed *Madonna del Latte*, a figure in a robe with many folds which Nino, the son of Andrea Pisano, carved for the church of Santa Maria della Spina. Further notable works are parts of a 15th-century Annunciation group by Francesco di Valambrino, a bust of Christ attributed to Andrea del Verrocchio and a reliquary bust of St Rossore, a Sardinian martyr from the 3rd century, worked in gilded bronze by Donatello in 1427.

❶ Tue – Sat 8.30am – 7.30pm, Sun 9am – 1.30pm, admission: €5

Giardino Scotto, Fortezza

From the Museo Nazionale it is not far to the Giardino Scotto on the south bank of the Arno. The park was laid out in the 19th century and begins right behind the Ponte alla Fortezza.

NORTH-EASTERN OLD CITY

San Francesco

East of Piazza dei Cavalieri lies the quarter of San Francesco. The small church on the piazza of the same name was documented as early as 1211, while St Francis was still alive. The building was completed in 1270. In the second chapel on the right is the **grave of Count Ugolino della Gherardesca and his sons**, who were starved to death in Palazetto dei Gualandini (Palazzo dell'Orologio). The paintings on the legend of St Francis and a 14th-century marble polyptych by Tommaso Pisano, which shows the Virgin with saints, are also worth seeing. Walk through the sacristy to a chapel with frescoes by the Sienese Taddeo di Bartolo (1397).

Santa Caterina

Between 1251 and 1310 the Dominican order had a church built over older buildings not far to the north-west of San Francesco on Piazza

Santa Caterina. Around 1327 the façade was added and decorated in Pisan style with a tracery rosette and dwarf gallery. A campanile was added later. Inside note the marble Annunciation group (around 1360) and the elaborate marble grave for Archbishop Simone Saltarelli, both by Nino Pisano. One of the main works of Pisan 14th-century painting, *The Gloria of St Thomas Aquinas* (around 1342) by Francesco Traini, is on the north wall of the nave.

SOUTH-WESTERN OLD CITY

In the Museo della Grafica, which is located in Palazzo Lanfranchi, the design collections that Carlo Ludovico Ragghianti began in 1957, the private collections of Timpanaro and Argan and donations of significant artists are on display.

Museo della Grafica

❶ Lungarno Galilei 9; Tue – Fri 5pm – 9pm, Sat, Sun 10am – 12pm, 5pm – 10pm; admission: €3; www.museodellagrafica.unipi.it

Palazzo Gambacorti (14th cent.) on Lungarno Gambacorti near the Ponte di Mezzo is today the seat of the city administration. The former owner Pietro Gambacorti ruled Pisa and was killed in his palace by conspirators in 1393. Nearby are the Logge dei Banchi, the covered cloth market which was built from 1603 to 1605.

Palazzo Gambacorti

In the BLU Palazzo d' Arte e Cultura, Palazzo Blu for short, large art exhibitions are held regularly. The collection of the city pank is permanent and includes furniture, paintings and sculptures that let life in the old ruler's palace come alive again.

Palazzo Blu

❶ Lungarno Gambacorti 9; Tue – Fri 10am – 7pm, Sat, Sun until 8pm; www.palazzoblu.org

About 300m/1,000ft further to the west stands what is probably the most famous of the smaller Pisan churches. It was established as an open prayer hall for travellers and bargemen and was converted to a Gothic oratory in 1332. The reason for the reconstruction was a thorn (spina) from the crown of Christ brought back from the Holy Land, which was to be kept here. The **richly decorated façade** with three gables, tabernacle-like towers and tracery rosettes is striking for such a small church. Behind the Renaissance altar is a group *Madonna with St Peter and John the Baptist* (around 1345) by Andrea Pisano and assistants. Pisa-

***Santa Maria della Spina**

Insider Tip

! **SMS – for friends of modern art**

MARCO POLO TIP

Apart from Palazzo Blu, the Centro Espositivo San Michele degli Scalzi (Centro SMS) on Parco delle Piagge also shows contemporary art. The renovated medieval complex with 1600 m² of exhibition space is located on Viale delle Piagge to the east of the old city on the Arno River.

Palazzo Blu, interesting exhibition venue for modern art

no's *Madonna del Latte* is a replica of the original in the Museo Nazionale di San Matteo.

❶ Mar 1 – Oct 31 Tue – Fri 10am – 1.30pm, 2.30pm – 6pm, Sat, Sun 10am – 7pm, Nov 1 – Feb 28 Tue – Sun 10am – 2pm, second Sun/month 10am – 1pm, 2.30pm – 5pm; admission: €1.50

San Paolo a Ripa d'Arno

About 300m/330yd south-west not far from the Arno is the church San Paolo a Ripa d' Arno. It was built in the 12th century as a Romanesque domed church – a building type that is not often found in Tuscany. The influence of the cathedral is obvious on the façade decorated with round arches and dwarf galleries (12th century). The interior of the basilica holds the tomb of the scholar Burgundio (late 12th century), an ancient Roman sarcophagus. Another was set in the wall over the door of the left transept.

* Sant 'Antonio Abate

The church and convent of Sant' Antonio Abate on the piazza with the same name just a few steps from Piazza Vittorio Emanuele II go back to the year 1341. The imposing **painting on the convent's wall** *Tuttomondo* (The Whole World) owes its existence to the accidental meeting between a Pisan student and the artist **Keith Haring** (1958 – 1990) in New York. It was created in 1989 and is considered to be the artist's last work. The 30 intertwined figures are supposed to symbolize various aspects of peace.

The remains of an Etruscan and Roman harbour were found in December 1998 on the grounds of the Pisa-San Rosso railway station. During the excavations **several ancient ships and their cargo** – amphorae, ceramics, oriental crafts, Celtic gold jewellery among other things – were found. The finds were on display in the Arsenali Medicei; a re-opening of the exhibit is planned.

Cantiere delle avi Antiche di Pisa

AROUND PISA

6km/3.5mi south-west of Pisa, San Piero a Grado is worth a visit. Legend has it that the apostle Peter landed here on his way to Rome, at a time when this was still a coastal area. From an early date the church said to have been founded by St Peter, »ecclesia ad gradus« (church at the steps), was an important station for pilgrims going to Rome from the north. The basilica was built in the 11th century from tuff and marble. Excavations prove the existence of a previous church from the 6th century. Unusually this church also has an apse in the west. The main decoration of the simple interior is the important **fresco cycle** in the main aisle. It was probably painted around 1300 by an artist from Lucca, Deodato Orlando. The lower part consists of portraits of popes; the middle part depicts scenes from the life of the apostles Peter and Paul, and the top part shows the heavenly Jerusalem.

*San Piero a Grado

> **!** **MARCO POLO TIP**
>
> *Pasta fresca* **Insider Tip**
>
> Fans of Italian pasta who would like to see how it is made should make a side trip to Lari 35km/21mi south-east of Pisa – when driving from Pisa to Florence for instance (motorway to Florence, exit at Ponsacco and drive 10km/6mi south). The Martelli family has had its pasta factory here since 1926 and offers tours (Via S. Martino 3, tel. 05 87 68 42 38, www.martelli.info).

Beautiful pine groves and forests of holm oak extend about 4km/2.5mi west of Pisa as part of the 23,000 ha/57,000-acre Parco Naturale di Migliarino – San Rossore – Massaciuccoli (►Versilia). In the visitor's centre of San Rossore **excursion** on foots, by bike, in the »trenino« (train) or by bus are offered.

*Parco Naturale di Migliarino

❶ Guided tours: Sat, Sun 8am – 7.30pm; winter until 5.30pm; bicycle rental; http://centrovisitesanrossore.it

*Marina di Pisa, Tirrenia 10km/6mi from downtown Pisa on the mouth of the Arno River lies the popular seaside resort Marina di Pisa with a modern yacht harbour. The former fishing village became popular as a resort at the beginning of the 20th century, as the pretty art nouveau villas show today. There is only one narrow beach but the fish restaurants, which stand on piles in the water, are excellent and popular. A bit further to the south the modern resort Tirrenia has broad beaches of fine sand.

Monte Pisano, San Giuliano Terme North-east of Pisa lies Monte Pisano, a mountain range that is very pleasant and not over-run with hikers. With Bagni di Pisa Natural Spa Resort (www.bagnidipisa.com) the spa tourism in San Giuliano Terme, a small spa at the foot of Monte Pisano was greatly improved. San Giuliano Terme is the mecca of kite flyers in Tuscany.

Calci Calci lies on the south-west flank of Monte Pisano in Valgraziosa surrounded by olive groves. In the middle of the village stands the parish church ***Pieve di Sant'Ermolao**, which was mentioned already in 823. The present building dates from the 11th and 12th centuries. The elegant façade has blind arcades in Pisan Romanesque style; the campanile was never finished. The Romanesque baptismal font by an unknown master of the 12th century is the main attraction in the church. The influence of ancient sarcophagi is clear.

*Certosa di Pisa/Museo Nazionale della Certosa di Calci The Carthusian monastery was founded in 1366 about 1km/0.5mi outside Calci. It is the **second-largest Carthusian monastery in Italy** after Pavia, and today a national monument. The monastery was converted to Baroque in the 17th/18th cent. and it has two cloisters. The smaller one was designed by Lorenzo da Settignano in the 15th century, the larger with the monks' cells by the master builder Cartoni in the early 17th century. The Baroque church has a 17th-century dome fresco; the Sala del Granduca in the guesthouse was reserved for the grand dukes of Tuscany. The **natural science museum of the University of Pisa** is also part of the monastery. It displays fossils and minerals, mounted mammals and birds from the various regions of Italy.

❶ Monastery: Tue – Sat 8.30am – 6.30pm, Sun until 12.30pm (tours every hour), admission: €4
Museum: Mar 1 – Sep 30 Mon – Fri 9am – 5pm, Sat 9am – 6pm, Sun 10am – 7pm; Oct 1 – Feb 28 Mon – Fri only until 2pm; admission: €7

Pontedera A fine selection of beautiful old Vespas can be admired in the **Museo Piaggio** in Pontedera, 21km/13mi to the south-east. In 2010 more than 33,000 visitors saw the famous Vespa 98cc 1946 (valued today at €66,000), a Paperino (1943/44), the Ciao and the famous Ape (Italian for bee), a three-wheeled lorry from the 1950s/60s.

❶ Tue – Sat 10am – 6pm; free admission; www.museopiaggio.it

* Pistoia

F 8

Province: Pistoia (PT)
Altitude: 65m/213ft above sea level
Population: 90,300

Pistoia lies about 35km/21mi north-west of Florence in the fertile Ombrone valley. The old city has kept its medieval charms very well and has worthwhile buildings and museums. This is especially true of the cathedral square and market district, which are among the prettiest in Tuscany.

Pistoia started as a trading settlement on the Roman military road Via Cassia. In the 12th and 13th centuries the city flourished. However, disputes with neighbouring cities had consequences. Pistoia quarrelled with Bologna to the north over control of the Apennine passes; in the west Pisa lay in waiting, and Guelf Florence expanded in the east. A military defeat in 1254 brought on Florentine rule. The razing of the city walls in 1307 meant the submission of Pistoia, which was incorporated into the Tuscan grand duchy in the 16th century.

Old merchant city

> **MARCO POLO TIP**
>
> ! *Giostra dell' Orso* **Insider Tip**
>
> If the Palio in Siena or the Giostra del Saracino in Arezzo is too crowded for you, try Pistoia's city festival. On July 25 Pistoia holds the Giostra dell' Orso in honour of St Jacopo with a parade and a competition on horseback on the cathedral square, in which four teams symbollically fight against a bear. Tickets: APT Pistoia or www.giostradellorso.it (Standing room €8, seats €22).

WHAT TO SEE IN PISTOIA

The surprisingly large cathedral square, centre of the historic quarter, has always presented an appearance of harmonious austerity and – unusual for an Italian city – has neither shops nor street cafés. Clerical and secular power are united peacefully here: the Romanesque cathedral with campanile and baptistery, the bishop's palace, Palazzo del Podestà and Palazzo Comunale, decorated with coats of arms, as well as the medieval residential tower Torre di Catilina.

*Piazza del Duomo

The Romanesque cathedral was built in the 12th and 13th centuries in place of a 5th-century building. The **Pisan-Luccan Romanesque façade** is fronted by a portico. The colourful majolica coffered vault in front of the main portal is by Andrea della Robbia, as is the terracotta relief in the lunette of the door, which shows the Madonna with two angels (1505). The the three-aisled interior was restored to the 13th-century style. Next to the entrance is the grave of Cino da Pistoia with

*Duomo San Zeno

Pistoia

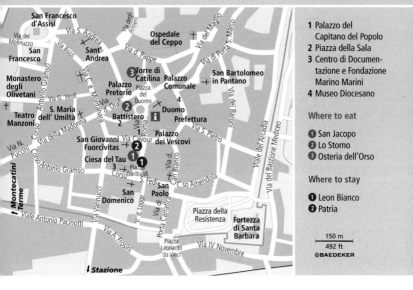

1 Palazzo del
  Capitano del Popolo
2 Piazza della Sala
3 Centro di Documen-
  tazione e Fondazione
  Marino Marini
4 Museo Diocesano

Where to eat

❶ San Jacopo
❷ Lo Storno
❸ Osteria dell'Orso

Where to stay

❶ Leon Bianco
❷ Patria

150 m
492 ft
©BAEDEKER

a seated figure of the poet. It is the work of an unknown master, done in 1337. The most important work in the Capella di San Jacopo, which can be entered from the right aisle is the **silver altar of St James**, a masterpiece of Italian gold and silver work created between 1287 and 1456 for a relic of St James, which the bishop of Pistoia obtained in 1144 from the archbishop of Santiago de Compostela in Spain. The 628 figures are made of silver metal, in part gilded and mounted on a core of wood, wax and resin. 15 scenes from the New Testament are depicted (1316) on the front. The right side has nine scenes from the Old Testament (1361–1364); the left side nine scenes from the life of James (1367–1371). The statue of St James enthroned is by Giglio Pisano. The two figures of prophets have been attributed to Brunelleschi.

❶ daily 8am – 9.30am, 10.30am – 12.30pm, 3.30pm – 7.30pm; free admission, admission to the silver altar (Altare argenteo): €2

*Campanile The campanile next to the cathedral, the emblem of Pistoia, is 66m/217ft high. It is reminiscent of Venetian bell towers. The three upper storeys with delicate arcades and green-and-white striped marble cladding from the 13th century are especially beautiful. The bell storey and the brick-covered tower top are 16th century additions.

❶ access on appointment (minimum of 4 people) in the APT Pistoia tourism office, Piazza del Duomo 4; admission: €6

Pistoia

INFORMATION
Piazza Duomo 4
Tel. 057 32 216 22
www.pistoia.turismo.toscana.it

PARKING
Shuttlebus »M« (Navetta »Il Micco«)
runs from Parcheggio Cellini south-
east of the old city. Parking is also
available along the southern city wall
(Viale A. Pacinotti) and on the Pertini
parking lot (signposted; Fri/Sat evenings from 8pm to 3am every 20 min.
a free shuttlebus »La Civetta« runs to
the old city).
Bus 1 (BluBus) runs from the railway station around the Centro Storico.
Taxi: »Amico Pistoia«
Tel. 05 73 50 95 30.

MUSEUM SYSTEM
(SISTEMA MUSEALE) PISTOIA
Museo Civico, Rospigliosi museums,
Diocesan museum, Museo del Ricamo,
Centro e Fondazione Marino Marini and
Palazzo Fabroni (museum for visual contemporary art) can be visited with a collective ticket A (admission to two museums €6, with Pal. Fabroni €7) or
collective ticket B (all museums €9,
with Pal. Fabroni €12).

WHERE TO EAT
❶ *San Jacopo* €€€
Via Crispi 15
Tel. 057 32 77 86
www.ristorantesanjacopo.it
Closed Mon
Small but up-market restaurant directly
opposite Hotel La Patria. Popular, so re-
serve your table! Try the maccheroni alla
Pistoiese (with duck ragout).

❷ *Lo Storno* €
Via del Lastrone 8
Tel. 057 32 61 93
Closed all day Sun, Mon/Tue evenings
and Aug.
Historic osteria with local cuisine in the
heart of the city. Wide selection of tradi-
tional primi and secondi.

❸ *Osteria dell' Orso* €
Via del Presto 9
Tel. 05 73 204 91
www.osteriadellorso.net
Wed – Sun only evenings, closed Mon/
Tue
In Osteria dell' Orso everything revolves
around the Crescentine Emiliane (filled
pastries). They are available wit a good
selection of sausage and dips or with
cheese.

WHERE TO STAY
❶ *Albergo Leon Bianco* €€
Via Panciatichi 2
Tel. 05 73 266 76
www.hotelleonbianco.it
Comfortable hotel with 30 simply-fur-
nished rooms in the pedestrian zone
near the cathedral square. Parking lot at
the hotel.

❷ *Patria* €€€
Via Crispi 8/12
Tel. 05 73 35 88 00
www.patriahotel.com
Its charms are already a bit faded but
the central location of this traditional
hotel makes up for that. Caffè Patria is
open mornings, noon and for five-
o'clock tea.

Shops with workshops like this one have become rare in Tuscany – Pistoia is the place for craft lovers

Palazzo dei Vescovi

The Romanesque palace next to the right-hand aisle of the cathedral was once the bishop's palace. The front is decorated with 14th-century coats of arms. Today the palace is home to the tourist information office and the cathedral chapter museum where the exhibited items include sacred objects and the Bigongiari painting collection with Florentine works from the 17th cent.

❶ Tue, Thu and Fri 10am–1pm and 3–5pm, tours 10am, 11.30am, 3.30pm; admission: €4

*Battistero S. Giovanni

The baptistery has the characteristic eight-sided ground plan of a baptismal church. The building was begun in 1338 by Cellino di Nese to plans by Andrea Pisano. The outer covering is made of green and white marble. In the tympanum of the Gothic main door there is a Madonna, while the lintel below it bears scenes from the life of John. Inside the baptismal font by Lanfranco da Como dating from 1226 has been preserved.

The austere Palazzo del Podestà or Palazzo Pretorio to the right of the baptistery was built in 1367 as the seat of the city ruler (podestà) appointed by Florence. Only the inner courtyard is in its original condition. A restoration between 1844 and 1846 gave the palace its present appearance. Today it holds part of the city court.

Palazzo Pretorio

Opposite stands the Palazzo Comunale, decorated with coats of arms, which radiates medieval elegance with its street-level arcades and bundled trefoil windows in the upper storeys. The building was begun in 1294 under Guelf government and only finished in 1385 by the Sienese architect Michele di Memmo. In 1637 the bridge-like connection to the cathedral was added. In the middle is the Medici coat of arms with the papal keys, which refers to Clement VII's intervention in the city history. Today the palace is the seat of a documentation centre on the work of the Pistoian architect Giovanni Michelucci (1891–1990) and the city museum, which includes a large number of frescoes and paintings from the 13th to 18th centuries in its collection.

*Museo Civico

City museum: Tue – Sat 10am – 6pm
Michelucci collection: Tue – Sat 10am – 7pm, Sun 9am – 12.30pm; admission: €3.50

The palace of the Rospigliosi family stand at Via Ripa del Sale 3. Pope Clement IX was the illustrious offspring of this influential family. The palace houses several museums. **Museo Clemente Rospigliosi** presents historic furnishings and paintings (16th/17th cent.), the **diocesan museum** presents old choir books and manuscripts from Pistoia and the **Museo del Ricamo** is dedicated to Pistoia's tradition of embroidery with exhibits of various techniques of brocade »in bianco« (white) and »sul bianco« (on white cloth) showing items from the 18th – 20th cent. (hours: Tue–Sat 10am–1pm and 4–7pm).

Palazzo Rospigliosi

Museo Clemente Rospigliosi, diocensan museum: Tue – Sat and 2nd Sun of the month 10am – 1pm, 3pm – 6pm; admission: €3.50
Museo del Ricamo: Tue – Thu 10am – 1pm, Fri, Sat and 2nd Sun of the month 10am – 1pm, 3pm – 6pm; admission: €3.50

The hospital on Piazza Giovanni XXIII was founded in the 13th century as a hospital and pilgrims' hospice. Its nickname is a reference to the offertory box (ceppo) where alms were collected for the needy. At the beginning of the 16th century it was decorated with a portico with majolica frieze like its Florentine model. Artists from the della Robbia workshop created one of their most beautiful works here. The seven works of mercy are depicted here, corresponding to the duties of a hospital (clothing the naked, hosting pilgrims, nursing the sick, caring for prisoners, giving the last rites, caring for the hungry and the thirsty).

Ospedale del Ceppo

The majolica frieze on the Ospedale del Ceppo shows what charity can mean

Pistoia Sotterranea   Tours of the Renaissance vaulted cellars of the Ospedale show underground Pistoia, **»Pistoia Sotterranea«**, and include a tour of the anatomical theatre of the Accademia Medicea and the museum for surgical instruments (Museo dei Ferri Chirurgici) in the hospital.
❶ Apr 1 – Sep 30 daily 10am – 7pm, otherwise until 6pm, tours usually on the hour, max. 30 people; admission: €9

San Bartolomeo in Pantano   On the way back to the cathedral square make a detour to this church, which was built from 1159 in a swamp outside the city walls (pantano = swamp). Its façade, which has rounded arches on half columns, is decorated by a beautiful relief architrave above the main portal (1167). It resembles stylistically the reliefs on Roman sarcophaguses. The pulpit is a masterpiece of early Tuscan sculpture by Guido da Como (around 1250).

*Piazza della Sala   Pistoia is at its prettiest around Piazza della Sala with its traditional well. Here there are still medieval **workshops with stone benches** in front of the windows. A stroll through the **vegetable market** that is held every morning on Piazza della Sala is also worthwhile.

From the market it is only a few steps to Via Cavour, which runs along the path of the old city wall. Originally outside the city wall (fuor civitas = outside the city), the Benedictine church was begun in 1150 and completed in the 14th century with its white-green striped façade. On the lintel of the main door there is a **relief of the Last Supper** (1160) by the local sculptor Gruamonte, one of his most beautiful works. In the aisle-less interior the pulpit by Fra Guglielmo da Pisa (around 1270) is worth a look. The basin for holy water is probably the first independent piece by Giovanni Pisano. The figures on the six-sided basin include personifications of the three cardinal virtues faith, love and hope. A further masterpiece of sacred art, a polyptych (1353–1355) by Taddeo Gaddi, is next to the main altar.

*San Giovanni Fuorcivitas

Follow Via Crispi to the southern part of the old city, to the shopping street Corso Silvano Fedi. In the former church of Sant'Antonio dei Frati del Tau on the Corso Silvano Fedi a museum was started for the sculptor **Marino Marini**, who was born in 1901 in Pistoia and died in 1980, and was known for his archaic human and animal figures. The cafeteria in »Chiostro delle Ortensie« (hortensia crossing) is an oasis of peace and quiet and an official »Area destressizzata«, stress-free zone.

Centro di Documentazione e Fondazione Marino Marini

❶ Oct – Mar Mon – Sat 10am – 5pm, Apr – Sep Mon – Sat 10am – 6pm; admission: €3.50

The church to the south and opposite was started in 1300 and embodies the simple Gothic style of the mendicant orders. The church was heavily damaged in World War II but still has fresco fragments from the 14th century. Behind the right side altar is the imposing grave of Filippo Lazzari which was made from 1462 to 1468 by Bernardo and Antonio Rossellino.

San Domenico

Outside the old city to the west is an unusual church, Pistoia's most important Renaissance building. The central-plan church was begun in 1495 and completed in 1561 by **Giorgio Vasari**. Vasari also designed the **dome**, which looks like a miniature version of the cathedral dome in Florence. The octagonal main space is actually much smaller than the broad vestibule suggests. At the main altar is the miraculous Madonna fresco (Giovanni di Bartolomeo Cristiani, around 1370) from the previous building, which was the reason for the new building in 1490.

Madonna dell'Umiltà

The Romanesque church Sant' Andrea in the north-west part of the old city goes back to the 8th century. Its **beautiful façade** is constructed like that of other churches in Pistoia, especially of San Bartolomeo. The capitals and the relief over the main portal (1166) are especially fine work. The ***pulpit by Giovanni Pisano**, one of this artist's major works dating from 1298–1301, is the most valuable piece. It is supported by seven red porphyry columns which carry

*Sant'Andrea

pointed arches. The figures of sibyls and prophets appear on the elaborately decorated capitals. The pulpit relief tells the story of Christ in five panels. Giovanni Pisano also created the wooden crucifix in the chapel on the left side of the church.

Palazzo Fabroni

Palazzo Fabroni houses the **Centro di Arti Visive Contemporanee**. It exhibits Pop Art, Minimal Art and Arte Povera. The permanent collection is based on donations of works.

❶ Via Sant' Andrea 18; Thu – Sun 10am – 1pm, 3pm – 6pm; admission: €5

Giardino Zoologico

The zoo west of the city is considered to be one of the best in Italy; »residents« include a Siberian tiger, elephants and giraffes.

❶ Via Pieve a Celle 160a; Mon – Fri 9.30am – 6pm, Sat, Sun 9am – 7pm; admission: €12.50; www.zoodipistoia.it

✴ Pitigliano

✦ O 12/13

Province: Grosseto (GR)
Altitude: 313m/1,027ft above sea level
Population: 4,200

The medieval houses of Pitigliano look as if they grew out of the steep tuffstone cliff. The most impressive view of the plateau with the cliff town, which looks like a fortress without a wall, can be seen when coming from Manciano. The setting appears to be from a fairy tale and that's what Pitigliano looks like on a walk through the dimly lit, labyrinthine alleys.

History

The Etruscans settled here and the Romans followed them. The Roman Orsini family, which was allied with the Guelfs, made Pitigliano the seat of their county in 1293. The town later passed on to the Florentine Strozzi family and in 1604 to the Grand Duchy of Tuscany.

*Alleys and caves

Narrow flights of stairs and vaulted passageways are just as typical for Pitigliano as the caves that were dug into the soft stone. The Etruscans used them as graves and later as storerooms. The Romans already used the cool rooms as **wine cellars**, and today the best wines of the region, especially Bianco di Pitigliano, are stored here.

WHAT TO SEE IN PITIGLIANO

Palazzo Orsini, aqueduct

The 14th-century palazzo with the crenellated roof recalls the former city rulers, the Orsini family from Rome. It was later converted by the

Pitigliano

INFORMATION
Piazza Garibaldi 5
Tel. 05 64 61 71 11
www.lecittadeltufo.com

WHERE TO EAT
Il Tufo Allegro €€€
Vicolo della Costituzione 5, Pitigliano
Tel. 05 64 61 61 92
Closed Tue and Wed.
Small restaurant in a tuffstone cave near the synagogue, super food, great service. Reservations a must.

WHERE TO STAY
Hotel della Fortezza €€ – €€€
Piazza Cairoli 5
Tel. 05 64 63 20 10
www.fortezzahotel.it
A stylish hotel with 12 rooms in the Fortezza Orsini in Sorano. All of the

rooms all have a grand view. Guests get a friendly reception.

Hotel Relais Valle Orientina €€€
Loc. Valle Orientina
Tel. 05 64 61 66 11
www.valleorientina.it
Anyone looking for quiet will find it in this peaceful hotel, 3km/1.8mi outside Pitigliano in the Orientina valley. A tennis court is available for sports lovers.

Renaissance architect Giuliano da Sangallo to a palace with a courtyard fountain. The palace museum (with Museo Diocesano) shows gold and silver items, coins and the panel picture *Madonna Enthroned with Child Crowned by Two Angels between Saint Peter and Saint Francis* (1494), presumably the work of Guidoccio Cozzarelli from Siena. The aqueduct on Via Cavour was built 1636 – 1639 at the behest of the Medici.

❶ Aug daily. 10am – 1pm, 3pm – 7pm, other months only Tue – Sun, (Nov – Apr only until 6pm); admission: €3

Museo Civico Archeologico della Civiltà Etrusca exhibits Etruscan vases and ceramics woth seeing and more recent finds from the region around Pitigliano. The museum includes the **archaeological park** »Alberto Manzi« 2km/1mi outside of town. **Museo Civico Archeologico della Civiltà Etrusca**

Museum: Piazza Fortezza Orsini 59c; Aug 1 – Aug 31 daily 10am – 7pm; July 1 – July 31 Mon – Fri 10am – 5pm, Sat/Sun 10am – 6pm; June 13 – June 30 closed Tue, Apr 9 – June 12 closed Tue and Wed, Sep 1 – Nov 8 Mon – Fri 10am – 1pm, 3pm – 4pm, Sat/Sun 10am – 1pm, 2pm – 7pm; Dec 23 – Jan 6 Mon – Fri 10am – 1pm, 3pm – 4pm; admission: €2.50
Park: Via Cava del Gradone; opening times like museum; admission: €4

Piazza Gregorio VII   Piazza Gregorio VII is dominated by the Baroque façade of the cathedral, which was built in the Middle Ages and altered in the 18th century, and its massive campanile. A travertine column on the square bears the Orsini coat of arms with the bear (Italian *orso*).

Synagogue, Little Jerusalem   There was a large Jewish community in Pitigliano until well into the 20th century; it has had a synagogue since 1598. The synagogue and the old ghetto, called the »Piccolo Gerusalemme della Maremma« (little Jerusalem of the Maremma), can be viewed; there is an old women's ritual bath, a kosher butcher, winery, dyer and bakery as well as the Museo di Cultura Ebraica. The entrance to the quarter is at Vicolo Marghera/Vicolo Manin. The Jewish cemetary (Cimitero Ebraico) outside of Pitigliano on the SS 74 towards Manciano can also be viewed.

❶ Apr 1 – Sep 30 Sun – Fri 10am – 1.30pm, 2.30pm – 6.30pm, Oct 1 – Mar 31 Sun – Fri 10am – 12.30pm, 3pm – 5.30pm; admission: €3; www.lapiccolagerusalemme.it

> !   *Lo Sfratto*   **Insider Tip**
>
> **MARCO POLO TIP**
>
> In the bakery »Panificio del Ghetto«, Via Zuccarelli 167, Giovanni Bianchini sells »Lo Sfratto dei Goym«. This biscuit shaped like a stick is a reminder of how Jews were commanded in the 16th cent. to move into the ghetto. The order to vacate (sfratto) their homes was given by hitting the doors with a stick.

Vie Cave   Pitigliano is surrounded by defiles (Vie Cave) that the Etruscans carved into the tuffstone. They were used to transport goods, but also for religious purposes. Eight defiles lead into the surrounding region (information and map aavailable at the tourism office). The Via Cava di San Giuseppe and Via Cava di Poggio Cani are easy to follow.

AROUND PITIGLIANO

*Sorano   The medieval town of Sorano is situated, crowned by an Orsini castle, on the peak of a tuffstone plateau. Even though it is only a short distance from Pitigliano (9km/5.5mi), Sorano has remained unnoticed to this day and thus still has a very special charm. Close to Sorano, dark openings in the cliff walls are visible. They hold cave-like grave chambers from the 3rd/2nd century BC. In the **medieval and Renaissance museum** in Sorano's fortress (13th cent.), which is a masterpiece of military architecture, there is an interesting tower room with grotesques (16th cent.). On the ground floor is the office of the archaeological park »Città del Tufo«. The park includes the rock along Provincial road 22, which is named San Rocco after the chapel (18th cent.) and which has an **Etruscan necropolis** (3rd/2nd cent. BC). **Masso Leopoldino** (Via del Poggetto) offers a magnificent view. The tuffstone plateau was fortified by Leopold of Lorraine in the 18th century.

Museum: Mar 27 – Oct 3 Tue – Sun (Aug also Mon) 10am – 1pm, 3pm – 7pm, Oct 4 – Nov 1, Dec 26 – Jan 9 Tue – Sun 10am – 1pm, 2pm – 5pm; admission: €4; www.leviecave.it

Etruscan necropolis: Jan 1 – Nov 1 daily 11am – 6pm; admission: €2

Masso Leopoldino: Jan 1 – Oct 31 daily 10am – 1pm, 3pm – 7pm; admission: €2

The cave dwellings of Vitozza were built on the edge of San Quirico, about 5km/3mi south-east of Sorano, probably around 1000 BC. With about 200 grottoes the settlement is the largest of this kind in Italy. The caves were inhabited into the 19th century and are now part of the »Città del Tufo« park. **San Quirico / Vitozza**

❶ Apr – Oct daily 10am – 7pm, Nov – Mar only Fri – Sun 10am – 5pm; admission: €2

Sovana is a picture-book town just like Pitigliano and Sorano. It flourished in the 11th century. In 1021 it was the birthplace of the ***Sovana**

Rock city: Pitigliano looks like an conquerable city with houses growing right out of the tuff stone plateau

Steam rising from the thermal waterfalls south of Saturnia

monk Hildebrand, who in 1077 as Pope Gregory VII brought the Holy Roman Emperor Henry IV to his knees at Canossa. The fortress of the Aldobrandeschi, who were loyal to the emperor, and the double-aisled hall crypt of the cathedral were built in the 11th century. Its low Gothic vaulting was added in the 14th century. Lombard and southern French stonemasons created the remarkable **relief scenes on the pillar capitals** in 1100. The late Romanesque church of Santa Maria on Piazza del Municipio has an excellent example of Lombard-Carolingian stone carving: the high altar is covered by a stone ciborium (9th cent.) with fine ornamentation. Palazzo Pretorio has the **visitor's centre** for the »Città del Tufo« park and a museum

Visitor's centre: Piazza del Municipio 12a; Mar 27 – Oct 3 daily 10am – 1pm, 4pm – 7pm, Oct 4 – Nov 2, Dec 26 – Jan 6 10am – 1pm, 2pm – 5pm; Nov 3 – Nov 30 only Sat, Sun 10am – 1pm, 2pm – 5pm

*Tomba Ildebranda

Two trails make it possible to explore the signposted Etruscan necropolis (4th – 2nd cent. BC). The Hildebrand grave (late 3rd / early 2nd cent. BC) on the Poggio Felceto is especially impressive. The grave, which was carved into the rock, gets its name from Gregory VII, formerly the monk Hildebrand. Ribbed columns with beautifully decorated capitals rise above a base with steps at the sides. The imitation temple was originally covered with stucco and had colourfully painted lintels in the upper part, traces of which are still visible. An underground dromos leads to the square grave chamber with a stone bench for the dead.

❶ Apr – Oct daily 10am – 7pm, Nov – Mar only Fri – Sun 10am – 5pm; admission: €5

Saturnia

Terme di Saturnia on the ancient Via Clodia in the high valley of the Albenga river. According to legend the god Saturn sought refuge here. The Etruscans called it Aurinia; it became Roman in 280 BC. Saturnia's **37.5°C/ 99.5°F warm, sulphurous springs** were already appreciated in antiquity. They promise relief from from rheumatism, bronchial disorders and digestive problems. 5km/3mi outside Saturnia towards Manciano the thermal water bubbles over the travertine waterfalls **Cascate del Molino** into natural basins, where free bathing is possible. A parking lot and a bar are nearby. The four-star hotel Terme di Saturnia with the Blackrose Spa, **Europe's largest thermal spa resort**, offers more amenities. Treatments are available to non-residents as well.

> **MARCO POLO TIP**
>
> **❗ The right shoes**   Insider Tip
>
> For swimming and exploring the basins of Cascate del Molino, waterproof shoes are essential because the natural stone is in part rough and also very slippery!

✱ Prato

✦ F 9

Province: Prato (PR)
Altitude: 63m/206ft above sea level
Population: 189,000

Don't expect pretty countryside between the cities, as the heavily industrialized suburbs of Prato and Florence have almost joined up. Prato is the second-largest and also one of the richest cities in Tuscany. It has been the centre of the textile industry for a long time – now it is known for its outlet centre. And even though this is a surprise in an industrial city like Prato, the historic centre is completely intact and well worth a visit.

Textile city

Prato was probably founded on the ruins of an Etruscan-Roman settlement. During the glorious period of the Staufer dynasty, the city was the seat of an imperial viceroy. In the 14th century Prato was acquired by Florence for 17,500 gold florins, and despite occasional revolts the histories of these two cities have been tightly knit ever since. As in Florence, the **textile industry** developed early in Prato.

Prato

INFORMATION
Piazza delle Carceri
Tel. 057 42 41 12
www.prato.turismo.toscana.it

WHERE TO EAT
❶ *Il Piraña* €€€€
Via Guiseppe Valentini 110
Tel. 05 74 257 46
www.ristorantepirana.it
Closed Sat midday and Sun
First-class fish restaurant in a post-modern setting.

❷ *Osteria Cibbè* €
Piazza Mercatale 49
Tel. 05 74 60 75 09
www.cibbe.it
Closed sun and all of Aug.
Simple, friendly osteria that serves a Pra-

to speciality: Sedani ripeni alla Pratese,
filled celery

WHERE TO STAY
❶ *Flora* €€ – €€€
Via Cairoli 31
Tel. 05 74 335 21
www.pratohotels.it www.hotelflora.info
This spotless three-star hotel lies in the middle of the old city. 31 tastefully decorated rooms. Service is important here.

❷ *Villa Rucellai* €€ – €€€
Via di Cannetto 16
Loc. Canneto
Tel. 05 74 46 03 92
www.villarucellai.it
Comfortable B&B hotel (12 rooms) in a Renaissance villa with medieval tower.
4km/2.5mi north-east of Prato

The industry had its greatest upswing after World War II when Prato collected the rags of worn out clothing from war-bombed Europe and turned them into new fabric. This business flourished and the population tripled by 1975. Asian competition caused economic stagnation in the late 1970s, but further specialization soon led to recovery: today Prato is »**outlet city**«. In 1992 the city in the lower Bisenzio Valley also gained something it had wanted for a long time: administrative independence from Florence and the status of an independent province.

WHAT TO SEE IN PRATO

*Castello dell' Imperatore The massive fortress of the Staufer emperors on Piazza Santa Maria delle Carceri, built in 1237–1248 **for Holy Roman Emperor Frederick II**, is unique in northern central Italy for its building style and excellent state of preservation. Castello dell'Imperatore (or Fortezza di Santa Barbara) was built as an enlargement of a 10th-century castle of the counts of Prato and is similar to the numerous defensive structures that Frederick II built in his favourite southern Italian provinces. The imperial castles looked like a Roman castrum on the

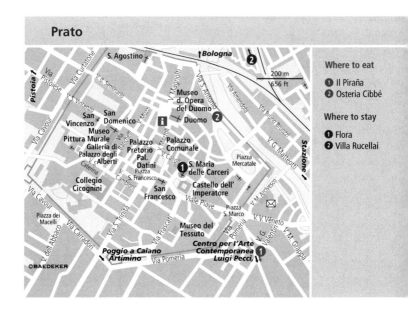

Prato

Where to eat
❶ Il Piraña
❷ Osteria Cibbé

Where to stay
❶ Flora
❷ Villa Rucellai

outside and primarily served defensive purposes, but the interiors are very liveable – unfortunately no interiors of Castello dell' Imperatore remain in their original form.

❶ Mon, Wed – Fri 4pm – 7pm, Sat, Sun 10am – 1pm, 4pm – 7pm; admission: €2.50

The Cassero in the street of the same name was a medieval enclosed walkway, which led from the castello to the city wall and served as an invisible escape route. Its floor was made so that even horses' hooves cannot be heard.

❶ Apr 1 – June 30, Sep /Oct Wed – Mon 4pm – 7pm

Cassero

The church opposite the northern corner of the castle was built for a miraculous image of the Virgin, which once hung on the wall of a prison (carcere) here. Giuliano da Sangallo designed a Renaissance church of outstanding beauty (1484–1495) on the ground plan of a Greek cross. A restrained dome crowns the crossing, coloured marble covers the façade and inside there are terracotta medallions by Andrea della Robbia.

❶ daily 7am – 12pm, 4pm – 7pm

Santa Maria delle Carceri

Piazza del Comune is the centre of the city. Here is a statue of the textile merchant Francesco di Marco Datini who was famous beyond

Palazzo Pretorio, Museo Civico

Prato's boundaries. The medieval, completely regular façade of Palazzo Pretorio dominates the square. Capitano del Popolo Fresco de Frescobaldi bought the residence in 1284 and made it into the first office of the city government. The open stair with balcony, crenellations and the bell tower were added in the 16th century. The palace houses the Museo Civico with the city art gallery. It masterpieces from the 14th/15th centuries, including by Fra Filippo Lippi, Filippino Lippi, Bernardo Daddi and Giovanni da Milano (closed for restoration at present). The crucifixion by Filippino Lippi that Prato bought at auction in New York in 2010 is being exhibited in the museum of San Domenico until the restoration is finished.

*Palazzo Datini Francesco di Marco Datini, whose statue adorns Piazza Comunale, lived in a palace in Via Rinaldesca, built at the end of the 14th century. It is a rare example of late Gothic secular architecture and foreshadows the developments of the 15th century. Only fragments of the

The outside pulpit on the Prato cathedral catches the eye

paintings on the outer façade, which show the family history, can be discerned. The frescoes in the inner courtyard are well preserved. **Casa Museo Francesco di Marco Datini** presents an exhibit on the life of the late medieval textile manufacturer and businessman (ca. 1335 – 1410) on the ground floor. Sales contracts, account books, insurance policies and the voluminous correspondence have been archived electronically.

❶ June – Aug Mon – Fri 9am – 12.30pm, 4pm – 7pm, Sat only mornings; Sep – May Mon – Fri 9am – 12.30pm, 3pm – 6pm, Sat only mornings; free admission

The cathedral is dedicated to St Stephen and John the Baptist and has been the spiritual centre of the city since the 10th century. It acquired its present form between 1385 and 1457. The wealthy city of Prato could afford the best artists, including Giovanni Pisano and Donatello, Michelozzo and Filippo Lippi. The festive, decorative character of the green-and-white stone covering of the façade is augmented by the **outside pulpit**, a joint work of Donatello and Michelozzo 1434–1438 (copy; original in the cathedral museum) for the veneration of the belt of the Virgin, which is shown several times a year including Easter, 15 August and Christmas. The church has retained its Romanesque character. The pulpit in the nave, which is decorated with reliefs, was created by Mino da Fiesole and Antonio Rossellino in 1437.

Duomo Santo Stefano

**Frescoes by Filippo Lippi: The painting of the main choir chapel (1452–1466) by the Dominican monk Fra Filippo Lippi – and his assistant Fra Diamante – is one of the most beautiful fresco cycles of the early Renaissance in Italy. The frescoes were restored over seven years in the early 21st cent. The cycle shows scenes from the life of the two patron saints of the church, which the artist interpreted in a relatively undramatic, even playful manner by the standards of the time. This can be seen especially clearly in Herod's Feast, painted in a wonderfully light style with the dancing Salome, for whom Filippo Lippi's mistress is supposed to have been the model.

*Cappella del Sacro Cingolo: The holy belt of Mary is kept in Cappella del Sacro Cingolo (1385–1395) to the left of the entrance. The frescoes executed by Agnolo Gaddi between 1392 and 1395 tell the legend of the relic: Mary gave the belt to the apostle Thomas when she went to heaven, who gave it to a priest. A merchant from Prato brought the miraculous belt back to Prato on a trip to the Holy Land, where he turned it over to both the clerical and the secular powers. For this reason both the bishop and the mayor have keys to the shrine today.

Cathedral: Mon – Sat 7.30am – 7pm, Sun 7.30am – 12pm, 1pm – 7pm
Chapel: Mon – Sat 10am – 5pm, Sun 1pm – 5pm; admission: €3, tours Thu 3.30pm, 4.30pm, Sat 10am, 11am, 3.30pm, 4.30pm; €5.50

*Museo dell' Opera del Duomo
The treasures of the cathedral museum in the bishop's palace include medieval panel paintings, liturgical utensils, gold work, a Madonna with the Archangel Michael and Saints Peter and Paul dated 1262 by Giroldo di Jacopo da Como and Donatello's seven original reliefs for the cathedral outside pulpit.

❶ ? Piazza del Duomo 49; Mon, Thu, Fri 9am – 1pm, 2.30pm – 6.30pm, Wed 9am – 1pm, Sat 10am – 1pm, 2.30pm – 6.30pm, Sun 10am – 1pm; admission: €5; www.diocesiprato.it

*San Domenico, Museo di Pittura Murale
The church was built between 1283 and 1322. No one knows why the marble façade remained unfinished. Apart from a polychrome wooden cross from around 1400 the church is decorated in Baroque style. The religious reformer **Fra Girolamo Savonarola** lived in the adjacent monastery until he went to Florence. The monastery holds a museum with frescoes and sketches from the churches in Prato and offers insights into the technique of mural painting (pittura murale).

❶ Apr 1 – May 30 Mon, Thu, Fri 9am – 1pm, 2.30pm – 6.30pm, Wed 9am – 1pm, Sat 10am – 1pm, 2.30pm – 6.30pm, Sun 10am – 1pm; Oct 1 – Mar 31 Mon, Wed, Thu 9am – 1pm, Fri, Sat 9am – 1pm, 3pm – 6pm, Sun 10am – 1pm; admission: €5

> **!** *Shopping in fabbrica* **Insider Tip**
>
> **MARCO POLO TIP**
>
> The textile city of Prato offers various factory putlets (www.prato-turismo.it, category »Dove comprare«, also in English), the tourism office publishes the brochure *Shopping in fabbrica*. Other Tuscan cities also have factory outlets. The site: www.factory-outlet-italy.com/deu/NI/Toskana/Florenz.html has an overview.

Museo del Tessuto south of the old city is dedicated to the history of textile manufacturing from the 12th cent. in Prato, but also in other places. It exhibits machines involved in processing textiles and making patterns from various centuries and countries.

❶ Via Santa Chiara 24; Mon, Wed – Fri 9.30am – 2.30pm, Sat 10am – 6pm, Sun 4pm – 7pm; admission: €6; www.museodeltessuto.it

Galleria di Palazzo degli Alberti
Palazzo degli Alberti exhibits the painting collection of the Banca Popolare di Vicenza, including works by Filippo Lippi, Giovanni Bellini or Caravaggio.

❶ Via degli Alberti 2; tours by appointment (tel. 05 74 61 75 94); free admission; audio guide in English; www.galleriapalazzoalberti.it

*Centro d'Arte Contemporanea Luigi Pecci
On Viale della Repubblica south-east of the city is a museum complex for modern art. The museum conceived by Italo Gamberini with an large sculpture park (including works by Enzo Cucchi, Barbara Kruger and Mauro Staccioli) is a centre for modern art in Tuscany and symbolizes the wealth of Prato. Prato also displays **modern art**

in **public places**, e. g. by Henry Moore on Piazza San Marco, by Salvadore Messina in the apside garden of San Francesco (Piazza S. Maria delle Carceri) or by Giò Pomodoro a homage to Pablo Neruda (*Isla negra*; garden on Via C. Marx).

❶ Wed – Mon 10am – 7pm; Wed – Mon 4pm – 11pm; free admission; www.centropecci.it

AROUND PRATO

The country houses built in the gentle hills around Prato testify to the enthusiasm that wealthy city-dwellers of the 15th and 16th centuries developed for rural life. While Prato's wealthy sited their country homes in the fertile Bisenzio valley, the Florentine Medici built two of their most beautiful villas south of Prato at the foot of Monte Albano, one near Poggio a Caiano, one near Artimino.

Country villas

One of the most magnificent Medici villas of all stands on the edge of Poggio a Caiano south of Prato in the middle of a wonderful park with hothouses and exotic decorative gardens. The summer residence was built for Lorenzo il Magnifico from 1485 by Giuliano da Sangallo. The owner did not live to see it completed; but Leo X, the first Medici pope, enjoyed the rural luxury to the utmost. It possessed residential quarters of considerable size. The ground floor is decorated by arcades; large terraces surround the first floor and a stately loggia with columns and architrave recalls ancient temple and palace architecture. The **painting of the interior** was done by the most famous fresco artists of the 16th century, including Andrea del Sarto, Pontormo and Alessandro Allori. As the royal residence of Vittorio Emanuele II the noble Medici country residence experienced a few architectural changes in the second half of the 19th century, e.g. the construction of the outside stairs. The interior furnishings have survived only in part, but the main hall (Salone di Leone X) with frescoes painted by Allori in 1580 is original. The villa houses Italy's only **museum for still life painting** (Natura morta). The museum in the Scuderie shows the works of **Ardengo Soffici** from 1904 to 1962

**Poggio a Caiano, Villa Medicea

❶ June – Aug 8.15am – 7.30pm, Apr, May, Sep until 6.30pm, Mar, Oct until 5.30pm, Nov – Feb until 4.30pm, closed every 2nd and 3rd Mon of the month; free admission; tours hourly 9am – 12pm, 2pm until one hour before closing

Museo Ardengo Soffici: May 1 – Sep 30 Tue – Sun 10am – 6.30pm, Oct 1 – Apr 30 Sat, Sun 10am – 5pm; admission: €3

The Medici villa in Artimino, also called La Ferdinanda, which can now be rented for conferences and meetings. From 1587 Buontal-

*Artimino, Villa Medicea

enti built this stylish country villa for Ferdinando I, obviously following the model of the nearby Medici villa in Poggio a Caiano. But La Ferdinanda is comparatively modest and suits the landscape better – no arcades and terraces and the loggia is also much simpler. Instead of decorative roof constructions, chimneys decorate the tiled roof, giving the house its nickname Villa dei Cento Camini.

Inside the reserved style of the architecture is continued. The expressly **rural garden** suits it with its beautiful wine and olive plants. La Ferdinanda has an **archaeological museum** with Bucchero ceramics, bronze vases and iron statues; it is part of the Carmignano archaeological park.

Villa: Mon, Tue, Thu – Sat 9.30am – 12.30pm, Sun 10am – 12pm, admission: €4;

Arch. Museum/Arch. Park: Feb 1 – Oct 31 Mon, Tue, Thu, Fri 9.30am – 1.30pm, Sat 9.30am – 1.30pm, 3pm – 6pm, Sun 9.30am – 1.30pm, 2pm – 4pm, Nov 1 – Jan 31 Sat, Sun 9.30am – 1.30pm, 2pm – 4pm; admission: €4; www.parcoarcheologicocarmignano.it

✴✴ **San Gimignano**

✦ I 9

Province: Siena (SI)
Altitude: 334m/1,096ft above sea level
Population: 7,100

They can be see from afar, rising skywards on a hilltop in the Elsa Valley: the famous towers of San Gimignano, which were restored through UNESCO funds. The »Manhattan of the Middle Ages« gives us a picture of what urban life must have been like in the Middle Ages place in Tuscany.

Rivalries   The hill was already settled by the Etruscans, but the community is first mentioned in the 8th century. An ancient trade route to Rome led right through the town and brought it lucrative business. As in many cities **the rival noble families** of San Gimignano built towers as an expression of their political power – there were 72 at the end of the Middle Ages; today there are only 15. Since every family wanted to out-do the others with its tower, the city had to intervene in the end: in 1255 it was decided that the tower of the city hall should be the highest and no other should exceed it. The final standard was set in 1311 when the new town hall tower was completed at 54m/177ft. In 1353, after the Great Plague, the free commune was taken over by Florence – and from then on there was no more building.

Bird's eye view of San Gimignano: 15 of the original 72 towers still exist

WHAT TO SEE IN SAN GIMIGNANO

Porta San Giovanni is the best-preserved city gate in the medieval wall that dates from around 1300. Here is the Museo della Tortura, with exhibits including gruesome »aids« used by the Inquisition. There are detailed descriptions in English and Italian. Attached to this museum is the Museum of Capital Punishment (Museo della Pena di Morte) in Via San Giovanni 15 a, with displays including an electric chair; not suitable for children.

Museo della Tortura, Museo della Pena di Morte

Both museums: daily 10am – 7pm, winter only Sat, Sun 10am – 7pm; admission: €12; www.museodellatortura.it

Follow Via San Giovanni past small souvenir shops, cafés and wine shops north about 100m/110yd towards the centre to reach the Romanesque façade of the former parish church San Francesco, today an enoteca with a beautiful view of the valley. The 14th-century Palazzo Pratellesi diagonally opposite now holds the public library. In the reading room there is a fresco by Vincenzo Tamagni (1528) *Mystical Marriage of St Catherine of Alexandria*.

San Francesco, Palazzo Pratellesi

San Gimignano

INFORMATION
Piazza del Duomo 1
Tel. 05 77 94 00 08
www.sangimignano.com

EVENTS
Fiera delle Messi
is the name of the festival on the third weekend in June. With a parade in historical costumes and competitions. Festa di Santa Fina is held on March 12. There are markets every thursday. The cultural high point is the summer festival San Gimignano Estate.

JOINT TICKET
A joint ticket for Palazzo Comunale, Pinacoteca, Torre Grossa, Museo Archeologico, Galleria d' Arte Moderna and Speziera di Santa Fina costs €7.50. Tickets and information at the tourist information or the museums.

WHERE TO EAT
❶ *Dorandó* €€€
Vicolo dell'Orto 2
Tel. 05 77 94 18 62
www.ristorantedorando.it
Closed Mon, and Dec. – Feb.
Rustic Slow Food restaurant not far from the cathedral with creative traditional cuisine. To finish off: Crema di Procopio, halff-rozen dessert with honey, nuts, chocolate and rum.

❷ *Osteria delle Catene* € – €€
Via Mainardi 18
Tel. 05 77 94 19 66
www.osteriadellecatene.it
Closed Wed
Katerina, Gino and Virgilio offer a selection of five menus. The pot roast in Chianti is incomparable. Beautiful dining room with old vaulted ceilings.

WHERE TO STAY
It has to be seen to be believed: San Gimignano by day and San Gimignano in the evening are two completely different places. An overnight stay within the city walls is worthwhile for this if for no other reason. When the tourist buses leave, the town is yours!

❶ *La Cisterna* €€ – €€€
Piazza della Cisterna 23/24
Tel. 05 77 94 03 28
www.hotelcisterna.it
The house is a 14th-century palazzo with 50 pretty rooms furnished in the Florentine style. From the attached restaurant Le Terrazze there is a view over the Elsa valley.

❷ *L' Antico Pozzo* €€€
Via San Matteo 87
Tel. 05 77 94 20 14
www.anticopozzo.com
Hotel with 18 rooms in a tastefully restored medieval palazzo with patio in the middle of San Gimignano. Minibuses run between the parking lots outside the city wall and the hotel; garage parking available.

❸ *Podere Il Caggiolino* €
Loc. Picchena Castel San Gimignano
Tel. 05 77 95 31 90
www.caggiolino.com
A pleasant and reasonably priced B&B alternative to the hotels in San Gimignano 11km/7mi away. Generous breakfast, 5 rooms.

The atmospheric Piazza della Cisterna, the heart of the medieval city, got its name from the well built of travertine stone which was dedicated in 1273. The square is bordered by **towers and palaces**, including the Casa Razzi (no. 28) with the stump of a tower, Casa Salvestrini (no. 9), formerly Ospedale degli Innocenti and now Albergo La Cisterna, and Palazzo Tortoli and the Palazzo del Capitano del Popolo. Palazzo dei Cortesi has the high »devil's tower«. According to legend its owner returned from a trip to find it higher than it was before he left and thought that the devil was responsible. Arco dei Becci marks the path of the oldest city wall from the 11th century.

*Piazza della Cisterna

A broad outdoor stair leads up to the Romanesque church of the Assumption of the Virgin on the neighbouring **Piazza del Duomo**. The name is misleading since San Gimignano was never a bishop's seat. In 1456 Giuliano da Maiano enlarged the church, which was dedicated in 1148, but the front, which was reconstructed several times in the course of the centuries, was never given a façade. Inside a fresco (1456) by **Benozzo Gozzoli** shows the martyrdom of St Sebastian. There are also two wooden statues of the Annunciation (around 1421) by the Sienese sculptor Jacopo della Quercia, which were colourfully painted by Martin di Bartolomeo in 1426.

*Collegiata Santa Maria Assunta

Frescoes: The church is mainly worth seeing for its frescoes. The realistically portrayed **scenes of the Last Judgement (around 1393) on the western wall are by the Sienese Taddeo di Bartolo. In the right aisle Barna da Siena painted a monumental fresco cycle with scenes from the New Testament in the mid-14th century: the first row covers events from the Annunciation to the Flight to Egypt, the second from Jesus in the Temple to the Triumphal Entry into Jerusalem, the third from the Last Supper to Pentecost. As the artist biographer Giorgio Vasari relates, Barna fell from the scaffold while admiring his completed Crucifixion and died of his injuries. The frescoes were completed by his nephew and student Giovanni d'Asciano around 1380. In the left aisle there are similarly fine frescoes (around 1356 – 1367) by Bartolo di Fredi with scenes from the Old Testament.

At the end of the right aisle is the **Cappella di Santa Fina**, built 1468 – 1475 in purest Renaissance forms, the work of Giuliano and Benedetto da Maiano. The farmer's daughter Fina is said to have performed miracles and is the patron saint of San Gimignano. The top of the marble altar supports the sarcophagus that held the remains of St Fina until 1738. Domenico Ghirlandaio painted the frescoes *Pope*

San Gimignano

N ←

250 m
820 ft

1 Piazza della Cisterna
2 Palazzo Tortoli
3 Arco dei Becci
4 Palazzo del Podestà
5 Piazza del Duomo
6 Palazzo del Popolo

7 Museo d'Arte Sacra,
  Museo Etrusco
8 Torri Salvucci
9 Palazzo Cancelleria
10 Palazzo Pesciolini
11 Piazza Sant' Agostino

Where to eat
❶ Dorandó
❷ Osteria delle Catene

Where to stay
❶ La Cisterna
❷ L'Antico Pozzo
❸ Podere Il Caggiolino

©BAEDEKER

Gregory Announces to St Fina that She Will Die and *Funeral of the Saint* in 1475 and probably also the fresco of the Annunciation in the Loggia del Battistero dated 1476.

❶ Apr 1 – Oct 31 Mon – Fri 9.30am – 7.10pm, Sat 9.30am – 5.10pm, Sun 12.30pm – 5.10pm; Nov 1 – Mar 31 Mon – Sat 9.30am – 4.40pm, Sun 12.30pm – 4.40pm

*Palazzo del Popolo, Torre Grossa

To the left of the Collegiata stands the town hall, the Palazzo del Popolo, which was probably begun in 1288 by Arnolfo di Cambio and expanded in 1323. From the top of the 54m/177ft-high »broad tower«, completed in 1311 as the tallest of all towers in San Gimignano according to a city ordinance, there is a **beautiful panoramic view**. An inner courtyard decorated with coats of arms, a well from 1361 and three frescoes on the judge's loggia connects to a covered flight of steps leading to the * **Museo Civico**. Sala Dante on the second floor got its name because Dante came here on 8 May 1300 to persuade the city councillors to join the Guelf league. A wonderful Maestà by Lippo Memmi dated 1317 takes up the right wall of the room. The collection of paintings contains excellent Florentine and Sienese works of the 13th to 15th centuries, including a crucifix by Coppo di Marcovaldo (13th century), *Mother of God with Child and Saints* by Benozzo Gozzoli dated 1466, *Madonna in Glory* by Pinturicchio (1512) as well as *Annunciation* by Filippino Lippi, which consists of two round panels and was commissioned in 1482. In the adjacent Camera del Podestà frescoes by Memmo di Filippuccio (14th cent.) show scenes of medieval everyday life.

❶ Mar 1 – Oct 31 daily 9.30am – 7pm, Nov 1 – Feb 28, daily 10am – 5.30pm, admission €5

Opposite the Collegiata stands the old Palazzo del Podestà, which was built in 1239 on the houses of the Mantellini family and converted to a theatre in 1537. The 51m/135ft-high **Torre Rognosa** rises over the building.

Palazzo del Podestà

At the beginning of Via San Matteo are the 13th-century twin towers of the Salvucci family. The other buildings worthy of note are the 14th-century Casa-Torre Pesciolini (no. 32) with its arched windows and Palazzo Tinacci (no. 60/62) with windows in the style of different periods.

Via San Matteo

Behind the Collegiata a short, steep walk goes up to the castle, which was built in 1353 by the Florentines on the highest point of the town hill but razed in 1555 on the orders of Cosimo I de Medici. Parts of the wall and the defensive tower are preserved.

Rocca

The brick church in the north of the walled city was built 1280 – 1298 in the austere style of the mendicant orders. Inside the church the Cappella di San Bartolo is on the right. It has an elaborate marble altar by Benedetto da Maiano (1494) where the remains of St Bartolo of San Gimignano rest. The main altar is decorated by a panel *Coronation of the Virgin* (1483) by Piero del Pollaiuolo.

Sant' Agostino

**Frescoes by Benozzo Gozzoli: The main attraction is the fresco cycle dated 1464/1465 in the central choir chapel, a work by Benozzo Gozzoli. The painter represented the life of St Augustine (354 – 430) in 17 scenes.

The chronological scenes start on the left in the bottom row: Augustine is placed in the care of a schoolmaster by his parents; as a youth he is admitted to the university in Carthage; St Monica prays for her son Augustine; he travels to Italy by ship; Augustine is received on land; he teaches in Rome when he is barely 20; Augustine travels to

Milan. In the middle row: audience with the bishop of Milan and Emperor Theodosius; Monica prays for her son's conversion; disputation between Augustine and Ambrose; Augustine reads the epistle of Paul in the garden of his friend Alipius; Augustine is baptized by Ambrose on the following Christmas day and founds his order; Augustine and the boy at the sea; explanation of the rules of the order; death of St Monica. In the top row: Augustine as bishop of Hippo blessing his congregation; conversion of the heretic Fortunatus; vision of St Jerome; death and ascension of St Augustine.

The frescoes on the third altar to the left are worth seeing: *St Sebastian* (1524) by Benozzo Gozzoli, Sebastiano Mainardi's *St Bartolo* (1487) as well as *Birth and Assumption of the Virgin* (around 1400) by Bartolo di Fredi in the chapel next to the altar. The sacristy gives access to the adjoining cloister to the south (15th century) with the chapter house.

San Giovanni Valdarno
———————————————— ✦ H 12

Province: Arezzo (AR)
Altitude: 134m/439ft above sea level
Population: 17,150

The upper Arno valley (Valdarno) is bordered on the west by the hills of ►Chianti, on the east by the higher Pratomagno. The valley itself is heavily industrialized and not very inviting at first glance. However, San Giovanni Valdorno, about halfway between Arezzo and Florence, are worth a stop.

Sightseeing   San Giovanni Valdarno was designed in the 14th cent. with a grid street pattern, unusual for this time. The centrally located Piazza Cavour is extremely long; it was formed by making two squares with 13th-century Palazzo Preterio (or Palazzo d' Arnolfo) with its open arcades between them; its rich coat of arms also attracts the eye. There are plans to open a museum on the history of city planning in Tuscany in the palazzo. On the small Piazza Masaccio behind Palazzo Preterio stands the domed Basilica Santa Maria delle Grazie, which was dedicated in the 15th century and has a classical veranda dating from 1840. Inside the church is a miraculous picture of the Virgin Mary (around 1400). In the 14th-century Oratorio di San Lorenzo, also on the main square, there is an altar by Giovanni del Biondo (14th cent.).

In the **Museo della Basilica di S. Maria delle Grazie**, located in the building next to the basilica, several important paintings are exhibited, including the *Annunciation* by Fra Angelico (around 1430),

San Giovanni Valdarno

INFORMATION
Piazza Cavour 3
Tel. 055 94 37 48
www.comunesgv.it

WHERE TO EAT
Osteria di Rendola
€€€ – €€€€
Via di Rendola 72-86
Loc. Fattoria di Rendola, Montevarchi
Tel. 05 59 70 77 13
www.osteriadirendola.it
Oct. – May only evenings, at other times
also at noon

In the middle of the countryside in buildings from 1750, which include a hotel.
Creative seasonal cuisine is offered here.
Food is served on a beautiful veranda in
the summer.

WHERE TO STAY
Valdarno €€
Via Traquandi 13/15
Montevarchi
Tel. 05 59 10 34 89
www.hotelvaldarno.net
Modern hotel near the railway station.
61 elegant, very comfortable rooms.

which was brought here from the Convento di Montecarlo (15th cent.; 2 km/1mi away).

The house at Corso Italia 83 is considered to be Masaccio's birthplace, the brilliant early Renaissance painter. He was born here in San Giovanni Valdarno on December 21, 1401; but Gaiole in Chianti has also been put forward as his birthplace. **Museo Casa Masaccio**, a centre for modern art, was established in the house. Casa Masaccio's exhibits are usually held in other locations.

AROUND SAN GIOVANNI VALDARNO

No more than 5km/3mi south of San Giovanni Valdarno lies the medieval town of Montevarchi, which has an impressively harmonious and unspoiled appearance. The Piazza Varchi with the Palazzo del Podestà and the church of San Lorenzo is worth seeing. In the bulwarks of the Florentine city walls (1328) the art centre **Cassero per la scultura italiana dell' Ottocento e del Novecento** has 20 rooms with 19th/20th cent. sculptures, all of which are privately owned, including works by Michelangelo Monti, Alberto Giacomasso, Vamore Gemignani or Donatello (Dodi) Bortolotti.
❶ Via Trieste 1; Thu – Sun 10am – 1pm, 3pm – 6pm; admission: €3; www.ilcasseroperlascultura.it

*Montevarchi

A small artistic jewel is hidden 2km/1.3mi further in Gropina. The Romanesque parish church of St Peter was built between 1150 and

Gropina

1220 on Roman and Etruscan foundations. The monolithic columns and pillars with carefully worked early Romanesque capitals in the Lombard tradition are a joy to behold. They show a pig with her litter, a wolf with its prey, an eagle, lions, the battle of the virtues and vices, riders, leaf ornaments and grape vines. The beautiful pulpit with reliefs of the evangelists' symbols (lion, angel, eagle) and rich decorations is from the 12th century.

San Miniato

✳ **G 8**

Province: Pisa (PI)
Altitude: 156m/511ft above sea level
Population: 28,000

San Miniato – located on the intersection of Via Francigena and the old Roman road from Pisa to Florence became the important Tuscan base of the Holy Roman emperors in the Middle Ages. The town had the words »al tedesco« attached to its name until World War II. Today it is known for its white truffles.

San Miniato

INFORMATION
Piazza del Popolo 1
Tel. 057 14 27 45
www.comune-san-miniato.pi.it

WHERE TO EAT
Peperino €€€€
Via IV Novembre 1
Tel. 34 87 80 47 85
www.peperino.net
Open Wednesdays and evenings
Paolo Fiaschi will open for only 2 guests!
The smallest and most romantic restaurant of Tuscany is decorated in 19th-cent. style. Reservations necessary.

Pepenero €€
Via IV Novembre 13

Tel. 05 71 41 95 23
www.pepenerocucina.it
Closed Tue and all of Jan.
Chef Gilberto Rossi serves outstanding dishes with chanterelle mushrooms (finferli) or truffles (tartufi).

WHERE TO STAY
Fattoria Aglioni €€
Via Gello 12
Tel. 05 71 40 80 41
www.aglioni.it
Old farm house 6km/4mi from San Miniato with beautiful rooms in the main house and apartments (chic: maisonette in the former smithy) and pool. Excellent kitchen (cooking courses), gourmet truffle weekend in November.

Excavations in San Genesio brought a Roman settlement and early medieval structures to light. The Lombards built a church dedicated to the martyr San Miniato from AD 715. Already under the Holy Roman emperor Otto I in the 10th century there was an imperial castle on the hill and a village with increasingly Guelf sympathies outside the castle walls. In 1172 there was a revolt against the imperial castle that ended with the destruction of all houses and possessions outside the castle walls. Emperor Frederick II had the fortress renovated in 1217 – 1223.

On July 22, 1944 55 people were killed in the cathedral of San Miniato, ostensibly in a German act of revenge after one of their soldiers was murdered. At that time »al tedesco« was taken out of the town's name. The brothers Paolo and Vittorio Taviani, who come from San Miniato and who witnessed this event, made a film about it called *The Night of the Shooting Stars*. The story takes place in a fictitious location, San Martino. There is a plaque on the town hall to commemorate the events in the cathedral. New research has shown however that the carnage in the cathedral was cause by Allied artillery fire. On July 22, 2008 a second plaque was mounted on the town hall wall; on it the former Italian president, Oscar Luigi Scalfaro, explained that the responsibility for the bloodbath in April 1944 lay with the Allies.

WHAT TO SEE IN SAN MINIATO

The town lies on one of the highest points in the area. On the top of Rocca Federiciana is **Frederick's Tower**, a relic of the former imperial castle. It was destroyed in 1944 and rebuilt in 1958. It is the landmark of the town.
❶ Apr 1 – Sep 30 Tue – Sun 11am – 6pm, Oct 1 – Mar 31 until 5pm

Town with a view

Piazza del Popolo is a good starting point for a tour, with the church of San Domenico with its undressed façade. The aisle-less interior has frescoes on the life of St Dominic (around 1700) and the tomb by Bernardo Rossellino of the respected physician Giovanni Chellini († 1461), who founded the hospital next to the church of Santa Maria a Fortino.

Piazza del Popolo, San Domenico

Between 1650 and 1708 the episcopal seminary was built on the valley side of the Piazza della Repubblica. The building complex was extended over time by adding smaller houses along the city wall until it formed an uninterrupted, beautifully painted façade.

*Seminario Vescovile

The Palazzo Comunale, the town hall on Via Vittime del Duomo, houses San Miniato's collection of archaeological finds. The Palazzo

Palazzo Comunale

Comunale also includes the Oratorio del Lorentino, where a sacred cross was kept. In 1715 it was transferred to the **Chiesa del Santissimo Crocifisso** (1705 – 1718) on the other side of the street. In Chiesa del Santissimo Crucifisso there are beautiful frescos by Antonio Domenico Barberini.

Archaeological collection: Apr 1 – Oct 31 Sat 3pm – 6pm, Sun 11am – 6pm, Nov 1 – Mar 31 Sat, Sun 11am – 6pm; admission: €2.50

*Duomo, Museo Diocesano   A steep stairway leads from Piazza della Repubblica to the »cathedral meadow« (Prato del Duomo). The cathedral was built 1220 – 1250 on the remains of the previous church Santa Maria Assunta (8th cent.); in 1378 – 1489 the Florentines used it as an arsenal. After 1489 the fortified tower Torre di Matilde was included in the structure. Only in 1622 did Pope Gregory XV elevate the church, which had meanwhile been renovated in Baroque, to a cathedral. Museo Diocesano next door has worky by the Florentine school of Giotto.

Museo Diocesano: Apr 1 – Oct 31 Thu – Sun 10am – 6pm, Nov 1 – Mar 31 Thu – Sun 10am – 1pm, 2pm – 5pm; admission: €2.50

EMPOLI

Industrial city   The modern town lies in the Arno valley about 8km/5mi north-east of San Miniato and is known for its glass and textile industry. 30 years ago there was almost no Tuscan family that did not have some item handmade out of green glass from Empoli. But today the small workshops have disappeared. Despite its industrial character Empoli has a small centre with pleasant pedestrians streets such as Via del Giglio.

Sightseeing   Empoli's centre, Piazza Farinata degli Uberti, is surrounded by arcades and decorated with a fountain with naiads. The square got its name from an illustrious 13th-century member of the Florentine patrician Uberti family. The most noticeable building on the square is the collegiate church of St Andrew with its façade of green and white marble which was added in the late 12th century.

A visit to the collegiate museum on the neighbouring Piazzetta della Propositura is recommended. The **art collection** contains Tuscan paintings and sculptures (late 14th to 17th cent.).

MuVe (Museo del Vetro) in the old salt storehouse (17th cent.) is dedicated to glass production in Empoli; it shows glass products from 1650 – 1970.

Collegiate museum: Tue – Sun 9am – 12pm, 4pm – 7pm; admission: €3
MuVe: Via Ridolfi 70; Tue – Sun 10am – 7pm; free admission

Montelupo   Excavations in the area of Montelupo 10km/6mi east of Empoli uncovered signs of Stone Age settlements of the Villanova culture as

It's how you get there: Tuscan country roads won't get you there quickly, but you'll enjoy the trip!

well as Etruscan and Roman habitation. The finds are exhibited in what is probably the best prehistoric collection of Tuscany: ***Museo Archeologico di Montelupo**. Under Florentine rule Montelupo developed into an important centre for ceramics with coloured glaze, the so-called majolica. **Museo della Ceramica di Montelupo** presents vases and coats of arms (14th – 18th cent.) such famous Florentine families as the Medici, Strozzi and Machiavelli. Palazzo Pretorio (around 1427) in Via Baccio Sinibaldi houses the Museo Contemporanea with an art collection of the 19th/20th cent. and modern ceramic design by Fernando Farulli, Ettore Sottsass or Eva Zeisel.

Museo Archeologico di Montelupo: Via S. Lucia; Apr 1 – Oct 31 Thu – Sun 11am – 7pm, Nov 1 – Mar 31 Sat, Sun 2pm – 7pm; admission: €5.50
Museo della Ceramica di Montelupo: Piazza Vittorio Veneto 11, opening times/admission like Museo Archeologico; www.museomontelupo.it

VINCI

11km/7mi north of Empoli on the southern slopes of Monte Albano lies the community of Vinci, birthplace of the artist, engineer and natural scientist Leonardo da Vinci (►Famous People) and centre of the Terre del Rinascimento.

Birthplace of Leonardo da Vinci

❶ Via della Torre 11; www.terredelrinascimento.it

Museo Leonardiano is located in the castle of the Conti Guidi (10th – 13th cent.) and in **Palazzina Uzielli**. Palazzina Uzielli on Piazza dei Guidi, which was designed by **Mimmo Palatino**, shows

* Museo Leonardiano

Leonardo's machines and ideas to mechanize the production of textiles. There are more than 60 built-to-scale models from Leonardo's drawings, such as of flying or military machines, on display in the **Guidi castle**. An outside staircase leads to the first floor with propulsion models, including the famous »automobile« (self-propelling vehicle) and the wooden »bicycle« as well as a model of the cathedral dome of Florence. The **library** has facsimiles of all of the universal genius' manuscripts and drawings as well as his books from 1651. The castle square is dominated by a wooden sculpture by Mario Ceroli which was inspired by Leonardo's ideas. It is part of the **sculpture path** that leads to the church Santa Chiara's baptistery and to Piazza della Libertà with the Bronze horse (1997) by the sculptress Nina Akamu.

Museum: Mar – Oct daily 9.30am – 7pm, Nov – Feb until 6pm; admission: €7 (tickets at Palazzina Uzielli); www.museoleonardiano.it

Library: appointment necessary; www.bibliotecaleonardiana.it

*Museo Ideale Leonardo da Vinci   In the large vaulted cellars below the castle a private museum has an interesting exhibition of traditional agricultural implements and models of utopian machines based on drawings by Leonardo.
❶ Via Montalbano 2; temporarily closed; www.museoleonardo.com

Casa Natale di Leonardo   Leonardo's supposed birthplace is located in Anchiano 3km/1.8mi away. Hiking trail 14 leads to Anchiano for anyone who wants to walk there. Casa Natale di Leonardo has a bust of the genius, the reconstruction of a bedroom (15th cent.), reproductions of designs by Leonardo and a Tuscan landscape.
❶ see Museo Leonardiano

A magical place: the thermal pool in the middle of Bagno Vignoni

★ San Quirico d'Orcia

✦ L 12

Province: Siena (SI)
Altitude: 424m/1,391ft above sea level
Population: 2,770

San Quirico d'Orcia is not spectacular, but it is an orderly and pleasant town with an almost complete town wall. It lies on the old Frankish road through the river valleys of Orcia and Asso, about 45km/28mi south-east of Siena. In 1154 Emperor Frederick Barbarossa received the emissaries of Pope Adrian IV here – an event that is celebrated every year with a festival on the third Sunday in June.

The Romanesque **collegiate church** was built in the 12th century in a locatin that already had a church from the 8th cent. The transepts were added in the 13th century. The Baroque choir was completed in 1653, the tower added in 1806. The simple façade has an impressive Romanesque west door (around 1080) with a depiction of Pope Damasus II in the lunette. The side door is attributed to the school of Giovanni Pisano (around 1288). Inside the choir stalls, decorated with intarsia work, built in 1502 are worth seeing. The little **park** Horti Leonini next to the medieval city gate Porta Nuova is ideal for a break. Behind a modest entrance lies an Italian-style garden designed by Diamide Leoni in 1540 with pretty flower borders and boxwood hedges.

Sightseeing

AROUND SAN QUIRICO D'ORCIA

The hilly landscape between San Quirico d'Orcia in the west, Sarteano in the east and Radicofani in the south is some of the most beautiful that Tuscany has to offer: forests and fields, small roads that wind through them, picture-perfect cypress avenues, remote hilltop farms, small hidden castles and villages with beautiful views. The valley is a UNESCO world heritage site.

*Val d'Orcia

The little spa resort Bagno Vignoni was valued by Catherine of Siena and Lorenzo de Medici, but also by the Romans already. It became famous when the Russian director Andrei Tarkovsky chose this place as the impressive setting for his cult film *Nostalghia*. The large pool filled with bubbling spring water and the Renaissance buildings around it make a wonderful ensemble. **Parco dei Mulini** with excavations of old mill foundations is open to the public. The millstones used to be propelled by thermal spring water. To the left of the exca-

*Bagno Vignoni

San Quirico d'Orcia

INFORMATION
Via San Giovanni 10
Tel. 05 77 88 89 86
www.comunesanquirico.it

WHERE TO EAT
Ristorante La Parata €€
Piazza del Moretto 40, Bagno Vignoni
Tel. 05 77 88 75 08
Closed Mon.
Giancarlo Diodato cooks Tuscan speciali-
ties, three times a week there is fresh
pasta (pici, filled ravioli and pappardelle

with wild boar ragout). In the summer
the best place is on the terrace.

WHERE TO STAY
Posta Marcucci €€€€
Via Arca Urcea 43, Bagno Vignoni
Tel. 05 77 88 71 12
www.hotelpostamarcucci.it
Traditional hotel below the town centre
of Bagno Vignoni with 36 rooms and its
own thermal pool (also open to the
public).

vations a signposted path leads downhill to a free swimming in a
torquoise-coloured pool. From June to Oct. the thermal pool Stabilimento Termale di Bagno Vignoni, Piazza del Moretto 32 is also
open. At the edge of town the luxurious resort Thermae Adler Spa
fulfils all expectations of a wellness resort (www.adler-thermae.
com).

Sansepolcro

※ outside

Province: Arezzo (AR)
Altitude: 330m/1,083ft above sea level
Population: 16,400

**Piero della Francesca is the most famous son of Sansepolcro in
the upper Tiber valley. Important works by this outstanding
Renaissance painter can be admired in the local art gallery.
The somewhat colourless industrial and trade city is also
known for its gold jewellery.**

Sansepolcro means »holy grave«. The town got its name according to
legend from two pilgrims, Arcano and Egidio, who brought relics of
the grave of Christ back from Jerusalem in the 10th century and built
an oratory for them. At first Camaldolese monks devoted themselves
to caring for the holy site and later founded an abbey here. In later
years the rulers of Sansepolcro changed repeatedly until it was attached to Florence in the mid-15th century.

Sansepolcro

INFORMATION
Via Matteotti 8
Tel. 05 75 74 05 36
http://turismo.provincia.arezzo.it

WHERE TO EAT / WHERE TO STAY
Relais Oroscopo di Paola e Marco
€€
Via Togliatti 68

Loc. Pieve Vecchia
Tel. 05 75 73 48 75
www.relaisoroscopo.com
Here you can sleep like a king and dine like a prince. Paola and Marco's kitchen is known far beyond Sansepolcro. The hotel with 10 individually furnished rooms also has a pool!

WHAT TO SEE IN SANSEPOLCRO

The municipal art gallery in the Palazzo della Residenza displays paintings from the 14th–16th centuries including works by Luca Signorelli and Santi di Tito, who was born in Sansepolcro, and terracottas from the della Robbia workshop, as well as 20th cent. art, including works by M. Baragli, M. Argenti, G. Lanfredini, Benedetto, Francesco and Salvatore d' Amore.. However, the gallery owes its fame to **Piero della Francesca** (around 1416 – 1492), who worked above all in Umbria and at the courts of Ferrara, Rimini and Urbino and who was highly honoured in his home town. He was interred in the cathedral on 12 October 1492 – the day when Columbus first set foot in the New World. The use of perspective, strict geometry and a new spatial style of composition are important elements of his art, which can be seen in his *Resurrection*, painted in 1463 for the council chamber of the palace. Piero's first large independent work was the Misericordia Altar for the lay brotherhood of Sansepolcro. Piero promised in 1445 to complete the 23 panels within three years, but it took him 15 years in the end. The centre picture is dominated by a Madonna of Mercy with the most important donors of the brotherhood at her feet.

*Pinacoteca Comunale

❶ Via Niccolò Aggiunti 65; June 15 –Sep 15 9.30am – 1.30pm, 2.30pm – 7pm, Sep 16 – June 14 9.30am – 1pm, 2.30pm – 6pm; www.museocivicosansepolcro.it

The herb museum in Palazzo Bourbon del Monte only a few steps away is dedicated to the history of medicinal herbs in the course of the last millennium. Its displays include old distillation devices, rare herbs, books on botany.

Aboca Museum

❶ Via Niccolò Aggiunti 75; Apr 1 – Sep 30 daily 10am – 1pm, 3pm – 7pm, Oct 1 – Mar 31 Tue – Sun 10am – 1pm, 2.30pm – 6pm; admission: €8; www.abocamuseum.it

Duomo San Giovanni Evangelista	The cathedral also lies on Via Matteotti. It was already part of the Camaldolese monastery, which was built from 1012 to 1049, as the abbey church. Behind the Romanesque façade is a basilica which already shows the **transition to the Gothic style**. The larger than life-size crucifix (12th century) of walnut wood in the left choir chapel shows the influence of the Volto Santo from Lucca. There is a beautiful terracotta tabernacle from the della Robbia workshop in the presbytery.
Palazzo delle Laudi	To the left of the cathedral the **Laudi palace** was built (1591 – 1609) on the threshold to Baroque with an arcaded inner courtyard; today it is the town hall. In Via Matteotti as well as in Via XX Settembre, on Piazza Torre di Berta and Piazza Gramsci worthwile weekly markets are held every Tuesday and Thursday.
San Francesco	Beyond the Portadella-Pesa gate is **Piazza San Francesco** with the church of the same name. The façade and the bell tower are all that remain of the original 13th-century building; the rest was changed considerably in the late Baroque period.
Museo della Vetrata Antica	New life moved into the altarless church of San Giovanni Battista when the Museo della Vetrata Antica moved in. Until 1810 Piero della Francesca's *Taufe Christi* had been on display here; in 1859 it found its way into London's National Gallery. The Bernardini collection and Fatti donation show 19th /20th cent. church windows, including a pre-Raphaelite crucifixion that is attributed to the circle around William Morris. Magical transparency is the characteristic of Rosa and Cecilia Caselli's adaptation of Leonardo da Vinci's *Last Supper*. ❶ Via Giovanni Buitoni 9; Apr 15 – Sep 30 Fri – Sun 10am – 1pm, 2.30pm – 5.30pm, Oct 1 – Apr 14 only Sat, Sun; admission: €2.50

AROUND SANSEPOLCRO

*Anghiari	This picturesque town 10km/6mi west of Sansepolcro is a labyrinth of narrow alleys. Anghiari is famous for the battle on 29 June 1440, when Florentines allied to the pope defeated the army of the Duke of Milan – a triumph that was commemorated in the Great Hall of the Palazzo Vecchio in Florence by Leonardo da Vinci. Anghiari's Palazzo Pretorio (14th cent.) with its coats of arms is worth seeing. A tip: cheese, porcini mushrooms, black truffles and fabric can be bought at the linen weaver Busatti (since 1842), Via Mazzini 14.
Monterchi	The main reason why visitors come to the modest village of Monterchi 10km/6mi south of Sansepolcro, is to see a famous work by Piero

Hidden in the Tuscan Province: Madonna del Parto is one of the most expressive works by Piero della Francesca

della Francesca : during restorations to the pilgrimage chapel in 1888 the beautiful *Madonna del Parto* (the Virgin Mary before giving birth, around 1460), a * **fresco by Piero della Francesca** came to light, which can be seen in the museum Madonna del Parto, Via della Regina 1.

❶ Apr 1 – Oct 31 9am – 1pm, 2pm – 7pm, Nov 1 – Mar 31 until 5pm; admission: €3.50

** Siena

✦ K 10/11

Province: Siena (SI)
Elevation: 322m/1,056ft above sea level
Population: 54,500

Siena's impressive silhouette with towers and domes can be seen from far away. The characteristic red-brown colour of the buildings is not a coincidence: the clay from this area was once used as a natural pigment by artists – the coveted warm Siena brown. Within the mighty Medici wall, the Gothic city spreads over three ridges which meet in the secular centre at the famous Piazza del Campo, one of the most celebrated squares in Europe and venue of the Palio horse race.

Siena

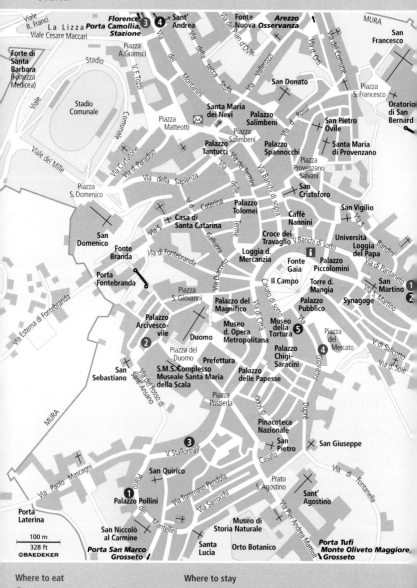

Where to eat

1 Il Canto
2 Antica Osteria da Divo
3 Il Mestolo
4 Trattoria Papei

Where to stay

1 Palazzo Ravizza
2 Santa Caterina
3 Hotel Duomo
4 Hotel Executive Siena
5 Locanda Gariba

escalator

Siena

INFORMATION
Piazza del Campo 56
Tel. 05 77 28 05 51
www.terresiena.it

TRAFFIC
Siena's old city is closed to private cars. It is surrounded by the Zona al Traffico Limitato (ZTL), which is video-controlled. There is parking at a fee at Fortezza Medicea, Piazza Santa Caterina and Piazza San Francesco (both connected to the old city by escalators) and in the parking garages (www.sienaparcheggi.com). There are also escalators from the main railway station to the upper city.

DON'T MISS!
2 July and 16 August are dates to take note of – on these two days the legendary horse race known as the Palio takes place in Siena, and the whole city flips out. Be sure to book tickets in time (►MARCO POLO Insight p. 90)

SHOPPING
Most of the shops are to be found on Via di Città and Via dei Banchi di Sopra. This includes the most expensive ones, such as Drogheria Manganelli (Via di Città 71–73), where cakes, especially the Sienese fruit cake **panforte**, are still made from old recipes. True wonders of confectionery can be found at Nannini (Via Banchi di Sopra 24) but the Sienesse shop at »Il Magnifico«, Via dei Pellegrini 27, und Enzo Bini, Via di Stalloreggi 91/93. Pizzicheria »Morbidi« (Via Banchi di Sopra 73/75) and the Sienese agricultural consortium's supermarket, Via Pianigiani 5 – 9 have high quality foods. Ham (Cinta Senese) and cheese: Gino Cacino, Piazza del Mercato 31.

JOINT TICKET
Siena offers a combined admission ticket (biglietto cumulativo) for two days as well as an expensive and comprehensive one for seven days. The tourist information office will help you choose the right one.

WHERE TO EAT
❶ *Il Canto* €€€€
Strada di Certosa 82 – 86
Tel. 05 77 28 81 80
www.ilcanto.it
Only evenings; closed Tue and
Dec. 10 – Feb. 10
One of the best restaurants in Tuscany. Chef Paolo Lopriore and his 5 cooks practice theri art for 20 guests at the most. The restaurant is part of a wonderful hotel in the former monastery Certosa di Maggiano.

❷ *Antica Osteria da Divo* €€€
Via Franciosa 25/29
Tel. 05 77 28 60 54
www.osteriadadivo.it
Open daily
Tuffstone grotto with wonderful vaulted ceilings and niches for romantic dinners for two. Fine Sienese and Avant-garde kitchen. The dishes made with saffron are interesting.

❸ *Il Mestolo di Gaetano e Nicoletta* €€€
Via Fiorentina 81
Tel. 0 57 75 15 31
www.ilmestolo.it
Closed Sun
Gaetano and Nicoletta serve the best Italian-Tuscan cooking in an elegant atmosphere. In the summer guests can be served under the pergola, or take part in

wine tasting or tasting menus. Excellent wine list.

❹ *Trattoria Papei* €€ – €€€
Piazza del Mercato 6
Tel. 05 77 28 08 94
Closed Mon.
Because of the good location lots of tourists eat here.

WHERE TO STAY
❷ *Santa Caterina* €€€
Via E. S. Piccolomini 7
Tel. 05 77 22 11 05
www.hscsiena.it
Quality hotel at the edge of the old city with 22 stylishly furnished rooms and a generous breakfast buffet. Be sure to request a room on the garden side!

❶ *Palazzo Ravizza* €€€
Piano dei Mantellini 34
Tel. 05 77 28 04 62
www.palazzoravizza.it
This hotel in an old city palace has been in business since 1924. The rooms with wooden and stucco ceilings and hand-painted terracotta tiles have an old-fash-ioned charm. Breakfast can be eaten in the garden.

❸ *Hotel Duomo* €€€
Via di Stalloreggi 38
Tel. 05 77 28 90 88
www.hscsiena.it
Very comfortable three-star hotel with 23 rooms near the cathedral.

❹ *Hotel Executive Siena* €€ – €€€
Via N. Orlandi 32
Tel. 05 77 33 12 10
www.hotelexecutivesiena.com
The unpretentiously basic hotel with 73 rooms is located outside of the old city, that is outside of the ZTL. Bus connections into the centre of town.

❺ *Locanda Garibaldi* €€
Via G. Duprè 18
Tel. 05 77 28 42 04
Reasonably priced hotel right in the centre behind Piazza del Campo. Reserve ahead, since there are only 7 rooms! Silvia Bettina also runs the osteria in the building.

City on three hills
Siena's three parts of a city (terzi) are spread over three hills. In the south lies the Terzo di Città around the shopping street Via di Città with the Pinacoteca Nazionale and the cathedral at the highest point of the city; in the north the Terzo di Camollia around Via Banchi di Sopra takes its character from the beautiful palaces of wealthy merchants; and in the east lies Terzo di San Martino.

History
The history of Siena has been documented since the Roman period. The rivalry between the city, which was loyal to the Holy Roman Emperor, and papal Florence ended in 1235 with a peace treaty that was severe for Siena and brought with it a reform of the city government. From this time the city was governed by a council of 12 noblemen and 12 commoners. The city owes its wealth partly to the **silver mines of Montieri** and the flourishing banking business – Sienese banking houses were among the most profitable in all Europe. After

a victory over Florence in the battle of Montaperti in 1260, Siena had to submit to Florence again in 1269 and place city government in the hands of the merchants. They established the Council of Nine as the governing body, which gave Siena a period of peace from 1287 to 1355. This in turn allowed **a magnificent flowering of the arts**. In 1348 the Great Plague caused the economy and population to decline. From 1487 until 1512 Pandolfo Petrucci, called »Il Magnifico«, ruled the city. Under his less popular successors Siena was again the object of rival imperial and papal interests. In 1559 in the Peace of Chateau-Cambrésis Siena was given to Duke Cosimo I – the end of the city republic was sealed, the government-in-exile formed of Sienese families in Montalcino powerless to restore the old status.

** PIAZZA DEL CAMPO

The centrally located Piazza del Campo was built in the 13th/14th centuries and became Italy's first pedestrian zone in 1956. The harmonious appearance of the piazza makes it one of the most beautiful squares in the world. The fan-shaped paving, which is divided into nine parts and made of light travertine stone and red brick, slopes toward the elegant Gothic palaces that line the north-west side of the square. The middle section is bordered at its higher end by the ***Fonte di Gaia** (Fountain of Joy). The richly decorated well, a **masterpiece by Jacopo della Quercia** (1419), was restored in 1868. The original reliefs are in the Palazzo Pubblico. Twice a year the Piazza del Campo becomes the scene of the legendary Palio races (▶MARCO POLO Insight p. 90).

Heart of the city

On the south side of the piazza stands the magnificent Palazzo Pubblico, a Gothic communal building erected in 1309 of travertine and brick. Its bulk is relieved by pointed triple windows and roof crenellations. The arches are decorated with the black-and-white arms of Siena, the »Balzana«. In the middle of the first upper storey are arms of the Medici, who ruled as grand dukes of Tuscany from 1570. The façade also bears several depictions of the Capitoline she-wolf – a **reference to the legendary founding of Siena by Senus**, the son of Remus.

**Palazzo Pubblico with Museo Civico

Today the palazzo houses the **Museo Civico** with the wonderful ****frescoes by Lorenzetti** reflecting the city's self-confidence in the 14th and 15th century. The most famous is the allegory of Good and Bad Government (1340), which Ambrogio Lorenzetti designed for the Sala della Pace (Room of Peace). This fresco is one of the earliest examples of secular pictorial art in Italy. **Buongoverno** is an impressive depiction of virtues like justice, generosity, love of peace and unity, as well as everyday scenes with a veduta of Siena. These are contrasted with **Malgoverno**, which shows the consequences of tyranny, pride, greed, deception, betrayal, malice and mismanagement.

In the ****Sala del Mappamondo** Simone Martini painted the magnificent fresco of the Maestà (= Madonna enthroned, around 1315), and facing it the portrait of the military commander Guidoriccio da Fogliani (1329), one of the oldest equestrian portraits in Gothic art, stylistically a pioneering work. The explanation for the numerous examples of a Maestà in Siena lies in the local **veneration of the Virgin**, since the keys to the city were dedicated to her for assistance before the victorious battle of Montaperti in 1260, after which Siena called itself »Civitas Virginis«. Two other large frescoes in this room, by Giovanni di Cristoforo and Francesco d'Andrea (1479), show the victory of the Sienese troops over Florentine forces near Poggio Imperiale. The Sala del Mappamondo takes its name from a world map by Ambrogio Lorenzetti dating from 1344, which was lost. Attached to this room is the palace chapel with an antechamber (anticappella), which Taddeo di Bartolo decorated with a fresco cycle in 1414. The Sala di Balia was painted by Spinello Aretino in 1407 with scenes from the life of Pope Alexander III. To end a tour of the Palazzo Pubblico on a high note, enjoy the view of the square and the city from the top floor (loggia dei nove).

❶ Nov 1 – Mar 15 10am – 6pm, Mar 16 – Oct 31 10am – 7pm; admission: €8

View from the observation platform on the Torre del Mangia: Piazza del Campo looks like fan from above.

To the left of the Palazzo Pubblico is the city hall tower, one of the most daring towers of the Middle Ages. It is 102m/335ft high to the top of the metal bell cage and was built by the brothers Minuccio and Francesco di Rinaldo 1338 – 1344. It got its name from the sexton Mangiaguadagni (which literally means »the one who eats up the wages«), who regulated working hours by ringing the bell. A spectacular panoramic view of the city and surroundings is the reward for the climb up to the tower platform. In front of the palace façade at the base of the tower lies the **Cappella di Piazza**, which was built in 1352 out of gratitude for salvation from the plague of 1348, and substantially altered in 1463. Its forms, which hark back to ancient architecture, are a striking contrast to the austere façade of the Palazzo Pubblico.

Torre del Mangia

❶ daily Mar 16 – Oct 31 10am – 7pm, Nov 1 – Mar 15 until 4pm; admission: €8

On the north-east corner of Piazza del Campo, with its main façade facing Via Banchi di Sotto, stands **Palazzo Piccolomini**, which was built by Nanni Todeschini, brother-in-law of the later Pope Pius II. The Renaissance building today holds the state archives and the little **Museo delle Tavolette di Biccherna**. These are little painted wooden panels, which developed into works of art; they were made from the 13th century for the financial administration of Siena, which used them as file covers.

❶ tours: Mon – Sat 9.30am, 10.30am, 11.30am; free admission

At the Vicolo del Bargello near Piazza del Campo is the **Museo della Tortura**. In the lower floor there is a torture chamber from the times of the Inquisition.

Museo della Tortura

❶ daily 10am – 7pm, special exhibits until 8pm; admission: €8

BETWEEN PIAZZA DEL CAMPO AND THE CATHEDRAL

**Via di Città, Loggia della Mercanzia

From Piazza del Campo it is only a few steps uphill to Via di Città, the main street of the old city. The Loggia della Mercanzia, the old

---

MARCO POLO TIP

! *Siena tickets* Insider Tip

Biglietto cumulativo: combined ticket for Museo Civico and Torre del Mangia (€13).
Combined ticket for Museo Civico and SMS (valid 48 hours; €11).
SIA Estate/ SIA Inverno: 7-day ticket for Museo Civico, SMS, Museo dell' Opera Metropolitana, Battistero S. Giovanni, Oratorio di San Bernardino and Sant' Agostino (SIA Estate: Mar 15 – Oct 31, €17, SIA Inverno: Nov 1 – Mar 14, €14; without Oratorio di San Bernardino and Sant' Agostino).
Opa Si Pass: 3-day cathedral museum ticket for cathedral, Libreria Piccolomini, Battistero San Giovanni, Museo dell' Opera Metropolitana and Oratorio di S. Bernardino (€10; tickets at the Info Point, cathedral square, Mon – Fri 9am – 5pm).

commercial court which was built in 1428, stands here. It is an example of the transitional style from late Gothic to Renaissance; the upper storey was added in the 17th century. On the pillars with richly decorated capitals that support open arcades, statues of St Peter and St Paul, St Victor and St Ansano can be seen.

*Palazzo Chigi-Saracini   The ground plan of Palazzo Chigi-Saracini has been fitted to the bend in Via di Città; it was completed around 1320 and enlarged in 1787. A massive crenellated tower rises above the façade, which has windows with pointed arches and is one of the most beautiful in the city. The grey stone in the two lower storeys contrasts attractively with the brick on the top floor. The palazzo houses the music academy, which holds master classes, summer concerts and other events. The rooms can be viewed upon request.

Palazzo Piccolomini delle Papesse   On the corner where narrow steps go up to the cathedral stands the residential palace built around 1460 for Caterina Piccolomini, the sister of Pope Pius II. It is also called the »Palace of the Woman Popes«. The plans for this beautiful Renaissance palace in the Florentine style probably derive from Bernardo Rossellino.

** DUOMO SANTA MARIA ASSUNTA

❶ Mar 1 – June 14 Mon – Sat 10.30am – 7.30pm (June 15 – Sep 15 until 8pm, Nov 3 – Feb 28 until 6.30pm), Sun 1.30pm – 6pm (Nov 3 – Feb 28 until 5.30pm); order advance tickets: tel. 05 77 28 30 48; admission including Libreria Piccolomini (same opening times): €3, Aug 21 – Oct 21 €6; www.operaduomo.siena.it

Siena's most important building is the cathedral, one of the most impressive Gothic churches in Italy. It was begun over a previous building, probably around the middle of the 12th century, but the dome was not finished until 1264. In 1284 construction of the west façade began, and from 1316 the choir was extended toward the east. The bell tower, slender and covered with black and white marble, dates from the second half of the 13th century. In 1339 the citizens decided on an **enlargement** of the cathedral to make it the largest building in Italy: the existing structure was to become the transept of a church over 100m/110yd long, whose main axis was to run perpendicular to the present one. The project was slowed by lack of funds and problems in construction, and after the devastating

---

MARCO POLO TIP

!

The 2-star floor   **Insider Tip**

If you come to Siena in September or the first week of October you can see the entire cathedral floor daily 10am – 7pm in all its splendour. It is covered with wooden boards the rest of the year.

Duomo Santa Maria Assunta

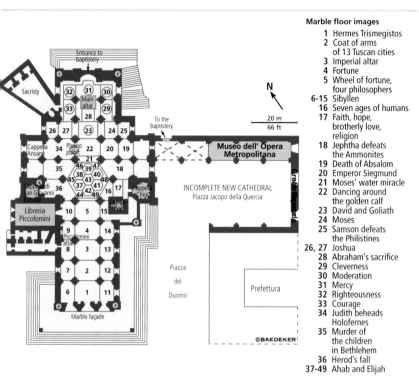

Marble floor images
1. Hermes Trismegistos
2. Coat of arms of 13 Tuscan cities
3. Imperial altar
4. Fortune
5. Wheel of fortune, four philosophers
6-15. Sibyllen
16. Seven ages of humans
17. Faith, hope, brotherly love, religion
18. Jephtha defeats the Ammonites
19. Death of Absalom
20. Emperor Siegmund
21. Moses' water miracle
22. Dancing around the golden calf
23. David and Goliath
24. Moses
25. Samson defeats the Philistines
26, 27. Joshua
28. Abraham's sacrifice
29. Cleverness
30. Moderation
31. Mercy
32. Righteousness
33. Courage
34. Judith beheads Holofernes
35. Murder of the children in Bethlehem
36. Herod's fall
37-49. Ahab and Elijah

plague epidemic of 1348 was abandoned. The unbelievable size of the planned new building can be seen from the parts that were completed in the extension of the right transept: the north-east aisle, which houses the cathedral museum today, the massive »great façade« and three bays of the south-west wall of the nave.

No less an artist than the eminent Giovanni Pisano was brought in from Pisa to design the west façade of the cathedral, which was completed in 1297. Pisano abandoned Romanesque architectural vocabulary in favour of the style of **French cathedral façades**, producing a composition of powerful spatial depth, a lavish programme of sculptures and three doorways set well back into the façade. Except for the storey with the rosette window, all of the sculptural decoration is by Pisano.

**West façade

Interior The interior, which is divided by high arcades, is a marked contrast to the radiant façade. The dark green-and-white striped marble, the atmosphere of gloom and the lack of pews are reminiscent of Arab architecture. The middle door is decorated on the inside of the façade with reliefs of the life of the Virgin (1483) and the legend of St Ansano (around 1480). The busts of Christ and 172 popes – from St Peter to Lucius III (†1185) on the prominent cornice below the clerestory are complemented by 36 medallion portraits of Roman emperors (15th/16th cent.) in the spandrels of the arches.

The ****floor** of the cathedral is a unique work of art. Its 56 images cut into the marble or made of inlay work are like an open book relating events from the Old Testament and showing virtues and allegories. The floor was started in 1369 and took about 200 years to complete, and numerous renowned artists were involved, including Pinturicchio (Happiness).

The tour of the cathedral begins with the ***Piccolomini Altar** in the third bay of the northern aisle. Andrea Bregno made it in 1485 for the Sienese Cardinal Francesco Piccolomini. It was intended to be decorated with sculptures afterwards, including 15 by Michelangelo. Opinions differ about which sculptures the artist actually made himself.

The cathedral of Siena is a Gothic masterpiece

The entrance to the Piccolomini Library is next to the Piccolomini Altar. The entrance wall, a high Renaissance masterpiece, was constructed by Lorenzo di Mariano in 1497; the library itself is one of the most beautiful and best- preserved rooms of its time. The building was begun in 1495 on behalf of Cardinal Francesco Piccolomini, from 1503 Pope Pius III, who wanted to provide a worthy place for the book collection of his uncle, Enea Silvio Piccolomini (Pope Pius II, ►Pienza). The wonderful **frescoes on the ceiling and walls** were painted between 1502 and 1509 by Pinturicchio of Perugia and his pupils. Beginning at the right-hand window, the murals depict the following scenes: Enea Silvio Piccolomini accompanies Cardinal Capranica to the Council of Basle (1432); as emissary of the council Piccolomini appears before the Scottish King James I; Emperor Frederick III crowns Piccolomini as poet; Piccolomini submits to Pope Eugene IV; as archbishop of Siena he brings Frederick III and Eleanor of Portugal together; Pope Calixtus III gives him the cardinal's hat; Piccolomini becomes Pope Pius II; in Mantua Pius II tries to unite the Christian rulers against the Turks; canonization of Catherine of Siena; Pius II arrives in Ancona in order to prepare for the military campaign against the Turks. The display cases on the walls hold valuable manuscripts from the 15th century. The Roman marble group of the three graces, a copy of a Greek original, was found in Rome around 1500.

**Libreria Piccolomini

The tour continues with the Renaissance chapel of John the Baptist (1482) with the bronze statue of the Baptist (1457), an expressive late work by Donatello, a statue of St Catherine of Alexandria (1487) by Neroccio and frescoes with scenes from the life of St John by Pinturicchio. In the chapel of St Ansanus, who is supposed to have brought Christianity to Siena and died under Emperor Diocletian, the tomb of Cardinal Riccardo Petroni (1317–1318), an early masterpiece by Tino di Camaino, is notable. Four supporting figures bear the sarcophagus with reliefs and figures of apostles. The bronze graveplate of Bishop Giovanni Pecci, dated 1430, is by Donatello.

Cappella di San Giovanni Battista, Cappella Ansano

Among the most important works of art in the cathedral is the pulpit, created in 1266–1268 by Nicola Pisano with the assistance of his son Giovanni and Arnolfo di Cambio. It rests on nine columns of granite, porphyry and marble. The outer ones stand on bases or on figures of lions, while the foot of the middle column is decorated with allegories of the seven liberal arts and philosophy. Above the capitals are personifications of the Christian virtues; prophets are in the arch spandrels. The facing has outstanding reliefs in the style of ancient sarcophaguses.

**Pulpit by Nicola Pisano

Duomo Santa Maria

The stately cathedral of Santa Maria rises up on the highest point of the city with Romanesque and Gothic stylistic elements in the façade. Below the choirs is the baptistery of San Giovanni while the remains of the »new cathedral«, which was to expand the cathedral in the 14th century, can be seen on the side.

❶ Mar 1 – June 14 Mon – Sat 10.30am – 7.30pm (June 15 – Sep 15 until 8pm, Nov 3 – Feb 28 until 6.30pm) , Sun 1.30 – 6pm (Nov 3 – Feb 28 until 5.30pm),
Advance tickets at tel. 05 77 28 30 48; www.operaduomo.siena.it

❶ Marble façade
At the end of the 13th century Giovanni Pisano designed the façade of the cathedral, inspired by French Gothic style.

❷ Libreria Piccolomini
The Piccolomini library was founded by Cardinal Francesco Piccolomini (later Pius III) in honour of his uncle Pius II. Pinturicchio's famous frescoes with scenes from the life of the later pope and a collection of choir books are here.

❸ Capella di San Giovanni
In the Renaissance chapel are a fresco cycle by Pinturicchio and a bronze statue of John the Baptist by Donatello (1457).

❹ Pulpit by Nicola Pisano
The octagonal pulpit by Nicola Pisano (13th cent.) rests on pillars which are in turn supported by lions.

❺ Battistero di San Giovanni
When the choir was expanded in 1316, a lower church (baptistery) was built.

❻ Museo dell'Opera Metropolitana
On the ground floor of the cathedral museum are works including the larger than life sculptures for the facade made by Pisano and his co-workers, which were replaced by copies in the course of time.

❼ Il Facciatone
The expansion plans of Siena's city fathers were stopped by lack of funds, technical problems as well as the outbreak of the plague in 1348. A reminder is the partially completed outer wall called Il Facciatone (the big façade).

❽ Crypt
The entrance to the crypt (13th cent.) lies on the back wall of the cathedral. It was only rediscovered in 1999 after 700 years. Its wall are painted with well-preserved frescos from the 13th cent. by painters from the Sienese school.

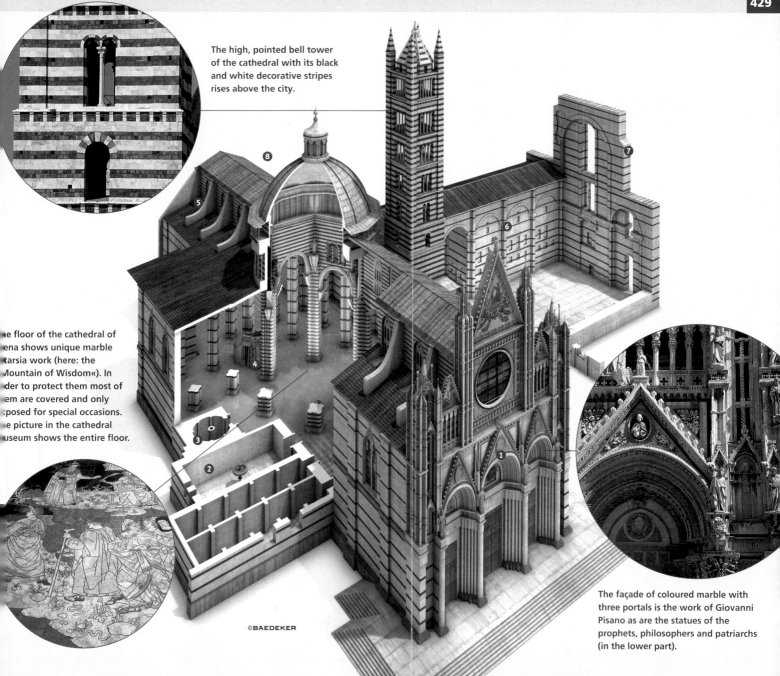

The high, pointed bell tower of the cathedral with its black and white decorative stripes rises above the city.

...e floor of the cathedral of ...ena shows unique marble ...tarsia work (here: the ...Mountain of Wisdom«). In ...der to protect them most of ...em are covered and only ...xposed for special occasions. ...e picture in the cathedral ...useum shows the entire floor.

The façade of coloured marble with three portals is the work of Giovanni Pisano as are the statues of the prophets, philosophers and patriarchs (in the lower part).

©BAEDEKER

Choir   The dominant feature in the choir is the large marble high altar by Baldassare Peruzzi (1532). Two angels flank the bronze ciborium (1472) by Vecchietta. At the top of the choir wall is a large round window with probably the oldest preserved stained glass in Italy, dating from 1288. The painter Duccio designed it. The **choir stalls** 1363–1397 are worth a closer look. Of more than 90 original seats, 36 have been preserved. The intarsia work on the backs of the seats (1503) gives a view from a window into the distance or into a cabinet of musical instruments.

Cappella Chigi   In the southern transept is the entrance to the Chigi chapel, constructed by the famous Baroque artist Gian Lorenzo Bernini between 1659 and 1662. The statues of St Jerome and St Mary Magdalene are dramatic late works of Bernini.

Campanile   The bell tower originally stood in a corner between the nave and transept, but the expansion of the cathedral brought it inside the church. On the wall above the door that leads into the base of the tower is the tombstone of Bishop Tommaso Piccolomini del Testa (1484).

*Battistero di San Giovanni   The baptistery lies under the choir. In order to see it leave the church and climb down the steps to Piazza San Giovanni. The tall church with its own façade commands the small square. The baptistery was built from 1316 to 1327, when the choir was extended. The frescoes inside the main room were created around 1450. The marble baptismal font (1417 – 1430) was probably created by Jacopo della Quercia, stands on a six-sided pedestal. It is decorated with personifications of the virtues and bronze reliefs on the life of John the Baptist by Jacopo della Quercia (announcement of the birth of John to Zacharias), Giovanni di Turino (birth and preaching of John), Lorenzo Ghiberti (baptism of Christ, imprisonment) and Donatello (beheading of John, Herod's feast).
❶ Mar 1 – June 14 9.30am – 7pm, June 15 – Sep 15 until 8pm, Sep 16 – Nov 2 until 7pm, Nov 3 – Feb 28 10am – 5pm; admission: €3

*Crypt   In 1999 the cathedral crypt, which had been hidden for 700 years, was rediscovered during restoration work. The room below the chancel goes back to the 13th cent. and was closed off in the 14th cent. Astonishingly well-preserved 13th-cent. frescoes from the sienese school were found behind masses of rubble.
❶ Opening times like Baptistery; admission: €6

**Museo dell' Opera Metropolitana   The cathedral museum is housed under three bays of the nave of the unfinished »new cathedral«. The rich collection contains, in addition to a Roman marble group of the three graces, above all works of me-

Interior with typical black and white marble decoration

dieval sculpture including **reliefs by Nicola Pisano**, works by Giovanni Pisano or his workshop, a wonderful relief *Madonna with Child, St Anthony and Cardinal Casini* by Jacopo della Quercia and the high-quality sculptures by Giovanni Pisano for the cathedral façade. Among the panel paintings the world-famous **Maestà** (1311), a painting of the Virgin by Duccio di Buoninsegna for the cathedral high altar, is the undisputed highlight. *The Birth of the Virgin* (1342) by Pietro Lorenzetti and the *Madonna degli Occhi Grossi* (Madonna with the large eyes), a work of the early 13th century that still reflects Byzantine influence, are also interesting. On the second floor valuable reliquaries such as the gilded 13th-century head reliquary of St Galgano and other items from the cathedral treasury are on display. From the top floor stairs lead to the »great façade« (Il Facciatone), a giant panorama terrace with a beautiful view of Siena.

❶ Piazza del Duomo 8; opening times like Baptistery; admission €6

S.M.S Complesso Museale Santa Maria della Scala

Opposite the cathedral façade the Ospedale di S. Maria della Scala founded in AD 823 and named after the cathedral steps (*scala*) retains its original form of the 13th and 14th centuries. The extensive museum complex S.M.S. Santa Maria della Scala was opened in the rooms. The exhibitiion centre is in the old ospedale. The frescoes in the pilgrims' hall were executed around 1440 by Domenico di Bartolo and show scenes of caring for the sick. Cappella del Manto is decorated with frescoes by Domenico Beccafumi (1512 – 1514) and older frescoes by Cristoforo di Bindoccio and Meo di Pero (1370). The Centro d'Arte Contemporanea, **S.M.S. Contemporanea** for short, is also attached to the complex. The permanent collection includes works by Cyprien Gaillard, Jenny Holzer or Gordon Matta-Clark; thematic and works exhibitions of the 20th cent. (e.g. Beuys, Burri, Bacon) are also held.

The educational museum of art for children **S.M.S. Museo d'Arte per Bambini** has, among other things, a painting collection on the history of childhood.

S.M.S. Santa Maria della Scala: Mar 17 – Oct 15 daily 10.30am – 6.30pm, otherwise until 4.30pm; admission: €6; www.santamariadellascala.com

S.M.S. Contemporanea: Tue – Sun 10am – 7pm; admission: €5

S.M.S. Museo d'Arte per Bambini: Mar 17 – Oct 15 daily 10.30am – 6.30pm, otherwise until 4.30pm; free admission; www.comune.siena.it/bambimus

*Museo Archeologico Nazionale
The collections in the left wing of the ospedale on Piazza del Duomo are also part of the SMS; they include mainly Etruscan finds – urns, bronze statuettes, sarcophagi, coins.

❶ Mar 17 – Oct 15 daily 10.30am – 6.30pm, otherwise until 4.30pm; admission: €6

Palazzo Arcivescovile
The Gothic forms of the archbishop's palace, which was built between 1718 and 1723 opposite the north wall of the cathedral nave, represent an early example of historicizing architecture. This return to an earlier style aimed to preserve the homogeneous appearance of the square. The bi-coloured marble covering of the cathedral has its counterpart on the ground floor of the palazzo.

** PINACOTECA NAZIONALE

❶ Sun, Mon 9am – 1pm, Tue – Sat 8.15am – 7.15pm; admission: €4

The Pinacoteca Nazionale is in the Palazzo Buonsignori, a late Gothic building that is considered to be one of the most elegant palaces in the region. This art gallery provides an excellent overview of Sienese painting from the 12th to the 16th century.

First floor
The main attraction on the first floor is the work of the high Renaissance painter Giovanni Antonio Bazzi, known as Sodoma, including

Flagellation of Christ (1511–1514) and *Deposition from the Cross* (around 1510), as well as paintings by Domenico Beccafumi, a representative of early Mannerism, including sketches for the floor decoration of the cathedral: *St Catherine of Siena Receives the Wounds of Christ* (around 1515) and *Birth of the Virgin* (around 1543).

The highlights of the second floor, where the tour should begin, include a damaged late 12th-century crucifix, one of the oldest works of Sienese art, as well as the altarpiece with Christ in the Mandorla from 1215 – the earliest dated example of Sienese painting (both room 1).

Second floor, room 1

The *Madonna and Child* (around 1262) by Guido da Siena in room 2 betrays Byzantine influences in the elongated bodies and the pronounced lines, while the retable with St John (around 1280) and the altar of St Peter (1280–1290) by anonymous masters demonstrate the transition from austere Byzantine forms to natural and colourful compositions. In room 2 there is also a diptych as well as five panels on the Passion of Christ, which were probably part of a Maestà in the Palazzo Pubblico, all from the workshop of Guido da Siena.

Room 2

The cathedral rises up from the highest point in the old city of Siena

*Room 3 / 4 **Altar panels** **by Duccio di** **Buoninsegna**	Rooms 3 and 4 contain two altar panels by Duccio di Buoninsegna, the founder of the Gothic school of painting in Siena (around 1310): *Madonna between Saints Augustine, Paul, Peter and Dominic*, lifelike and with delicate layers of colour, as well as *Madonna between Saints Agnes, John the Evangelist, John the Baptist and Mary Magdalene* with clear figure forms and a small panel *Madonna dei Franceschi* (around 1300). Other works from Duccio's circle are also exhibited here.
Rooms 5 / 6	Gothic panel paintings from the second half of the 14th century by Bartolo di Fredi (*Adoration of the Magi*, 1370/1380), Taddeo di Bartolo (*Annunciation, Adoration of the Shepherds*) and Luca di Tommè (including *Virgin and Child with St Anne*, 1367) are in room 5, while a panel painting by the great Sienese master Simone Martini depicts the Blessed Agostino Novello (1330).
Rooms **7–11 **Paintings by** **the Lorenzet-** **ti brothers**	The generation of painters that followed Duccio is represented by important works of the brothers Ambrogio and Pietro Lorenzetti. Pietro Lorenzetti painted (room 7) *Madonna Enthroned with Saints and Angels* and scenes from the history of the Carmelite order (1328–1329) with clear figures and perspective rendering of space, while Ambrogio Lorenzetti is represented by two small landscapes (around 1340), the *City on the Sea* and *Castle on the Lakeside*, as well as with *Madonna in Glory* (around 1340) and *Annunciation* (1344).

Nannini pasticcerias still carry the name but are no longer owned by
the family

The next rooms are devoted to painters from the circle of Simone Martini, including Lippo Memmi (*Madonna and Child*, around 1340) and Naddo Ceccarelli (Madonna polyptych) with extreme Gothic use of form. Room 11 houses several works from around 1400 by Taddeo di Bartolo, including *Enthroned Madonna* and an Annunciation altarpiece with signs of international Gothic style.

Simone Martini and his circle

Works by Giovanni di Paolo, a leading master of Sienese painting in the first half of the 15th century, are on display in rooms 12 and 13. He painted extremely attractive works using central perspective in connection with the rich colours of the Sienese tradition: *Madonna with Child Surrounded by Angels Making Music* (1433), *Madonna dell' Umiltà* (around 1455) and *Presentation in the Temple* (1447–1448). The work of Stefano di Giovanni, called Sassetta, was influential in the development of Sienese painting in the 15th century,. Unfortunately only the predella and crown of a polyptych painted between 1423 and 1426 are exhibited.

Rooms 12–13

The second half of the 15th century is represented in rooms 14–19 by Matteo di Giovanni's *Madonna among Saints* (1470), three Madonna panels (around 1476–1495) by Neroccio di Bartolomeo Landi in late Gothic-Mannerist style, and *Annunciation* (around 1470) by Francesco di Giorgio Martini, partly with extremely delicate lines, partly with clearly modelled figures in front of landscape and architectural scenes.

Rooms 14–19

The **third floor** holds the collection of the Sienese Spannocchi family with paintings from the 16th and 17th centuries, including works by Flemish masters as well as by Tintoretto and Albrecht Dürer.

Third floor

At the **Prato Sant'Agostino** in the church of Sant'Agostino, built in 1258, a *Crucifixion* by Perugino (1506), late 15th-century frescoes attributed to Francesco di Giorgio Martini (*Birth of the Virgin*, *Adoration of Christ*) and a Maestà fresco by Ambrogio Lorenzetti in the Cappella Piccolomini can be seen.
❶ Mon – Sat 2.30pm – 5.30pm; admission: €2.50

Sant' Agostino

The former Camaldolese monastery now accommodates an interesting natural history museum. The neighbouring botanical garden (orto botanico) already existed in 1588 and is open to the public.
Museo di Storia Naturale: Mon – Wed, Fri 9am – 1pm, 3pm – 6pm, Thu 9am – 1pm; free admission
Orto Botanico: Via Pier Andrea Mattioli 4; Mon – Fri 8am – 12.30pm, 2.30pm – 5.30pm, Sat 8am – 12pm; free admission

Museo di Storia Naturale, Orto Botanico

FROM THE CATHEDRAL SQUARE TO
FORTE DI SANTA BARBARA

Via Diacceto From the cathedral cross Piazza San Giovanni downhill and continue on the narrow Via Diacceto. About 50 yards along there is a beautiful view of the church of San Domenico. Via della Galluzza is covered by **high supporting arches** and leads down to the Dominican church.

*Casa di Santa Caterina In Via Santa Caterina, a narrow street which branches off to the left, is the birthplace of St Catherine of Siena (1347–1380) with a sanctuary built in 1464, three years after she was canonized. The Renaissance portal has the inscription: »Sponsae Kristi Catherinae Domus« (house of Catherine, bride of Christ). Catherine's intervention for the return of the pope from Avignon to Rome and her visions led to her canonization in 1461 by Pope Pius II, who came from Siena. For the stream of pilgrims the upper oratory was built in the 16th century and decorated with **frescoes from the life of St Catherine**. According to tradition she received the wounds of Christ in 1375 in front of the Romanesque crucifix now in the Oratorio del Crocefisso.

❶ Costa di S. Antonio 6; daily 9am – 12.30pm, 3pm – 6pm; free admission

Fonte Branda About 100m/110yd further to the west is a large fountain with Siena's oldest stone inscription (1198) by Bellamino. The fountain was given its present form mainly by Giovanni di Stefano around 1246.

San Domenico On Piazza San Domenico stands the Dominican church of San Domenico. The massive plain brick building has a nave without aisles and a square-ended choir as well as a tall transept from which two chapels extend to flank the choir. The fresco in the cross-vaulted chapel was painted by Andrea Vanni around 1370–1380, probably while Catherine was still alive, and is the ***oldest portrait of St Catherine**. The chapel of St Catherine also has two major works by Sodoma: *Ecstasy of St Catherine* and *St Catherine Fainting* (both around 1525). There is also a marble tabernacle (1466) by Giovanni di Stefano, which holds the head of St Catherine, who died in Rome and was buried there in the church of Santa Maria sopra Minerva.

On the other side of Viale dei Mille, beyond the athletics stadium, lies Forte di Santa Barbara, which Duke Cosimo I commissioned in 1560. The walls of the massive Fortezza Medicea give an attractive view of the city. In the vaults of the first bastion on the left is the *** Enoteca Ital-**

! *Happy Hour* Insider Tip

MARCO ⊕ POLO TIP

The Enoteca Italiana has a happy hour every Tuesday from 8pm – in the summer outside on the terrace, in the winter in the wine bar. There is a large buffet, the best aperitifs and cocktails, music with a DJ or live. And of course, excellent wines.

iana with an excellent selection of wines and an exhibition on Italian wine growing. Ristorante Millevini, which is run by Alberto Degortes, is attached. The wine list has more than 1,000 wines.

❶ Mon– Sat 12pm – 1pm; www.enoteca-italiana.it

FROM THE CAMPO TO THE NORTH-EASTERN OLD CITY

At Croce di Travaglio, the »Cross of Troubles«, near the the Loggia di Mercanzia, Via di Città meets the two other main shopping streets of the city centre: **Via Banchi di Sopra** and **Via Banchi di Sotto**.

Croce di Travaglio

About 100 metres north of Croce di Travaglio, Via Banchi di Sopra opens into a little piazzetta. On the left is one of the oldest palaces in Siena, Palazzo Tolomei, which was built in 1207. The front has windows with pointed arches and Gothic tracery. Opposite it is the church of San Cristoforo, originally Romanesque but completely remodelled in the 18th century. It has a remarkable 14th-century crucifix.

Palazzo Tolomei, San Cristoforo

Piazza Salimbeni also has a pretty collection of buildings. It is dominated by the 14th-century fortified Gothic **Palazzo Salimbeni** (14th cent.), the home of one of the oldest public credit institutions in Italy. It was established under the name Monte della Pietà in 1472: the »money mountain of mercy« offered low-interest loans to citizens who were in need. The banking house Monte dei Paschi – Monte loans are backed by income from the pastures (pascoli) of the Maremma – was established in 1624. To the right of the Salimbeni palace stands **Palazzo Spannocchi**, which was begun in 1470 for Ambrogio Spannocchi, treasurer of Pope Pius II of the Piccolomini family. The beautiful loggia was added to the elegant Renaissance building in 1880.

*Piazza Salimbeni

The foundation stone of the Gothic Franciscan church of San Francesco was laid in 1326, but it was completed only in 1484. The church has characteristic features of the architecture of mendicant orders in the large nave for preaching to a numerous congregation and flat-ended choir. The campanile was added in 1765; the façade was remodelled in the years from 1894 until 1912. The interior has an open truss roof and imitates in its black and white walls the marble cladding of the cathedral. The banners of the old craft guilds hang on the nave walls. In the left transept 14th cent. frescoes are worth seeing: *Crucifixion* (around 1336) by Pietro Lorenzetti, as well as the two frescoes by his brother Ambrogio Lorenzetti from the same period: *St Louis of Toulouse before Pope Boniface VIII* and the *Martyrdom of the Seven Franciscans of Ceuta*.

San Francesco

After a long city tour the cafés on the Piazza del Campo invite guests to take a well-earned break

**Oratorio di San Bernardino

A small two-storey oratory was built for St Bernard (1380–1444), a member of the order of St Francis, in the place where he usually preached. It stands next to the church and is worth visiting for its frescoes. They include works from the 16th century by Sodoma (*St Louis, Mary in the Temple, St Anthony of Padua*, St *Francis of Assisi, Visitation, Assumption and Coronation of the Virgin*), by Domenico Beccafumi (*Marriage of the Virgin, Madonna with Angels, Death of the Virgin*) and by Girolamo del Pacchia (*Birth of the Virgin, St Bernard of Siena, Gabriel, Annunciation*). Side rooms of the Oratory now house the Museo Diocesano di Arte Sacra (MDAS) with works of the Sienese school from the 14th cent. on. Especially expressive is the »Oratorio Superiore« with early 16th cent. frescoes.

❶ Mar 1 – Nov 1 daily 1.30pm – 7pm; admission: Oratory and MDAS €3

*Terzo di San Martino, Via Banchi di Sotto

SOUTH-EASTERN DISTRICT

Via Banchi di Sotto is the main axis of the south-east part of the city, the Terzo di San Martino with a lively atmosphere, small shops and

many cafés. It is obvious that the University of Siena and the renowned Università per Stranieri, the university for foreigners, are
located here.

In Via Banchi di Sotto is the delicate Loggia del Papa, completed in
1462. This building with three arches by the architect Antonio Fed-
erighi takes its name from Pope Pius II (Enea Silvio Piccolomini),
whose family had close ties to Siena.

**Loggia di
Papa**

Follow Via Banchi di Sotto, Via Pantaneto and Via Roma out of town
and turn off into Via San Clemente, which in turn leads to the
church of Santa Maria dei Servi (13th cent.). This church of the Servite order was remodelled in contemporary style in the 15th/16th
centuries. The austere façade was not changed; next to it stands the
13th-cent. campanile. Points of interest inside are the painting *Madonna del Bordone*, a picture of Mary with child and two angels by
Coppo di Marcovaldo (1261), and in the second chapel in the right-
hand transept the famous **fresco *Massacre of the Innocents***
(around 1330) by Pietro Lorenzetti. From Santa Maria dei Servi it is
not far to the city wall with the **Porta Romana**, a simple gate built
in 1327.

**Santa Maria
dei Servi**

South-east of Piazza del Campo is Siena's synagogue, which was
built in 1786, on Vicolo delle Scotte; it can be viewed in a guided
tour. A museum on 700 years of Jewish city culture is being built.
Two memorial plaques on the outer wall commemorate the Holocaust and the desctruction of the Siena ghetto on June 28, 1799
by the anti-Napoleon movement »Viva Maria«. 13 people were
killed.

Synagogue

❶ Mon – Thu 11.30am – 2pm, Sun 10am – 5pm; make appointments with
the Jewish congregation in Florence: tel. 05 52 34 66 54; admission: €4

AROUND SIENA

3km/2mi to the north of the old city is Chiesa dell'Osservanza, which
was built in 1476 over an older church that was donated by St Bernard. After being almost completely destroyed in a bombing raid in
1944, the church was rebuilt in its original form. The nave has no
aisles but eight side chapels. In the third chapel on the right is a reliquary of St Bernard, made in 1454 by Francesco d'Antonio; in the
fourth chapel a beautiful triptych (*Madonna with Saints Ambrose and
Jerome*, around 1436) by an unknown master. The **Annunciation
scene of colourful terracotta** on the pillars of the triumphal arch
between the nave and choir is by Andrea della Robbia; the Pietà (15th
century) in the sacristy by Giacomo Cozzarelli.

**Chiesa dell'
Osservanza**

*Monteriggi-
oni

For the journey from Siena to Monteriggioni, the autostrada is much less attractive than the beautiful drive on a country road through woods, vineyards and fields of dark brown earth. The town, founded in 1203, lies about 10km/6mi north-west of Siena on a hill over the Elsa valley. Parts of the well-preserved medieval wall, which dates from the 13th century and is fortified with 14 towers are accessible; the city wall was mentioned by Dante in *Divine Comedy*. The **castle museum** shows reproductions of medieval suits of armour and weapons.

Monteriggioni is the seat of all Tuscan events along the **Via Francigena**, including the new cultural festival along the pilgrimage route (June until Sept.; www.francigena.provincia.siena.it).

Castle museum: Feb 16 – Mar 31 10am – 1pm, 2pm – 4pm, Apr 1 – Sep 30 9.30am – 1.30pm, 2pm – 7.30pm, Oct 1 – Oct 31 9.30am – 1.30pm, 2pm – 6pm, Nov 1 – Jan 15 10am – 1.30pm, 2pm – 4pm; admission: €3

Ochre-coloured earth and dark green cypresses – impressions from the surroundings of Siena

A visit to the Romanesque basilica of the beautifully situated 11th/12th cent. Cistercian monastery Abbadia a Isola 2km/1.3mi west of Monteriggioni is also worthwhile. It was mentioned as Borgonuovo in notes by Archbishop Sigerich the Serious of Canterbury (994), a pilgrim's station on the later Via Francigena.

Abbadia a Isola

The Crete, a bizarre landscape of bare hills cut by valleys south-east of Siena has a unique aesthetic charm. The unwelcoming landscape, which is threatened by erosion, is the result of relentless deforestation and overgrazing. Where the topsoil has already been washed away, clay soil exposed – the name comes from *creta* (clay, chalk).

*Crete Sienesi

The medieval town of Murlo lies on the SS 2 south of Siena. Turn right just beyond Monteroni d'Arbia. The imposing Palazzo Vescovile houses the **Antiquarium**. Finds from the nearby necropolis Poggio Civitate are on display here, including an almost completely preserved roof construction and the gable of a building from the 5th century BC.

*Murlo

❶ ? Antiquarium: Apr – June, Sep Tue – Sun 10am – 1pm, 3pm – 7pm, July/Aug also 9pm – 11pm, Mar, Oct only until 5pm, Nov – Feb Tue – Fri 10am – 1pm, Sat, Sun also 3pm – 5pm; admission: €3.20

In the Crete foothills, 25km/16mi south-east of Siena, lies the town of Asciano. The Romanesque church of Sant'Agata, built of travertine stone (11th – 14th cent.) is remarkable. The neighbouring **Museo Civico Archelogico e d'Arte Sacra** in Palazzo Corboli shows Sienese paintings and sculptures, majolica and jewellery (13th – 19th cent.) as well as gold jewellery, bronze brooches and ash urns from five Etruscan chamber graves that were found on the Poggio Pinco east of town.

Asciano

Museo Civico Archelogico e d' Arte Sacra: Corso Matteotti 122; Mar 1 – Oct 31 Tue – Sun 10.30am – 6.30pm, Nov 1 – Feb 28 Fri – Sun 10.30am – 5.30pm; admission: €4.50

»White gold« or »kitchen diamonds«: – The first Italian **truffle museum** in the castle of San Giovanni d'Asso, Piazza Gramsci 1 is dedicated to the world of this delicacy, the white truffle.

San Giovanni d'Asso

Truffle museum: Jul 1 – Aug 31 Thu – Sun 11am – 1pm, 4pm – 7pm, Mar 1 – June 30, Sep 1 – Sep 30 Thu 2.30pm – 5.30pm, Fri – Sun 11am – 1pm, 2.30pm – 5.30pm; Oct 1 – Feb 28 only Sat, Sun 10am – 1pm, 2pm – 6pm; admission: €3

In Rapolano Terme there are two **thermal baths**. The remains of a rectangular Etruscan-Roman thermal bath can be seen in the Terme Antica Querciolaia (35 – 39°C/95 – 103°F; Via Trieste, www.termeaq.it). The temperatures in the Terme San Giovanni (39 – 40°C/103 –

Rapolano Terme

104°F, Via Terme di San Giovanni 52, www.termesangiovanni.it) are comfortable. **Museo dell'Antica Grancia** in a former oil press in Serre di Rapolano is dedicated to olives and oil-making. It cooperates with Siena's Museum SMS and also shows contemporary art.

❶ Apr 1 – Nov 1 Tue – Sun 10am – 1pm, 3pm – 6pm; admission: €2

** SAN GALGANO

Abbey church: morning until sunset, evenings also when there are concerts; www.sangalgano.org, www.sangalgano.info
Cappella Monte Siepi: daily 9am – 6.30pm; tickets Opera festival (June – Aug): www.festivalopera.it
Info Point: Mon – Fri 10am – 1pm, 3pm – 6pm, Sat, Sun 10am – 1pm, 2.30pm – 6pm

Ruins of an important Cistercian abbey

The ruins of the former abbey of San Galgano, which entered film history in Andrej Tarkowskys film *Nostalghia*, lies about 35km/22mi south-west of ▶Siena, a little distance from the road to ▶Massa Marittima. The monastery was founded in the 12th century. According to legend the archangel Gabriel appeared to the young nobleman by the nobleman Galgano Guidotti from nearby Chuisdino in a dream and told him to look for the way to God and nature in a **hermitage on the hill Montesiepi**. As a sign of his renunciation of violence and arms Galgano is said to have thrust his sword into a cleft in the rocks – the shaft sticking out of the rock has since then been honoured as a cross. The hermit died at the age of 33 and was canonized in 1185 by Pope Lucius III. A few years after his death the Cistercians came to Montesiepi, but soon the monastery was too small for them and they decided to move to the fertile valley floor. The building of the Abbazia di San Galgano began in 1224. It was almost finished at the end of the 13th century. Through donations, papal and imperial support the monastery continued to gain influence and property until the end of the 14th century. But raids by Florentine mercenaries and the exploitation of the estates by the commandery abbots in the 15th century ended the period of prosperity. The monastery closed in 1816.

Monastery church

The 69m/226ft-long church, whose roof has not been preserved, is a classic example of the Cistercian Gothic style that originated in Île-de-France. The walls of the three-aisled church, which has the plan of a Latin cross, are well preserved. It is built partly of **travertine** and partly of brick. The older part of the nave is divided into four storeys with pointed arcades and clerestory windows; the newer part has only three storeys. The door lintels have artistic floral capitals, and the main doorway is decorated with a 13th-century frieze of acanthus leaves. The enormous interior is unforgettable with its beautiful apse

The church ruins of the former Cistercian abbey of San Galgano are fascinating

and wonderful alignment of pointed arches and windows vaulted by the blue sky. Of the monastery the east wing and parts of the large cloister are preserved.

The original core of the Cistercian monastery is a small Romanesque rotunda, which was built in 1182 over the grave of St Galgano on Montesiepi. Above the natural stone base the walls consist of alternating layers of stone and fair-faced brickwork. The dome of San Galgano sul Monte Siepi recalls Etruscan grave monuments, while the tambour resembles the grave of Caecilia Metalla on the Via Appia in Rome. The countless spiralling stone rings are a medieval symbol for a person rising up to his maker. In the middle of the floor the sword of Galgano sticks out of a rock – however, it was placed here in the 19th century. The brick chapel was added in the 14th century and holds wonderful **frescoes by the Sienese Ambrogio Lorenzetti**. Parts of the two-row cycle are unfortunately in poor condition – the scenes from the life of St Galgano and the Annunciation, for example. The latter incorporates a window and the coffered ceiling into the composition, which gives a three-dimensional effect. A restoration revealed that the figure of the Virgin in a Maestà was paint-

*San Galgano sul Monte Siepi

ed in and was originally depicted as the queen of angels without a child. Eve, the original sinner, lies at Mary's feet; two kneeling women symbolize brotherly love (distributing fruits) and the love of God (offering a heart). The two Cistercian monks are presumably the founder of the order, Robert of Molesme, and St Bernard of Clairvaux.

Val di Chiana

✳ I–L 13/14

Provinces: Siena (SI) and Arezzo (AR)

The broad Chiana valley south of Arezzo was swampland for centuries. The Etruscans tried to drain it and planted grain.

With the fall of the western Roman Empire the Chiana valley reverted to swamp. Dante called it the »uninhabitable plague swamp«, and it was successfully drained only in the mid-18th century under the Habsburgs. Val di Chiana quickly developed into the granary of Italy. Sugar beets, olives and wine are today part of the intensive agriculture of the region, which is also known for its Chianina cattle.

WHAT TO SEE IN VAL DI CHIANA

Castiglion Fiorentino

Between ▶Arezzo and ▶Cortona the town of Castiglion Fiorentino is situated on a hill on the eastern edge of Val di Chiana. On the main square, Piazza del Municipio, the Vasari loggias (later 16th cent.) offer a wonderful view of the Chiana valley. The **Torre del Cassero** (1325), the city's landmark, is accessible; the bell Calfurnia has been ringing here since 1804. In the **Pinacoteca Comunale** in Via del Cassero there is high quality gold art and masterpieces from the schools of Arezzo and Siena to be admired, including a panel by Margaritone d'Arezzo *St Francis* (around 1280) and a Madonna by Taddeo Gaddi (around 1350).

The **archaeological museum** in Palazzo Pretorio including the underground tour is highly recommended. It shows 2,800 years of local history that begins with an Etruscan fortified settlement. The **Percorso Archeologico Sotteraneo** leads into the crypt of the church Sant' Angelo, whose walls consist in part of sections of Etruscan wall (4th cent. BC), and to excavations under Piazza del Cassero with a rectangular Etruscan temple (4th – 2nd cent. BC). The polychrome temple frieze with the head of a gorgon, lotus blossoms and red roses is in the museum.

The two-storey pilgrimage church Madonna della Consolazione at Porta San Michele was built in 1607 in late Renaissance style on an octagonal plan; it has a Baroque high altar with a Madonna fresco attributed to Luca Signorelli.

Torre del Cassero: May 1 – Sep 30 Sat, Sun 10am – 1pm, 4pm – 7pm; admission: €1.50

Pinacoteca Comunale: Apr 1 – Oct 31 Tue – Fri 10am – 12.30pm, 4pm – 6.30pm, Sat, Sun 10am – 12.30pm, 4pm – 7pm, Nov – Mar Tue – Sun 10am – 12.30pm, 3.30pm – 6pm; admission: €3

Archaeological museum: Via del Tribunale 8, opening times like pinacoteca; admission: €3

3km/2mi to the south lies Castello di Montecchio Vesponi with an almost intact castle (11th/13th cent.), whose 270m/295yd-long crenellated walls and eight massive fortified towers and 30m/100ft-high square central tower are impressive. In the late 14th cent. it was given to the English mercenary John Hawkwood alias Giovanni Acuto as a fiefdom; he was the successful commander of the Florentine mounted forces 1377 – 1394. Orietta Floridi Viterbini, the last descendant of Sir John, greeted Queen Elizabeth II here in 1992 and now uses her castle grounds for exhibitions by prominent artists like Giacomo Manzù.

Castello di Montecchio Vesponi

Lucignano's harmonious medieval appearance and cobblestone streets makes it a pearl amongst Tuscan towns. The highest point of the town is crowned by the parish church San Michele (late 16th cent.). The Palazzo Comunale behind the church houses the **museum**, which is worth a visit. The Sala Tribunale was painted by an unknown master with a fine fresco cycle depicting Roman emperors, poets and clerics with equal status (later 15th cent.). The main attractions, however, are the two works by Luca Signorelli (*St Francis Receives the Stigmata*, *Madonna with Child*) and the so-called Tree of Life (L' albero della vita; from 1350). After 1438 it was converted into a reliquary, The Sienese goldsmith Gabriello d' Antonio gave it the finishing touches in 1471.

*Lucignano

Museum: Mar 27 – Oct 31 Mon, Wed – Fri 10am – 1pm, 2pm – 6pm, Sat, Sun until 7pm; Nov 1 – Mar 26 Mon 10am – 1pm, Wed – Fri 10am – 1pm, 2pm – 5pm, Sat, Sun until 6pm; admission: €5

It may not have the charm of Lucignano, but 7km/4.5mi to the north the neighbouring town of Monte San Savino is also an attractive place. The elongated main square, Piazza Gamurrini, is dominated by the Cassero. This fortified building (14th cent.) houses the **municipal museum** and a ceramics collection. On Corso Antonio da Sangallo there are several proud palazzi as well as the merchants' loggia (1520). The arcaded hall is the work of the town's most fa-

Monte San Savino

mous son, the architect and sculptor Andrea Sansovino (around 1460 – 1529). A look into the the massive Palazzo del Monte (early 16th cent.) opposite is worthwhile. Cardinal Antonio del Monte had the pretty inner courtyard and terraced garden with an amphitheatre built.

Museum: Easter until Sep 30 Tue – Sun 9am – 12pm, 3pm – 6pm, Oct 1 until Easter only Sat and Sun as well as Wed mornings; admission: €1.55

Versilia

※ **E–G 3/4**

Province: Massa-Carrara and Lucca

Sand and sea in front of the magnificent Alpi Apuane backdrop: these are the attractions of the Versilia coast in northwest Tuscany on the border to Liguria.

* Tuscan Riviera
When Viareggio was developed into a sophisticated seaside resort in the 19th century, the other seaside towns soon followed its lead. Today route no. 1, the ancient Via Aurelia, connects the resort towns of the Tuscan Riviera. Hundreds of hotels in all categories border the coast, and on every beach one sun-shade nudges the next in July and August.

FORTE DEI MARMI

*Elegant seaside resort
Forte dei Marmi (population 7,750), around the fortress built by Grand Duke Leopold I 1782 – 1788, became the most exclusive resort on the Versilia coast in the 19th century. Since the beginning of the 20th century it has welcomed illustrious guests such as d'Annunzio and his muse Eleonora Duse, Thomas Mann and Aldous Huxley. Forte dei Marmi has kept up its high-class appearance with many street cafés in the pedestrian zone around Piazza Garibaldi, with renovated houses decorated with flowers and shops in the upper price range. In the sophisticated Forte dei Marmi people go shopping and the boutiques leave no desires unfulfilled – from Armani to Zegna. The slightly sloping beach of fine-grained sand makes Forte dei Marmi attractive to families as well. The recently extended seabridge is worth seeing, as is an enjoyable **museum of satire and caricature** in the fortress that gets lots of visitors.

❶ Museum: June 1 – Sep 14 daily 5pm – 8pm, 9pm – midnight, Sep 15 – May 31 only Fri – Sun 3.30pm – 7.30pm; free admission; ww.museosatira.it

Versilia

INFORMATION
Piazza Dante (railway station)
Viareggio
Tel. 058 44 63 82
www.aptversilia.it

EVENTS
Viareggio is a centre of carnival with extravagant parades along the coast promenade. In the summer the Puccini opera
festival takes place at Torre del Lago
(www.puccinifestival.it). The market in
Forte dei Marmi (Wed and Sun; www.il-
mercatodelforte.it) is one of the best in
Italy and even sells designer fashions. Pietrasanta's antiques market is also popular (every first Sun in the month).

WHERE TO EAT
Da Lorenzo €€€€
Forte dei Marmi, Via Carducci 61
Tel. 05 58 48 96 71
Mid-June to Mid-Sept. only evenings;
closed Mon, Tue midday and Dec 12 –
Jan 31
Gourmet destination where you can ex-
pect first class service!

Trattoria Il Marzocco €€
Pietrasanta

Via Marzocco 64
Tel. 05 84 714 46
www.trattoriailmarzocco.it
Here in the centre of Pietrasanta you can
expect a touch of Sicily. In this popular
trattoria with friendly owners down-to-
earth dishes are cooked extremely well.

Antica Locanda »Da Luca« €
Viareggio, Via Buonarroti 63
Tel. 05 84 42 55 29, www.hotelpinoblu.it
Open every day
Luca Lucchesi serves excellent fish dishes
and his brother Andrea runs the hotel
next door.

WHERE TO STAY
Viareggio is expensive, like the whole
Versilia coast. The town has several fine
traditional hotels, but also a large selection of small bed & breakfasts, especially
along the city park.

Plaza e de Russie €€
Viareggio, Piazza d'Azeglio 1
Tel. 058 44 44 49
www.plazaederussie.com, 52 rooms
Built in belle époque style in 1871 as the
top hotel in Viareggio on the main square
of the resort and still one of the best addresses. Meals are served on the roof terrace; the beach is about 100m away.

Hotel Bacco €€ – €€€
Via Michele Rosi 24
Lido di Camaiore
Tel. 05 84 61 77 66
www.hotelbacco.it
The Bacco is an orderly, hospitable hotel;
some of the rooms have fabulous views.
There is a beautiful roof terrace and a
pool for relaxing.

PIETRASANTA F 4

*Sculptors' town

Anyone interested in the artistic use of marble should go not just to Carrara, but definitely to Pietrasanta (population 24,800) too. The capital of the Versilia has been home to sculptors' workshops and bronze foundries for centuries, and there are countless small studios and workshops where visitors can watch sculptors at work. The town was named after Guiscardo Pietrasanta, governor of Lucca, who founded the settlement in the mid-13th century.

Sightseeing

The heart of the old town centre is the spacious cathedral square. Broad steps lead up to the **Duomo San Martino**, which was begun in 1296. Its brick campanile is the landmark of the city. To the right the baptistery holds a baptismal font by Donato Bentis (around 1509); diagonally opposite is the Torre dell'Orologio (1534). At the upper end of the piazza Palazzo Moroni is the home of the local archaeological museum (currently closed). The **museum's ceramics collection** is exhibited in the Luigi Russo Cultural Centre in the cloister of Sant' Agostino church. **Museo dei Bozzetti** is also located in the Luigi Russo Cultural Centre; it has a collection of more than 500 plaster models and sculpture designs, including works by Henri Georges Adam, André Bloc, César, Niki de Saint Phalle, Jean Robert Ipousteguy, Alicia Penalba oder Kan Yasuda. The church of **Sant' Antonio Abate**, Via Mazzini 103, also attracts many visitors with two **altar frescoes by Fernando Botero**. The subjects are Paradiso and Inferno. Botero clearly lets the »greatest field commander of all times« (A. Hitler) roast in hell.

Ceramics collection in the Luigi Russo Cultural Centre: Via S. Agostino 1; July 1 – Aug 31 Tue – Sun 6.30pm – 8pm, 9pm – midnight, Sep 1 – June 30 Tue – Sun 4pm – 7pm; free admission.

Museo dei Bozzetti: June 13 – June 24 Tue – Sun 4pm – 7pm, June 25 – Aug 28 Tue – Sun 6.30pm – 8pm, 9pm – midnight, Aug 29 – June 12 Tue – Sat 4pm – 7pm, Sun 4pm – 7pm; free admission; www.museodeibozzetti.it

Sant' Antonio Abate: Via Mazzini 103; daily July 1 – Aug 31 8am – 11pm, Sep 1 – June 30 8am – 7.30pm; free admission

VIAREGGIO F 4

*Vibrant seaside resort

Viareggio (population 64,500) is the »city« beach of the Versilia coast, lined by villas, hotels and cafés, which were rebuilt in typical Italian **art nouveau** (stile liberty) or art deco style after the fire of 1917 that destroyed the earlier wooden houses. In the early 19th century Maria Louuisa of Spain, duchess of Lucca, initiated the development of the fishing village. It was laid out with a right-angled street grid and granted a town charter in 1820. In the second half of the century the first luxury hotels appeared around Piazza d'Azeglio with its pine trees, Piazza Mazzini and Piazza Puccini, which soon welcomed noble and prominent guests, including Thomas Mann, who was inspired here to write his novella Mario and the Magician (1930), Arnold Böcklin and Lord Byron.

More than 200 hotels and guesthouses, the older ones with magnificent stucco façades, line the miles-long, four-lane coast road. The broad **beach promenade**, lined with palm trees, jasmine bushes and pine trees, runs parallel to it. On the beach side of this promenade art nouveau pavilions stand in a row. The little houses are built close together and for the most part date from the 1920s and 1930s. The legendary **Grand Caffè Margherita** with its two towers is a nice example. Today a walking tour leads to the art nouveau high points. The **Centro Matteucci per l' Arte Moderna** is dedicated to this heritage; it also shows works by the Macciaioli art group, Tuscan Impressionists.

Villa Paolina Bonaparte, which was built in 1822, now houses two interesting city museums. **MUS (Museo degli strumenti musicali)** exhibits more than 200 musical instruments from all over the world. **MAB (Museo Archeologico A. C. Blanc)** shows finds from the Neolithic era to the time when writing was introduced as well as ancient finds from the Versilia. The halls of the former summer residence are also worth seeing.

Galleria d' Arte Moderna e Contemporanea (GAMC) in Palazzo delle Muse has a high-quality collection of international 20th-century art (including Robert Rauschenberg) as well as exhibiting the oeuvre of Lorenzo Viani (1882 – 1936), a painter who was born in Viareggio. His monumental paintings of life on the Versilia coast from 1900 to 1920 leave a lasting impression on visitors.

Sightseeing

Centro Matteucci per l'Arte Moderna: Via d' Annunzio 28; July/Aug Mon – Fri 5pm – 11pm, Sat, Sun 10am – 1pm, 5pm – 11pm, June, Sep daily 10am – 1pm, 3.30pm – 7.30pm, otherwise daily 10am – 1pm, 3pm – 7pm; admission: €8; www.centromatteucciartemoderna.it

MUS and MAB: Via Machiavelli 2; Jul, 1 – Aug 31 Tue – Sun 6pm – 11pm, Sep 1 – June 30 Tue – Sun 3.30pm – 7.30pm; admission: €2.50; www.viareggiomusei.it

GAMC: Piazza Mazzini 22; Jul 1 – Aug 31 Tue – Sun 6pm – 11pm, Sep 1 – June 30 Tue – Sun 3.30pm – 7pm, morning by appt.; admission: €3; www.gamc.it

Cita del Carnevale on the northern edge of Viareggion consists of 16 hangars where carnival floats are on display.

Citta del Carnevale

❶ Via Santa Maria Goretti; June 1 – Sep 30 Thu – Sat 5pm – 8pm, otherwise Thu – Sat 4pm – 7pm; free admission; www.viareggio.ilcarnevale.com

Villa Borbone, a restored villa complex south of the town centre, goes back to Maria Louisa of Spain, the duchess Lucca. In the mid-19th century a previously modest house chapel was converted into the impressive burial place of the Bourbon-Parma dynasty. The chapel and park are open to the public.

❶ Viale dei Tigli; Mon – Sat 9am – 12pm, Mon, Wed also 3pm – 6pm; free admission

✳ PARCO NATURALE AND LAGO DI MASSACIUCCOLI

South of Viareggio along the coast to Livorno lies **Parco Naturale di Migliarino – San Rossore – Massaciuccoli**, a 23,000 ha/56,830-acre nature reserve. The **Lago di Massaciuccoli** (7 sq km/2.7 sq mi) constitutes the last remains of a lagoon which silted up through the sediment transported by the rivers Arno and Serchio. The visitor's centre on the farm San Rossore is a good place to start a tour of the park.

Visitor's centre: Viale delle Cascine; daily 9am – 6pm; guided tours: tel. 05 84 38 37 26; www.oasilipumas-saciuccoli.org

In his Villa del Torre del Lago Puccini composed *La Bohème* and *Madame Butterfly*

Torre del Lago on Lake Massaciuccoli got its nickname from Giacomo Puccini (▶Famous People), who composed operas in his art nouveau villa here, including *La Bohème* and *Madame Butterfly*. The villa is a **museum** today. The great composer found his final resting place in a chapel next to his study. There is a bronze monument to the great composer on Piazza Belvedere.

Gran Teatro Giacomo Puccini right on the shores of Lago di Massaciuccoli has an open-air theatre with more than 3,000 seats, which have a wonderful view of the lake. The foyer is decorated with costumes from Puccini operas.

Puccini Museum: Apr 1 – June 30, Sep 1 – Oct 31 Tue – Sun 10am –
12.30pm, 3pm – 6.20pm, July/Aug Tue – Sun 10am – 12.40pm, 4pm –
8.40pm, Nov 1 – Jan 31 Tue – Sun 10am – 12.40pm, 2pm – 5.20pm, Feb 1
– Mar 31 Tue – Sun 10am – 12.40pm, 2.30pm – 5.10pm, Mon only
afternoon; admission €7; www.giacomopuccini.it

✶✶ Volterra

✦ I 8

Province: Pisa (PI)
Altitude: 545m/1,788ft above sea level
Population: 11,200

**The once important city that was part of the Etruscan League
occupies a steep hill 60km/37mi south-east of ►Pisa. It is famous for its alabaster art.**

Excavacations have shown that the hill has been inhabited since the
Neolithic period. When iron ore was discovered around the Etruscan
city of Velathri, the settlement flourished from the 4th century BC
onwards. It minted its own coins and was protected by a wall more
than 7km/4.5mi long. In the Middle Ages Volterra developed into a
wealthy free state, which was conquered in 1361 by Florence.

WHAT TO SEE IN VOLTERRA

In the heart of the old city Piazza dei Priori has been Volterra's market and assembly place since the 13th century. Today the Coopera-
tiva Artieri Alabastro offers guided tours to alabaster workshops
(www.artierialabastro.it). Coats of arms and inscriptions for Florentine governors and commissioners decorate the façade of **Palazzo
dei Priori**, (1208 – 1254). It is the former residence and seat of the
podestà and the oldest preserved Tuscan city palace. The Palazzo Pretorio opposite was the seat of the Capitano del Popolo until 1511 and
later the Florentine administration. The Torre del Podestà towers
over this crenellated building, which is a combination of several
structures going back to the 13th century; the cornice is decorated
with an alabaster pig nicknamed »Porcellino«.

*Piazza dei
Priori*

❶ Palazzo dei Priori: Mar 16 – Nov 1 daily 10.30am – 5.30pm, Nov 2 –
Mar 3 Sat, Sun 10am – 5pm; admission: €1.50

The narrow Via Turazza leads to the cathedral, which was dedicated
in 1120 and enlarged around 1254 in Pisan Romanesque style. The
campanile was rebuilt after collapsing in 1493, but one storey had to

*Duomo
Santa Maria
Assunta*

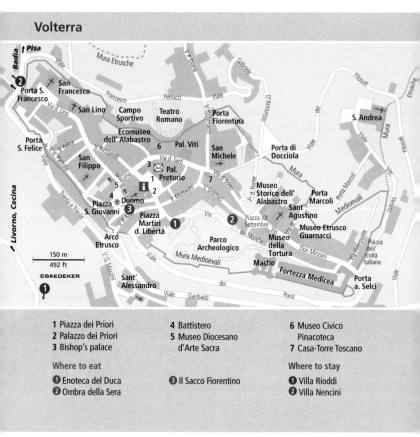

Volterra

1 Piazza dei Priori
2 Palazzo dei Priori
3 Bishop's palace

4 Battistero
5 Museo Diocesano
   d'Arte Sacra

6 Museo Civico
   Pinacoteca
7 Casa-Torre Toscano

Where to eat
❶ Enoteca del Duca
❷ Ombra della Sera

❸ Il Sacco Fiorentino

Where to stay
❶ Villa Rioddi
❷ Villa Nencini

be removed afterwards for structural reasons. The interior got its present appearance in Renaissance forms mainly in the 16th century, when the walls were adorned with stripes, the capitals and column shafts were redecorated and a wooden coffered ceiling was added. The surviving **Romanesque furnishings** are the large Deposition from the Cross in the right transept – with its slender figures from that time a rarity in Italy. The pulpit which was assembled in the 17th century using fragments from the 12th and 13th centuries. Its 12th-century reliefs show scenes from the Old and New Testament. Wonderful examples of the transition from Mannerism to Baroque can be seen on the wings of the altars in the aisles, as in the Immaculate Conception by the Mannerist **Pomaranchio** (1592). The three dark

Volterra

INFORMATION
Piazza dei Priori 20
Tel. 058 88 72 57
www.volterratur.it

EVENTS
Cene Galeotte
Once a month 27 prisoners, most of
whom are serving life sentences, cook
for a maximum of 100 guests in the
high security prison in Fortezza Medicea.
Cene Galeotte is headed by Luca Marin
(Rist. Il Santo Bevitore, Florence) and is a
rehabilitation project. The profits from
the admission (€35) and donations is in
turn donated to a project in Brazil. The
event is very popular. Admission is at
7.30pm. Reservations at: Argonauta
Viaggi, Tel. 05 52 34 50 40, or the tourist information office.

WHERE TO EAT
❶ *Enoteca del Duca* €€€
Via di Castello 2, Tel. 0 58 88 15 10
www.enoteca-delduca-ristorante.it
Closed Tue and all of mid-Jan. to mid-
Feb.
Enoteca del Duca creates an award-win-
ning ribollita with truffles. There are reasonably priced dishes for lunch. The garden in the courtyard offers especially
pleasant seating.

Insider
Tip
❷ *Ombra della Sera* €€ – €€€
Via Gramsci 70, tel. 058 88 15 10
Closed Mon and all of Nov. to end of
Jan./beginning Feb.
This stylish little restaurant has been
open for more than 25 years. Two of the
many house specialties: zuppa alla Volt-
errana and ravioli alla Maremma.

❸ *Il Sacco Fiorentino* €€
Via G. Turazza 13
Tel. 058 88 85 37
Closed Wed and all of Jan.
Elegant restaurant and enoteca, sophisti-
cated seasonal cuisine

WHERE TO STAY
❶ *Villa Rioddi* €€€
Loc. Rioddi
Tel. 058 88 80 53
www.hotelvillarioddi.it
Small comfortable hotel with 13 rooms in
a 15th-century former coaching station.

❷ *Villa Nencini* €€
Borgo Santo Stefano 55
Tel. 058 88 63 86
www.villanencini.it
Hotel (14 rooms) opposite Porta San
Francesco with a garden and swimming
pool. There is an enoteca in the former
stables.

paintings in the Capella Inghirami, depictions of the life and martyrdom of St Paul by Domenichino, embody Baroque drama by means
of chiaroscuro effects. The marble canopy from the year 1471 on the
altar and, in the Cappella dell'Addolorata, the colourful terracotta
group *Mary and Joseph with Child* in front of Benozzo Gozzoli's fresco (*Arrival of the Magi*) are also of interest.

The baptistery opposite the cathedral also dates from the 13th cen-   **Battistero**
tury. A dome was added about 300 years later. It faces the cathedral

and is covered with white and green marble stripes and has a portal decorated with figures. The main attraction inside is the beautiful baptismal font by Andrea Sansovino (1502).

Arco Etrusco From Palazzo dei Priori steps (Via Porta all'Arco) lead down to Arco Etrusco, the only preserved **Etruscan city gate** in the ancient wall. The masonry in the sides and the three weathered heads on the outer gate have been dated to the 4th–3rd century BC. The vaulted arch was renovated in the 1st century by the Romans, and the walls are medieval.

Museo Dioce-sano d'Arte Sacra The Museo d'Arte Sacra is in the cloister just a few steps north-west of the cathedral (Via Roma 1). It displays religious art from the diocese of Volterra including glazed terracotta busts of St Linus, the first disciple of St Peter, by Andrea della Robbia, a bust reliquary of St Ottaviano of embossed silver (15th century) by Antonio del Pollaiuolo, a tabernacle with miniature painting (15th century) of the Umbrian school as well as a gilded bronze crucifix (16th century) by Giambologna.

❶ Via Roma 1; Mar 16 – Nov 1 daily 9am – 1pm, 3pm – 6.30pm, Nov 2 – Mar 15 8.30am – 1.45pm; €10 (combined ticket)

*Side trip to San Francesco Frescoes by Cenni di Francesco The church of San Francesco (13th cent.) on Piazza M. Inghirami in the north-western part of the old city is worth visiting. A chapel of the cross was added in 1315 and painted in 1410 by **Cenni di Francesco** with a **fresco cycle** on the Legenda Aurea and the childhood of Christ – about 25 years after Gaddi's cycle in Santa Croce (▶Florence) and 50 years before Piero della Francesca created his famous cycle on the Legend of the Holy Cross (▶Arezzo).

Via Riccarelli, residential towers Back in the centre walk through Via Ricarelli, where there are two beautiful examples of medieval residential towers of the 12th and 13th centuries: Casa-Torre Buonparenti (at the intersection with Via Roma) and Casa Ricciarelli (no. 34 – 36). There is another tower in Via Matteotti: Casa-Torre Toscano.

*Pinacoteca and Museo Civico The Renaissance palace Minucci-Solaini in Via dei Sarti is the location of the art gallery and Museo Civico. The high quality of the collection, which contains works by artists from Florence, Siena and Volterra, derives from such important pieces as the large wooden statues of the *Annunciation* (around 1420) by Francesco di Domenico Valdambrino from the cathedral of Volterra, Luca Signorelli's graceful *Madonna and Child with Saints* (1491) and his *Annunciation* (1501), two triptychs from the 14th or 15th century by Taddeo di Bartolo, and Domenico Ghirlandaio's lifelike depiction *Christ with Saints Attinea, Greciniana, Benedict and Romuald* (1492), which was made for the Benedictine convent San Giusto. The highlight of the collection is the **Deposition** by Rosso Fiorentino, which glows in bright colours and was designed for the cross chapel of the church of San Francesco on Piazza M. Inghirami in 1521. This large-scale painting is a masterpiece of Florentine Mannerism and takes its appeal from its dynamic composition. The figures are connected with each other as in a net in front the ground of the picture, and the light illuminates certain areas of the scene like a spotlight.

❶ ? Via dei Sarti 1; Mar 16 – Nov 1 daily 9am – 7pm, Nov 2 – Mar 15 8.30am – 1.45pm; admission: €6

The adjacent alabaster museum in Torre Minucci is dedicated to the material that has always been important for Volterra. Its exhibits include two Etruscan urns, two capitals – the only examples of medieval alabaster work, a collection of outstanding 18th- and 19th-cent. alabaster sculptures, alabaster medallions from the workshop of Alberto Funaioli as well as works of the Volterran artist Raffaello Consortini.

Ecomuseo dell'Alabastro

❶ Piazza Minucci; Mar 16 – Nov 1 daily 11am – 5pm, Nov 2 – Mar 15, Sat, Sun 9am – 1.30pm; admission: €3

MARCO ❂ POLO TIP

Biglietti Cumulativi   **Insider Tip**

Whoever plans on visiting several sites in Volterra can save money by buying a collective ticket that is valid in Museo d' Arte Sacra, Museo Etrusco Guarnacci and in the art gallery. Thes »Biglietto Cumulativo« costs €10.

The construction of Viti Palace was begun at the end of the 16th century on behalf of the nobleman Attilio Incontri. In the second half of the 19th century it was acquired by Benedetto Giuseppe Viti, a wealthy businessman whose **alabaster workshop** was one of the most important artisan businesses in Volterra before it closed in 1874. The sculptures in the stairwell as well as the chandeliers in the ballroom, among other things, come from there. There are also two magnificent alabaster candelabras which were intended for Emperor Maximilian of Habsburg, but which were never delivered because of his execution in 1867. In the cabinets are oriental birds of paradise, Chinese chess sets and a Bali temple of balsa wood, all Viti family souvenirs from their business trips. The Chinese drawings on rice paper in the dining room from the 18th and 19th centuries, two Lombard Louis XVI chests and the gilded furniture in the Red Salon are also notable.

*Palazzo Viti

❶ Via dei Sarti 41; Mar 26 – Nov 1 daily 10am – 1pm, 2.30pm – 6.30pm, Nov 2 – Mar 25, only by appt., tel. 0 58 88 40 47; admission: €5

The busy Via Guarnacci leads uphill towards Porta Fiorentina. Below the medieval city wall are the ruins of a Roman theatre (1st cent.), which was donated by the wealthy citizen Caecina and his son. The

Teatro Romano

building materials come from the surroundings area: sandstone for the walls, tuff for the seats and lava for the steps. In the second half of the 3rd century the stone of the theatre was used to build the nearby thermal baths. Spectator seating and the two-storey stage wall on Piazza Caduti Martiri dei Lager Nazisti have been partially reconstructed. A market is held every Saturday at the Teatro Romano.

❶ Mar 16 – Nov 1 daily 10.30am – 5.30pm, Nov 2 – Mar 15 Sat, Sun 10am – 4pm; admission: €3.50

Museo della Tortura

In **Museo della Tortura** on Piazza XX Settembre various instruments of torture from various centuries are exhibited, including a guillotine. The museum is constructed similarly to its branches in San Gimignano, Siena and the Republic of San Marino.

❶ Daily 10am – 7pm; admission: €8; www.museodellatortura.it

**Museo Etrusco Guarnacci

The Guarnacci Museum is considered to be one of the **most important Etruscan museums in Italy** owing in part to the fact that an astonishing number of Etruscan finds were discovered around Volterra. The museum owes its existence to the cleric Mario Guarnacci (1701–1785), who left his collection to the city.

It includes about 600 urns (cists), most from the 4th to the 1st century BC when Volterra was a centre of urn production. The lids of the urns were made of tuff, alabaster or terracotta and shaped like boxes. They have figures of the dead, while the sides are decorated with mythological reliefs and were originally painted. The motifs cover hunting, battle and funerary scenes, taking leave of life, the journey into the after-life – which the Etruscans thought was populated by fearful demons – and scenes from Greek mythology. The Urna degli Sposi (urn of the bridal couple) is noteworthy for the expressions on the faces of the couple during the feast. The most important piece among the Etruscan bronze stele is the 57cm/22in statue of a naked youth from the late 3rd century BC called **»ombra della sera«** (evening shadow), which could easily be taken for a 20th-century sculpture. The museum also has a wonderful black Volterran jug (4th century BC), a cyathos (cup with one handle) of Bucchero clay with a high decorated handle, bronze articles, votive stele, dishes and tools, jewellery, marble heads and floor mosaics from the Roman imperial period.

❶ Via Don Minzoni 15 ; Mar 16 – Nov 1 daily 9am – 7pm, Nov 2 – Mar 15 8.30am – 1.45pm; admission: €8

Fortezza Medicea

On the highest point of Volterra stands the massive Medici fortress, today a high-security prison. It is among the largest bulwarks of Renaissance architecture in Italy. The old castle in the east was built in the 14th century by the Duca d'Athene, the new castle between 1472 and 1475 for Lorenzo de Medici. The middle round tower of the new castle, was called »maschio« (little man), whereas the half-elliptical tower of the old castle is called »femmina« (little woman).

At the western foot of the Medici fortress is the archaeological park. In 1926 during an excavation the remains of an ancient acropolis were exposed, including the foundations of two temples from the 2nd century BC and a cistern (piscina).

Parco Archeologica

❶ Mar 16 – Nov 1 daily 10.30am – 5.30pm, Nov 2. – Mar 15 Sat, Sun 10am – 4pm; admission: €3.50

There are numerous remains of the wall that the Etruscans built to defend the wealthy city of Velathri. The 7km/4.5mi-long wall encircled an area that was much larger than the medieval city. The remains are especially well preserved in the north-west near the small Santa Chiara church.

Etruscan walls

AROUND VOLTERRA

The Balze (balza = cliff), an inhospitable landscape almost bare of vegetation whose hills are cut by deep fissures as a result of erosion, lies immediately north-west of the city and makes a deep impression. Etruscan necropolises, part of the ancient wall and a medieval church have all fallen victim to the continuous erosion of the soft sedimentary stone. The Camaldolese abbey (Badia) also had to be abandoned in 1861 because it was in danger of collapsing.

*Le Balze

The geothermal centre of Larderello is located about 35km/22mi south of Volterra a little away from the road between Volterra and Massa Marittima and near the 691m/2,267ft-high Monte Cerboli. For a long time it was the largest plant of its kind in the world. The cooling towers of the steam power plant, which uses the heat of the earth (90–230°C/195–450°F) to produce electricity, are almost 75m/250ft high. In an area of 240 sq km/90 sq mi about 180 bore holes deliver steam to the power plants from volcanic sources up to 4,000m/13,000ft deep. These steam sources are called »soffioni« and also deliver boric acid, borax and ammonium sulphate for industry. The city also owes its name to a producer of ammonia derivates, François de Larderel, who built a factory here in 1818. In the Museo della Geotermia of the electricity company E.N.E.L. geology, technology and the future of geothermics are explained.

Larderello, geothermal power plant

❶ Mar 16 – Oct 31 daily 9.30am – 6.30pm, Nov 1 – Mar 15 Tue – Sun 10am – 5pm; free admission. Tours of the geothermic facilities: tel. 8 00 90 01 37 or www.enel.it (May – Oct once or twice a week); free

PRACTICAL
INFORMATION

What is the best way to get to Tuscany and what should you definitely not leave at home? What is a ZTL and how do you ask for a good restaurant in Italian?

Arrival · Before the Journey

BY AIR

The most important Tuscan airport is Aeroporto Galileo Galilei (www.pisa-airport.com), just over one mile outside **Pisa** with good connections to the centre. Trains also run to Lucca, Pistoia, Montecatino, Empoli or Viareggio, buses to Florence and a car rental agency. There are connections to Pisa from the following destinations in the United Kingdom and Ireland: Belfast International (Jet2.com), Bournemouth (Ryanair, Tomsonfly), Bristol (easyjet), Coventry (Tomsonfly), Dublin (Ryanair), Doncaster (Ryanair, Tomsonfly), East Midlands (Ryanair), Edinburgh (Jet2.com), Glasgow Prestwick (Ryanair), Leeds-Bradford (Jet2.com), Liverpool (Ryanair), London Gatwick (British Airways, easyjet) and Stansted (Ryanair), Manchester (Jet2.com) and Newcastle (Jet2.com). Intercontinental flights land at Leonardo da Vinci airport in Rome.

The small Amerigo Vespucci Airport (www.aeroporto.firenze.it) lies 6km/3.5mi outside **Florence** in Peretola. There is a shuttle bus to the railway station in Florence. The airline Meridiana (www.meridiana.it) flies there from London Gatwick. Trains and buses run regularly between Pisa (railway station at airport) and Florence and take about one hour.

AIR TRAVEL
Alitalia
tel. *89 20 10 (within Italy)
www.alitalia.com
Aeroporto Galileo Galilei, Pisa
Tel. 05 02 20 48 11
www.pisa-airport.com
Tel. 06 22 22
(Airport Florence)
Tel. 0039 0 66 56 49
(making reservations abroad)

Meridiana
Aeroporto Amerigo Vespucci
Tel. 05 53 02 49 10, 199 11 13 33 or
Aeroporto Galileo Galilei
Tel. 05 04 30 48
www.meridiana.it

RAIL TRAVEL
In London
Rail Europe Travel Centre
178 Piccadilly
London W1V 0BA
Tel. 0870 8 37 13 71
www.raileurope.co.uk

In Italy
Trenitalia tel. 848 88 80 88 (toll-free)
www.trenitalia.com

BUS
Eurolines
Bookings online and in UK through
National Express, tel. 087 05 80 80 80;
www.eurolines. com and
www.nationalexpress. com

BY TRAIN

For those who do not like flying, the train is an option for getting to Tuscany, but is **less suitable for local travel**, since many small towns have no train connections. Florence is a major rail hub, and can be reached from London via Paris in about 17 hours as an over-night trip. There are also good direct connections from Germany, Austria and Switzerland. The main routes between Florence and Rome circle around Tuscany. The coastal line runs from Pisa via Livorno and Grosseto to Rome, the interior line from Pisa via Florence to Rome. Local lines are Empoli–Siena–Grosseto; Siena–Chiusi; Asciano–Grosseto and Cecina–Volterra.

Along with **Trenitalia**, the successor of the Italian national railway (Ferrovie dello Stato; FS) there are also some private rail lines.

There are different **kinds of trains**: slow Regionale, Interregionale and Espresso. Intercity, Eurocity, Eurostar and the Pendolino, a high-speed train, require seat reservations; there is also a surcharge on the regular fare (supplemento).

There are one-way (andata) and return tickets (andata e ritorno) for first and second (prima, seconda classe) class.

International **tickets** are valid for two months, and the journey may be interrupted as often as the traveller wishes. For tickets bought in Italy the following applies: for distances up to 200km/125mi the tick-et is valid for 6 hours, for journeys over 200km/125mi for 24 to 48 hours. **Don't forget:** tickets must be validated at the departure sta-tion! There are special rates for groups, senior citizens over 60 years, young people under 26 years and families.

BY CAR

There are no car-carrying »motorail« trains from Calais or Paris to Italy, so motorists will normally need to make the long journey on European highways. For those driving from the UK south-east through France the most obvious route is to go south to Lyon, then cross the Alps on the E70 to Turin; or, alternatively and further north, to pass Geneva and take the Mont Blanc tunnel to Turin (European route E25), then south to Genoa and along the coast into Tuscany. The coastal route is the E80 from the south of France parallel to the shore of the Mediterranean to Genoa, La Spezia and Livorno. **From the west**

Drivers who have been in the Swiss or Austrian Alps before travelling to Tuscany or are coming from Germany or other points further north have a number of options. One is to take the St Bernard Pass, entering Italy at Chiasso, and on to Milan and then either via Bologna on the E35 to Florence, or on the E62 to Genoa and then via the E80 **From the north** to La Spezia and south to the Tuscan coast. Alternatives from Switzerland are the Simplon Pass and St Gotthard Pass. Further east there is the route E45 from Munich to Innsbruck and the Brenner Pass, then on past Verona to Bologna and west into Tuscany.

From Austria

In **Austria** tolls are charged for use of the motorways. There are yearly, two-month and ten-day toll stickers (vignette). Extra tolls are collected on other routes as well; info: ASFiNAG (www.asfinag.at). Sprecial tolls and vignettes can be bought directly, online and by telephone. Buying a video toll card, which records the licence plate number automatically saves a lot of time waiting in line at the Brenner Pass (www.videomaut.at). Payment by credit card is possible at the Brenner Pass.

From Switzerland

For **Swiss motorways** an annual vignette is necessary. There are also special tolls on some routes. The vignettes can be bought at the border or online in advance.

Tolls

In **Italy** tolls are charged to use the motorways – either in cash, with a credit card or with the so-called Viacard. This card is available from automobile clubs, at main toll stations, at petrol stations and rest stops on the motorway (information: www.autostrade.it; tolls in Switzerland: www.ezv.admin.ch; in Austria: www.asfinag.at/toll).

BY BUS

Bus tours directly to Tuscany are offered by many operators. These are mostly group tours. The Euroline long-distance bus services which connect many European cities have no direct link from London; with changes in Paris and Milan the journey time to Florence is about 28 hours. Arrival by bus may be convenient for travellers who are moving on from other parts of continental Europe. Even then, the journey can take some time: for example, the trip from Munich takes about 14 hours, changing in Milan.

IMMIGRATION AND CUSTOMS REGULATIONS

Travel documents

The identity cards and passports of EU citizens are often no longer checked. However, since random inspections are carried out at the border and identification is required at airports, visitors should be able to show their passports when they enter the country. Children under 16 years of age must carry a children's passport. Entries into the parents' passports are no longer valid.

Always carry your driving licence, the motor vehicle registration and the international green insurance card. Motor vehicles must have the oval sticker showing their nationality unless they have a Euro licence plate.

Car documents

Those who wish to bring pets (dogs, cats) to Italy require a new **pet pass**. Among other things, it contains an official veterinary statement of health (no more than 30 days old), a rabies vaccination certificate that is at least 20 days and no more than eleven months old, and a passport photo. As of 2011, the EU requires that the animal must have a microchip or tattoo. A muzzle and leash are required at all times for dogs. Please bear in mind that dogs are not allowed on most beaches.

Pets and travel

The European Union member states (including Italy) form a common economic area, within which the movement of goods for private purposes is largely duty-free. There are merely certain maximum quantities which apply (for example 800 cigarettes, 10 litres of spirits and 90 litres of wine per person). During random inspections customs officers must be convinced that the goods are actually intended for private use.

Customs regulations for EU citizens

For travellers from outside the EU, the following duty-free quantities apply: 200 cigarettes or 100 cigarillos or 50 cigars or 250g of tobacco; also 2 litres of wine and 2 litres of sparkling wine or 1 litre of spirits with an alcohol content of more than 22% vol.; 500g of coffee or 200g of coffee extracts, 100g of tea or 40g of tea extract, 50ml of perfume or 0.25 litres of eau de toilette. Gifts up to a value of €175 are also duty-free.

Customs regulations for non- EU citizens

Citizens of EU countries are entitled to treatment in Italy under the local regulations in case of illness on production of their European health insurance card. Even with this card, in most cases some of the costs for medical care and prescribed medication must be paid by the patient. Upon presentation of receipts the health insurance at home covers the costs – but not for all treatments. Citizens of non-EU countries must pay for medical treatment and medicine themselves and should take out private health insurance.

Health insurance

Since some of the costs for medical treatment and medication typically have to be met by the patient, and the costs for return transportation may not be covered by the normal health insurance, additional travel insurance is recommended.

Private travel insurance

Electricity

Italy uses 220 volt electricity; an adapter (Ital. adattore) is generally necessary. If you don't have one you can buy the necessary adaptor (spina elettrica or spina di/della corrente) for the Italian outlets (presa di corrente, presa elettrica).

Emergency

General emergency numbers
Tel. 113 (national)

Police emergency number
Tel. 112 (national)

Fire department
Tel. 115 (national)

Accident and medical emergency
Tel. 118 (national)

Breakdown service of the ACI
Tel. 116; 800 116 800 (mobile phone)

Etiquette and Customs

What is acceptable in Italy and what isn't? Bella figura, a beautiful appearance , is a deep-seated need for most Italians. Everyone who goes out in public likes to dress up, even for a trip to the post office or market, following Coco Chanel's motto: always be dressed to meet the love of your life. When there is a choice, money is always spent on fashion (and good food) rather than furniture or a coat of paint for the façade. »Unlabelled« tourists who stroll into cathedrals with flip-flops on their feet, wear shorts to visit the art gallery, sit in a restaurant in sandals or even dare to stroll through the old city with a naked chest – something not even the tifosi, soccer fans from Juventus Turin, Lazio Roma or Sampdoria Genoa, would consider – are looked down upon with amusement or a complete lack of comprehension.

Coffee bars Take an example of bella figura every morning from the baristi, who play the leading role in hundreds of thousands of bars up and down the country: to prepare steaming espresso they usually wear smart waiter's jackets and snappy little caps; they are the sovereign rulers of the public standing before them, handing out foamed cappuccini, freshly-baked cornetti and of course glasses of fresh water with matchless elegance. A sit-down bacon-and-eggs breakfast is boring by comparison! Break out of the hotel routine at least once and treat yourself to a colazione all'italiana with a slice of Tuscan life thrown in. And leave a few coins for the men behind the counter – service jobs are often badly paid.

Bella figura also makes life easier for photographers. Most Italians are happy to get in front of a lens – this reveals their love of theatre. Take the opportunity for a chat. Often the neighbour will want to join in, the children wave over their whole class for the photo session and the padrone insists that the entire brigade of waiters gets into the picture. A photo is always a public event, an expression of joy, of being chosen.

Taking photos

Italians are also spontaneous behind the wheel. Although the traffic fines have become draconian, southern Italians in particular constantly prove their mastery of the art of living, airily attempting to overtake on the wrong side or parking their Fiats three deep – it's a relief when the chaos then unsnarls and as many people as possible join in with all the gestures at their command. Then the street becomes a living piazza, the machine-like routine of day-to-day life is interrupted. The purpose of all this is to communicate, and only rarely to be proved right, a fact proven by the Italians' chivalrous regard for pedestrians, which is a pleasing contrast to other Mediterranean countries.

Traffic

MARCO POLO INSIGHT

? *Did you know...?*

A vino or grappa with a cigarette – smokers have had to go without since January 2005 in restaurants and bars. Except in a closed, separately ventilated room. The fines go up to €275.

To enjoy life in Italy, approach people and let them know through a smile or a gesture just how much you appreciate dealing with such a competent and winning counterpart. Do not hesitate to ask for the waiter's first name, and call out a »bravo«, »grande« or »bello« too many rather than one too few. And if things are not working out, bring the ancient Italian art of »arriangiarsi« into play. With Tuscans and Romans, Milanese and Neapolitans, a sympathetic compliment is usually more effective than a threatening attitude, which – you guessed it – is detrimental to the bella figura. This is a nation that prefers to be adored than to be told what to do.

Arrangiarsi

Health

In many places there is a Guardia Medica for medical help. The medical emergency service at night (8pm–8am) and on holidays is provided by the Guardia Medica notturna e festiva. Medical emergency help or first aid (pronto soccorso) outside hospitals (ospedali) comes from the White Cross (Croce Bianca), Green Cross (Croce Verde) and Red Cross (Croce Rossa Italiana), whose addresses can be found on the first pages of the telephone book (Avantielenco). Dentists (dentista) can be found in the telephone book under »medici dentisti«.

Medical help

Medical emergency service
Tel. 118; www.118italia.net

Medical Service Firenze 24 hours (English spoken)
Tel. 055 47 54 11

Hours Via Lorenzo il Magnifico 59: Mon – Fri 11am – 12pm, 5pm – 6pm, Sat 11am – 12pm
Hours clinik Via Porta Rossa 1: Mon – Sat 1pm – 3pm
www.medicalservice.firenze.it

Pharmacies Pharmacies (farmacie) are generally open Mon–Fri 9am–1pm and 4–7.30pm. They are closed on alternate Wednesdays or Saturdays. Every pharmacy displays in the window or door a list of pharmacies (farmacie di turno) which are open at night and on holidays.

Information

Italian National Tourist Office ENIT (Ente Nazionale Italiano per il Turismo)
www.italiantourism.com

IN AUSTRALIA
Italian Government Tourist Office
Level 4, 46 Market Street
NSW 2000 SIDNEY
Tel. 02 92 621 666

IN CANADA
Italian Government Tourist Office
175 Bloor Street E, Suite 907
Toronto M4W 3R8
Tel. 416 925 48 82

IN UK
Italian State Tourist Board
1 Princes Street
London W1B 2AY
Tel. 207 408 12 54

IN USA
Italian State Tourist Board
630 Fifth Avenue, Suite 1565

10111 New York
Tel. 212 245 48 22

INTERNET
www.turismo.toscana.it
To get started: overview of the region, events, excursions, accommodation and much more.

www.emmeti.it
Descriptions of museums and accommodations in the larger towns in Tuscany.

www.tuscany.net
Short introduction to the most important destinations and accommodation.

www.chianti.it
Everything about the Chianti region, for example, wineries, gastronomy, accommodation and cultural highlights.

www.hotelsearch.it/alberghi/campeggi-toscana.htm
Overview of hotels, guest houses and camp grounds.

www.turismoverde.com
Tips and lots of background information
on Siena and surroundings: Along with
the usual tourist information there are,
for example, legends associated with the
region.

www.rivieratoscana.com/en/ct
Sightseeing attractions on the Tuscan
coast, many practical tips.

www.virtualuffizi.com
The Uffizi gallery in the net including
ticket sales

www.polomuseale.firenze.it/musei
All large museums in Florence, description of rooms, illustrated lists of expo-
nents, catalogue numbers

IN TUSCANY
Assessorato Regionale al Turismo
Via di Novoli 26, I-50127 Firenze
Tel. 05 54 38 21 11
www.regione.toscana.it
There are tourist offices in all of the larger communities in Tuscany, the Aziende
di Promozione Turistica (APT). (▶ Sights
from A to Z)

EMBASSIES AND CONSULATES
IN ITALY
Australian Embassy in Rome
Via Antonio Bosio 5, Tel. 06 85 27 21

www.italy.embassy.gov.au

British Embassy in Rome
Via XX Settembre 80A
Tel. 06 422 00 001
www.britishembassy.gov.uk

British Consulate in Florence
Lungarno Corsini 2
Tel. 055 28 41 33

Canadian Embassy in Rome
Via Zara 30, Tel. 06 44 59 81
www.canada.it

*Embassy of the Republic of Ireland
in Rome*
Piazza Campitelli 3
Tel. 069 697 91 21
www.ambasciata-irlanda.it

New Zealand Embassy in Rome
Via Zara 28
Tel. 06 441 71 71
www.nzembassy.com

United States Embassy in Rome
Via Vittorio Veneto 119
Tel. 06 4 67 41
www.usis.it

United States Consulate in Florence
Lungarno Amerigo Vespucci 38
Tel. 055 26 69 51

Language

Many Italian dialects can be heard in Tuscany. However, communica-
tion is not a problem compared with other regions, since the Tuscan
dialect is the foundation for written Italian. Anyone who tries to
speak a little Italian – no matter how ungrammatical and incorrect
– usually gains much support and is rewarded with a sincere »brava«
or »bravo«, which means »well done«.

Italian Phrases

At a glance

Sì/No	Yes/No
Per favore/Grazie	Please/Thank you
Non c'è di che	You're welcome
Scusi!/Scusa!	Excuse me!
Come dice?	Excuse me?
Non La/ti capisco	I cannot understand you
Parlo solo un po' di ...	I only speak a little ...
Mi può aiutare, per favore?	Can you please help me?
Vorrei ...	I would like ...
(Non) mi piace	I (do not) like that
Ha ...?	Do you have ...?
Quanto costa?	How much does it cost?
Che ore sono?/Che ora è?	What time is it?
Come sta?/Come stai?	How are you?
Bene, grazie. E Lei/tu?	Fine, thank you. And you?

Getting around

a sinistra	left
a destra	right
diritto	straight ahead
vicino/lontano	close/far
Quanti chilometri sono?	How far is that?
Vorrei noleggiare ...	I would like to rent ...
... una macchina	... a car
... una bicicletta	... a bicycle
... una barca	... a boat
Scusi, dov'è ...?	Excuse me, where is ...?
la stazione centrale	the central railway station
la metro(politana)	the metro/subway
l'aeroporto	the airport
all'albergo	to the hotel
Ho un guasto.	I have broken down.
Mi potrebbe mandare un carro-attrez-zi?	Can you please send a tow truck?
Scusi, c'è un'officina qui?	Is there a garage nearby?
Dov'è la prossima stazione di servizio?	Where is the next gas station?
benzina normale	regular gasoline
super/gasolio	super/diesel
Deviazione	detour
Senso unico	one-way street

sbarrato	closed
rallentare	drive slowly
tutte le direzioni	all directions
tenere la destra	drive on the right
Zone di silenzio	honking forbidden
Zona tutelata inizio	start of the no-parking zone
Aiuto!	Help!
Attenzione!	Attention!
Chiami subito ...	Quickly, call ...
... un'autoambulanza	... an ambulance
... la polizia	... the police

Going out

Scusi, mi potrebbe indicare ...?	Where can I find ...?
... un buon ristorante?	... a good restaurant?
... un locale tipico?	... an typical restaurant?
C'è una gelateria qui vicino?	Is there an ice cream parlour nearby?
Può riservarci per stasera un tavolo per quattro persone?	Can I reserve a table for four, for this evening?
Alla Sua salute!	Good health!
Il conto, per favore.	The bill, please.
Andava bene?	How was everything?
Il mangiare era eccellente.	The meal was excellent.
Ha un programma delle manifestazioni?	Do you have an events diary?

Shopping

Dov'è si può trovare ...?	Where can I find ...?
... una farmacia	... a pharmacy
... un panificio	... a bakery
... un negozio di articoli fotografici	... a photo shop
... un grande magazzino	... a department store
... un negozio di generi alimentari	... a grocery store
... il mercato	... the market
... il supermercato	... the supermarket
... il tabaccaio	... the tobacconist
... il giornalaio	... the newsagent

Accommodation

Scusi, potrebbe consigliarmi ...?	Can you please recommend ...?
... un albergo	... a hotel
... una pensione	... a bed and breakfast

Ho prenotato una camera.	I have a room reservation.
È libera ...?	Do you have ...?
... una singola	... a single room
... una doppia	... a double room
... con doccia/bagno	... with shower/bath
... per una notte	... for one night
... per una settimana	... for one week
... con vista sul mare	... with a view of the sea
Quanto costa la camera ...?	What is the cost of the room ...?
... con la prima colazione?	... with breakfast?
... a mezza pensione?	... with half-board?

Numbers

zero	0	diciannove	19
uno	1	venti	20
due	2	ventuno	21
tre	3	trenta	30
quattro	4	quaranta	40
cinque	5	cinquanta	50
sei	6	sessanta	60
sette	7	settanta	70
otto	8	ottanta	80
nove	9	novanta	90
dieci	10	cento	100
undici	11	centouno	101
dodici	12	duecento	200
tredici	13	mille	1000
quattordici	14	duemila	2000
quindici	15	diecimila	10000
sedici	16		
diciassette	17	un quarto	1/4
diciotto	18	un mezzo	1/2

Doctor and pharmacy

Mi può consigliare un buon medico?	Can you recommend a good doctor?
Mi puo dare una medicina per ...	Please give me medication for ...
Soffro di diarrea.	I have diarrhoea.
Ho mal di pancia.	I have a stomach ache.
... mal di testa	... headache
... mal di gola	... sore throat
... mal di denti	... toothache
... influenza	... influenza
... tosse	... a cough

... la febbre	... fever
... scottatura solare	... sunburn
... costipazione	... constipation

Menu

Prima colazione	breakfast
caffè, espresso	small coffee, no milk
caffè macchiato	small coffee with a little milk
caffè latte	coffee with milk
cappuccino	coffee with foamed milk
tè al latte/al limone	tea with milk/lemon
cioccolata	hot chocolate
frittata	omelette/pancake
pane/panino/pane tostato	bread/roll/toast
burro	butter
salame	sausage
prosciutto	ham
miele	honey
marmellata	marmelade/jam
iogurt	yogurt

Antipasti	Appetizers and soup
affettato misto	mixed cold cuts
anguilla affumicata	smoked eel
melone e prosciutto	melon with ham
minestrone	thick vegetable soup
pastina in brodo	broth with fine pasta
vitello tonnato	cold roast veal with tuna mayonnaise
zuppa di pesce	fish soup
Primi piatti	Pasta and rice
pasta	pasta
fettuccine/tagliatelle	ribbon noodles
gnocchi	small potato dumplings
polenta (alla valdostana)	corn porridge (with cheese)
agnolotti/ravioli/tortellini	filled pasta
vermicelli	vermicelli
Carni e Pesce	Meat and fish
agnello	lamb
ai ferri/alla griglia	grilled
aragosta	crayfish
brasato	roast
coniglio	rabbit
cozze/vongole	mussels/small mussels

fegato	liver
fritto di pesce	baked fish
gambero, granchio	lobster, crab
maiale	pork
manzo/bue	beef
pesce spada	swordfish
platessa	plaice
pollo	chicken
rognoni	kidneys
salmone	salmon
scampi fritti	small fried shrimp
sogliola	sole
tonno	tuna
trota	trout
vitello	veal
Verdura	Vegetables
asparagi	asparagus
carciofi	artichokes
carote	carrots
cavolfiore	cauliflower
cavolo	cabbage
cicoria belga	chicory
cipolle	onions
fagioli	white beans
fagiolini	green beans
finocchi	fennel
funghi	mushrooms
insalata mista/verde	mixed/green salad
lenticchie	lentils
melanzane	aubergine
patate	potatoes
patatine fritte	french fries
peperoni	paprika
pomodori	tomatoes
spinaci	spinach
zucca	pumpkin
Formaggi	Cheese
parmigiano	parmesan
pecorino	sheep's milk cheese
ricotta	ricotta cheese
Dolci e frutta	Dessert and fruit

cassata	ice cream with candied fruit
coppa assortita	assorted ice cream
coppa con panna	ice cream with cream
tirami su	dessert with mascarpone cream
zabaione	whipped egg cream
zuppa inglese	cake soaked in liqueur with custard
Bevande	Drinks
acqua minerale	mineral water
aranciata	orangeade
bibita	refreshing drink
bicchiere	glass
birra scura/chiara	dark/light beer
birra alla spina	beer on tap
birra senza alcool	alcohol-free beer
bottiglia	bottle
con ghiaccio	with ice
digestivo	digestive
gassata/con gas	sparkling, carbonated
liscia/senza gas	not carbonated
secco	dry
spumante	sparkling wine
succo	fruit juice
vino bianco/rosato/rosso	white/rose/red wine
vino della casa	house wine

Literature and Film

Boccaccio, Giovanni: *The Decameron*. Penguin Classics 2003. Col-   Fiction
lection of 100 stories, which were written after the great plague in
Florence in 1348 and are considered to be the genesis of Italian
prose.

Collodi, Carlo: *The Adventures of Pinocchio*. Simply Read Books
2002. The imaginative story of the long-nosed wooden puppet, wonderful for old and young.

Dante Alighieri, *The Divine Comedy*. Everyman's Library. Dante's
chief work, an allegorical epic poem in the Tuscan dialect composed
from 1311, contains many references to current events and contemporaries of Dante.

Forster, E. M.: *Room with a View*. Bantam Classics 1988. Florence 1907: an Englishwoman on a cultural journey falls in love with a young aesthete. At first she denies her feelings, but then she finds the courage to choose against all conventions.

Fruttero, Carlo und Lucentini, Franco: *An Enigma by the Sea*. Chatto and Windus 1994. A detective thriller set on the Tuscan coast, one of a series of gripping mysteries by the successful duo.

Nabb, Magdalena: *Death of an Englishman*. Soho Crime 2001. Thrill crime novel with the somewhat slow Inspector Maresciallo Guarnaccia as the focus.

Origo, Iris: *The Merchant of Prato*. David R. Godine 1986. The diary of Francesco di Marco Datini, a businessman from Prato in the early Renaissance.

Origo, Iris: *War in Val D'Orcia: An Italian War Diary, 1943-1944*. David R. Godine 1995. Description of the war years in Val d'Orcia (►MARCO POLO Tip p. 42).

Pratolini, Vasco: *A Tale of Poor Lovers*. Monthly Review Press, 1988. Life and love in Florence in Fascist times.

Mayes, Frances: *Under the Tuscan Sun*. Broadway Books 1999. Autobiographical, romantic love story; an American declaration of love for Tuscany!

? MARCO ⊕ POLO INSIGHT

Tuscany in the movies

Eight and a Half: an amusing self-portrait by Fellini with Marcello Mastroianni.
The English Patient: set in the last days of World War II in the deserted and mined Villa San Girolomo in Tuscany, among other places.
Life is Beautiful: Benigni succeeded here in making the tragedy of the Holocaust the subject of a bittersweet comedy.
Tea with Mussolini: a group of English ladies who have been interned in Tuscany believe themselves to be under Mussolini's special protection.
Room with a View: very beautiful, atmospheric adaptation of E.M. Forster's novel. Incidentally, there were Baedeker guidebooks back then too: when young Lucy Honeychurch strolled through the streets of Florence she always had the red guidebook with her to satisfy her thirst for knowledge.

Non-fiction **Hibbert, Christopher**. *The Rise and Fall of the House of Medici*. Penguin Books. Readable account by a leading cultural historian.

Hibbert, Christopher: *Florence*: The Biography of a City. Penguin Books 1994. An excellent account of the history of the city.

Burke, Peter: *The Italian Renaissance*: Culture and Society in Italy. Polity Books 1999. A standard work on a great period in the history of Tuscany

Silver Spoon Kitchen: *Tuscany*. Phaedon Press 2011. By the makers of the classic Italian cookbook *The Silver Spoon*. More than a cookbook, it tells the story of regional Tuscan cooking, beautiful pictures of the region and the dishes.

Vasari, Giorgio: *The Lives of the Artists*. Oxford World's Classics 1998. Around 1550 Vasari wrote his entertaining short biographies of the famous artists of his time.

Media

La Repubblica, Italy's biggest-selling daily newspaper, is published in Florence with a local section. Corriere della Sera is the number two national newspaper. La Stampa and Il Secolo XIX from Turiuscanyn are leading newspapers read outside their home region. La Nazione is the largest Tuscan daily newspaper and published in Florence, followed by Livorno's Il Tirreno, which is mainly read along the Tuscan coast. Leading European newspapers are available in the larger cities and in popular tourist locations.

Daily newspapers

The monthly Firenze Spettacolo (www.firenzespettacolo.it) in Florence has information on all important events. The tourist information centres and the hotels also have the twice-monthly Florence Concierge Information. It is published in English and Italian.

Calendar of events

Money

On 1 January 2002 the euro became the official currency of Italy.

Euro

Citizens of EU members countries may import to and export from Italy unlimited amounts in euros.

Currency regulations

With few exceptions the banks are open Mon–Fri 8.30am–1pm; afternoons vary (about 2.30–3.30pm). On days before holidays (prefestivi) the banks close at 11.20am.

Banks

Cash is available at ATM machines without problems round the clock by using credit and debit cards with a PIN.

ATMs, debit cards

Credit cards have limits. Loss of a card must be reported immediately. Most international credit cards are accepted by banks, hotels, restaurants, car rentals and many shops.

Credit cards

Receipts In Italy customers are required to request and keep a receipt (rice-vuta fiscale or scontrino). It can happen that a customer is asked to show a receipt after leaving a shop. This is intended to make tax evasion more difficult. Buying imitations of designer labels, usually sold on the street, is against the law and can lead to fines of up to 10,000 euros. This makes a customer receipt all the more important.

Post · Communications

Post offices Italian post offices offer regular mail and package delivery services as well as postal banking services . They are open Mon–Fri 8.25am–1.45pm and Sat 8.25am–noon. Post offices close at noon on the last day of the month.

Postage stamps Postage stamps (francobolli) can be bought in post offices or – more quickly – in tobacco shops, which have the »T« sign (tabacchi). In towns the next tobacco shop is never far away. Letters up to 20g/0.7oz and postcards within Italy and to EU countries cost 0.75 euros. Current postage rates for letters/packages: www.poste.it/azienda/tariffario

Public telephone Public telephone booths work with coins (only a few) or with **telephone cards** (carta telefonica), which can be bought in bars, newspapers stands or tobacco shops. **Area codes** are part of the Italian telephone numbers . This means that the **area code including the initial 0** must always be dialled when calling from another country as well as locally.

Mobile phones The use of mobile telephones (Ital. telefono cellulare, or telefonino) from other countries is generally problem-free in Italy. Mobile telephone numbers can be recognized by the 3-digit number at the beginning that starts with 3. Leave off the initial 0, also when calling from outside of Italy.

COUNTRY CODES
From Italy
to other countries: 00 followed by the country code, e.g.
to UK: 0044
to USA: 001

From other countries to Italy:
0039

TELEPHONE DIRECTORY INQUIRIES
In Italy tel. 412, tel. 1254
www.info412.it
http://1254.virgilio.it
www.paginebianche.it

Prices and Discounts

Almost all museums in Florence and many other large **museums** offer free admission to senior citizens over 65 years old (only EU citizens), discounts for children and youths as well as young adults up to 26 years. More information on discounts can be found at www.firenzemusei.it or www.polo-museale.firenze.it. Combination and tickets for several museums or people (family tickets) are available.

The **Florence Card** allows free admission to about 33 different museums. Public transportation is also free for card holders. (Valid for 83 days.) Information: www.firenzecard.it.
The electronic **VVC card** (Voglio-vivere-cosi-card – »Voglio vivere cosi«: I want to live like that.) entitles to discounts in 100 regional museums, in the future also in natureparks, spas and on golf courses. Free download via smartphone: www.turismo.intoscana.it.

Time

Italy is in the central European time zone (CET), one hour ahead of Greenwich Mean Time. For the summer months from the end of March to the end of October European summer time is used (CEST = CET+1 hour).

Toilets

Almost all museums have toilets. Of course there are also ones in cafés and restaurants, sometimes at a fee, while bars often do not have public rest rooms – or at least claim not to. *Museums, cafés*

All in all the standard of public toilets in Tuscany has been raised considerably, but in many places they are locked due to vandalism or in less than satisfactory condition. Toilet paper is often missing and toilets seats are not used for sanitary reasons. *Standards*

The question about public facilities (servizio igienico, bagno pubblico, bagno) is one of the most frequently-asked questions in Florence, especially by tourists with children. The city has recognized this and produced a brochure on the subject. *Florence*
In the historic centre there are a total of 14 public toilets with the following **opening times**: April 1 – Oct. 31 daily 9am – 9pm, Nov. 1 –

Mar. 31 9am – 7pm. They can be found at the Centro Arte e Cultura, Opera Santa Maria del Fiore ticket office on Piazza San Giovanni 7 opposite the baptistery (8.30am – 6.30pm) as well as Piazza Santa Maria Novella on the side of the Fratellanza Militare. In the S. M. Novella railway station on the lower level (sottopasso; daily 9am – 9pm). Other toilets are available in Santa Croce at the tourist office Borgo Santa Croce 29r, near the Palazzo Vecchio in Via Filippina, in San Lorenzo in Via della Stufa, near Palazzo Pitti (Oltrarno) in Via dello Sprone as well as in Via S. Agostino. The latter also has **showers** (doccia).

Public and barrier-free rest rooms, usually for a 0.60 € fee, are located near Piazzale Michelangelo in Viale Galilei, in the Parco delle Cascine (Viale Kennedy), at Fortezza da Basso as well as near Piazza Ghiberti at Piazza Madonna della Neve. The parking lots/garages Parterre (Piazza Libertà), Sant' Ambrogio, Porta al Prato and Calza (Porta Romana) have public toilets.

In Pistoia and Siena there are public toilets at the **Park & Ride places**, in Arezzo at the **escalators** on Piazza Giovanni Paolo II. Spas like those in Montecatini Terme, Chianciano Terme, Saturnia or Bagno Vignoni usually have very clean toilets.

Transport

The **speed limit** for vehicles, motorcycles and campers up to 3.5 t within city limits is 30mph (50 km/h), outside of city limits it is 54mph (90 km/h), on four-lane roads (two lanes in each direction) it is 66mph (110 km/h), on motorways 78mph (130 km/h); cars and campers over 3.5 t or cars with trailers: outside of city limits and on four-lane roads 48mph (80 km/h), on motorways 60mph (100 km/h). In the rain the speed limit on motorways is 66mph (110 km/h) at the most for everyone! Speeders in Italy can count on high fines if they are caught.

Cars must have **low beam lights** on during the daytime on motorways and outside of city limits; motorcycles must have low beam lights on on all roads.

The **permitted alcohol level** is 50mg of alcohol per 100ml of blood. Draconian fines running from cash immediately, loss of driving privileges, confiscation of the vehicle to prison sentences can be levied. **Telephoning** while driving is only allowed with a hands-free set.

Anyone not driving his own car in Italy needs **written permission** in Italian. Taking along a green insurance card is recommended; **warning triangles, first aid kit and warning vest** are required.

Traffic regulations

country by Vespa: fun on roads with little traffic, like this pine tree-lined road in the Maremma

AUTOMOBILE CLUBS
Automobile Club d'Italia (ACI)
Tel. 05 52 48 61
Tel. 80 31 16
(breakdown service; toll free from land-line and mobile)
Tel. 8 00 11 62 00
(breakdown service; when using foreign mobile network)
www.acifirenze.it, www.aci.it

Touring-Club Italiano (TCI)
Tel. 05 83 46 45 42
Tel. 8 40 88 88 02
(Pronto Touring, Italy-wide)
www.touringclub.it

Towing service
▶ Emergency numbers

CAR RENTALS IN ITALY
Avis
tel. 06 45 21 08 391
www.avis.com

Europcar
tel. 06 96 70 95 92
www.europcar.com

Hertz
tel. 055 307370
www.hertz.com

Sixt
tel. 06 65 21 11
www.sixt.com

Maggiore
Florence: Via Finiguerra 11/R
Tel. 0 55 29 45 78
Airport Florence: tel. 0 55 31 12 56
Airport Pisa: tel. 05 04 25 74
www.maggiore.it

Further regulations If a vehicle is wrecked completely, customs must be notified since there might be an import duty on it. **Private towing** is not allowed on motorways. If a car breaks down, foreign travellers in cars or on motorcycles will be towed to the next garage by the Italian automobile club.
Helmets are required on motorcycles of over 50cc. Non-compliance can mean that the motorcycle will be confiscated for 60 days.

Motorway Almost all motorways (autostrada) in Italy charge tolls (pedaggio). The tolls can be paid either in cash, with a credit card or with the so-called **Viacard**. They are available in Italy from the automobile clubs, the ACI offices at the borders, motorway entrances, in tobacco shops as well as at petrol stations.

Petrol stations The import and transport of petrol in jerry cans is not allowed. Unleaded **super petrol** (97 octane, super senza piombo) and **diesel** (gasolio) are available. Petrol stations are generally open from 7am until noon and from 2pm until 8pm. Along the motorway they are usually open 24 hours. Automatic petrol pumps are available on weekends, increasingly also during the midday hours and at night.

Minibuses and expensive or relatively new cars are particularly vulnerable to break-ins or theft. The most important rule when parking a car is never to leave anything inside, to empty the glove compartment and leave it open, and to remove the radio when possible. If you can, leave the car in a locked parking lot or garage overnight. If the worst happens anyway, always notify the police. This is absolutely necessary for the insurance claim!

Car theft

Most cities in Tuscany are closed to vehicles in the centre (ZTL – Zona Traffico Limitato) or only open for local residents. Violators can expect hefty **fines**; the main access roads are monitored by video cameras which record all licence plates. Since 2012/2013 all EU traffic fines are collected in the home country after the holidays.

ZTL and parking

Almost all cities have **parking lots** outside the historic centre. From there the old city is generally within a few minutes walking distance or – more rarely – a bus ride away. Many city centres that lie higher up now have escalators (e.g. Arezzo, Siena). **P&R offers** are in place or being established. Buses run back and forth to the old citiies (e.g. Pisa, Pistoia, Florence).

Parking is free of charge along kerbs without any marking and without any no-parking signs or in white parking spaces; sometimes a parking disk (disco orario) is required. Parking is **charged** for blue parking spaces and kerbs, pay at the parking meter. Parking is **prohibited** in spaces marked in yellow (for example, reserved for taxis and busses), along kerbs marked in black and yellow. Watch out for unauthorized »parking guards« in Florence! **Parking fines** can be high (in Florence appr. €80).

In order to rent a car in Italy, you have to be at least 21 years old, have a credit card and have had a national driving licence for at least a year. Bookings can be made with the well-known international car hire firms before travelling to Italy. This usually saves money. They have services at the airports of Pisa and Florence (daily 8.30am – 11pm) and right in Florence. Local car rentals are in the telephone book under »Noleggio« »Autonoleggio«.

Rental cars

Travellers with Disabilities

Detailed information and individual help before your journey and when you arrive, links for barrier-free offers as well as hotels, restaurants and museums, first aid, dialysis emergencies, taxi service, public rest rooms and parking for the disabled are offered by **Turismo senza barriere** (»barrier-free tourism«; www.turismosenzabarriere. it) in Florence.

Turismo senza barriere

Hotels Barrier-free **hotels** and hostels can be found under »Holidays without barriers« on www.toskana.net/en/. Holidays on farms and estates on http://www.agriturist.it/agriturismo-per-disabili/.

Projects »Turismo senza barriere« is an ambitious **Tuscan regional project**, which can be thanked for the fact that most of the Tuscan museums are barrier free. According to their slogan »Turismo per tutti, turismo a misura« (tourismus for everyone, made to measure tourism) it offers tips, ideas, suggestions for holiday and overnight accommodations at http://www.turismo.intoscana.it/site/en/itineraries/Tuscany-Tourism-without-barriers/.

> **?**
> MARCO ⊕ POLO INSIGHT
>
> *Turismo senza barriere*
>
> Viale XX Settembre 157 a
> Sesto Fiorentino
> 50019 Florenz
> Tel. 0039 05 54 48 13 82
> www.turismosenza
> barriere.it

This includes improved facilities in **nature parks**. Parco Naturale della Maremma, Parco Naturale delle Alpi Apuane, Parco dell' Orecchiella, L' oasi Lipu Massaciuccoli or the parks in the Casentino have special offers for people with special needs.
Access to beaches and beach facilities has also been improved, for example in Livorno. Swimming and splashing is possible there in the Stabilmento balneare dei Tre Ponti, in Quercianella, Bagni Paolieri or the Bagni Cala Bianca.

When to Go

Climate Dry, hot summers and damp, mild winters are typical for Tuscany. The temperatures along the Tuscan coast are more moderate than inland: in winter a little higher and in summer a bit lower. The Apennines and the Apuan Alps get the most rain, over 2,000mm/80in annually, while the coasts get less than 1,000mm/40in annually, and the interior has the driest climate (Florence 840mm/33in, Siena 860mm/34in annually).

Spring and fall The best time for hiking or cultural trips to Tuscany are the months April, May and June or September and October. It is possible to enjoy **spring** in April already, but there can be cool days with rain and wind just as in the **fall**. In Florence the normal daily temperatures in May are 20–22°C (68–72°F). The months of May and June are considered to be ideal, when the poppies and gorse are in full bloom and the temperatures on nice days are warm enough to enjoy sitting on the piazza or a picnic outdoors. The large number of traditional festivals and events are also a reason to go in May / June, and the wine festivals, which are held mainly but not only in the Chianti region, are an argument for visiting Tuscany in the autumn.

From July to September the weather is mostly dry and very warm in Tuscany – the preferred time for a beach holiday on the coast or on one of the islands. In Florence temperatures vary in July between 28°C and 33°C (82–91°F) by day and between 18°C and 20°C (64–68°F) by night. In the towns at higher elevations there is always a breeze that makes the heat bearable in the warmest months.   Summer

Index

List of Maps and Illustrations

Photo Credits

Publisher's Information

1st Edition 2016
Worldwide Distribution: Marco Polo
Travel Publishing Ltd
Pinewood, Chineham Business Park
Crockford Lane, Chineham
Basingstoke, Hampshire RG24 8AL,
United Kingdom.

Photos, illustrations, maps::
173 photos, 34 maps and and illustra-
tions, one large map
Text:
Jürgen Sorges (Revison),
Eva Maria Blattner, Achim Bourmer,
Marlies Burget, Michael Machatschek,
Andreas März, Dr. Reinhard Paesler,
Peter Peter, Dr. Madeleine Reincke,
Reinhard Strüber, Ursula Thurner,
Andrea Wurth
Editing:
John Sykes, Robert Taylor
Translation: David Andersen, Barbara
Schmidt-Runkel, John Sykes, Robert
Taylor
Cartography:
Franz Huber, Munich;
MAIRDUMONT Ostfildern (large map)
3D illustrations:
jangled nerves, Stuttgart
Infographics:
Golden Section Graphics GmbH, Berlin
Design:
independent Medien-Design, Munich
Editor-in-chief:
Rainer Eisenschmid, Mairdumont
Ostfildern

Printed in China

Despite all of our authors' thorough
research, errors can creep in. The publishers do not accept any liability for thi
Whether you want to praise, alert us to
errors or give us a personal tip Please
contact us by email or post:

MARCO POLO Travel Publishing Ltd
Pinewood, Chineham Business Park
Crockford Lane, Chineham
Basingstoke, Hampshire RG24 8AL
United Kingdom
Email: sales@marcopolouk.com

FSC
www.fsc.org
MIX
Paper from
responsible sources
FSC® C011918

Curious Facts Tuscany

What a lottery ticket can lead to, how Silvio Berlusconi once made his money and why the Chinese are coming to Tuscany – Tuscany has some odd stories on offer.

▶Tuscan Las Vegas
In August 2009 a bar in Bagnone (Massa-Carrara province) became a tourist attraction when a €2-lottery ticket that had been turned in there cracked the national jackpot worth €147,807,299.

▶Celebrating in November
Since 2001 Tuscany has celebrated its regional holiday every year on November 30. It commemorates the abolishing of the death penalty in the Grand Duchy of Tuscany in 1786.

▶The devil visits Pisa?
On the northern side of the cathedral of Pisa there is a block of marble from Roman times with a row of 150 black marks. Ask for the »Unghiate del diavolo,« the devil's scratches.

▶Chinese already here
About 10% of the residents of Tuscany are foreigners (about 340,000), mostly from Romania (about 71,000), Albania (about 66,000), Africa, Latin America and Asia. In the province of Prato and in Florence the largest foreign ethnic group is Chinese. They have taken over large parts of the textile industry and are bringing about another »economic miracle«.

▶Job miracle on Elba: rocking with Silvio
In July 2012 the Kontiki Bar in Rio Marina offered Silvio Berlusconi his old, secure job back in case he resigns as prime minister. In the 1950s Berlusconi started his career by entertaining guests on cruise ships and in the Kontiki Bar as a singer of romantic love songs.

▶Busy as a bee on Elba
Elba's flag has three bees on it. It was raised for the first time at Napoleon's command on May 4, 1814. It is possible that Napoleon wanted to comment on the Elban people's hard work but it is certain that he used the flag of the Polish cavalry as his model.

▶No building error: holes for wine
Many Florentine palazzi have 15-inch holes in the walls at ground level, called »bucchette di vino«, which were once used to pass wine barrels into the houses. They were conceived in the 14th century when winegrowing and consumption fairly exploded and about 60,000 cogne (1 cogne = about 450 l) of wine were delivered to Florence in one year and sold through these openings.